Economics of
Watershed Planning

Southeast Land Tenure
Research Committee

Economics of

WATERSHED
PLANNING

*Symposium on the Economics of
Watershed Planning.*

Edited by
G. S. TOLLEY
and
F. E. RIGGS

The Iowa State University Press, *Ames,* **Iowa**

LITHOPRINTED IN THE UNITED STATES OF AMERICA BY
CUSHING - MALLOY, INC., ANN ARBOR, MICHIGAN, 1966

Foreword

FRONTIERS USED TO MOVE WEST, but a symptom of our national maturity is that some of the frontiers in water resources development are moving in the opposite direction. The spreading interest in water in the East does not stem from the same urgent concern about water scarcity found in the West. Where serious problems do occur in the East, they often concern only one facet of water use such as flood control, pollution due to growing industries, or the reaching out of growing cities for water supplies. These lead naturally to an awareness of the interrelatedness of all water uses. Irrigation is increasing, partly due to reductions in the cost of pumping and transporting water. In most eastern areas irrigation still does not use a large fraction of the water supply, but the agricultural effects can be seen and are dramatic even if as yet localized.

The increased interest in water resources all over the country suggests that the desirability of advance planning is being recognized. Programs now under way are helping to accumulate experience that will be ever more valuable as water problems increase in importance. Watersheds are being developed throughout the country by building small dams, clearing stream channels, adjusting cropping patterns to control water runoff and improve incomes, and by making other investments in a small-area context. While this book is concerned partly with how small watershed development can best fit into river basin and regional planning, its more general aim is to contribute to a variety of working-level planning decisions that concern technicians, administrators, and legislators in on-going water resources development.

Examination of small watershed development gives an opportunity to build on the many improvements that have occurred in project formulation and evaluation. Procedures in natural resources planning that drew criticism a few years ago have been improved by developing and enforcing a more adequate theoretical framework and by obtaining personnel well qualified to do planning. Small watershed planning has been a forerunner in these improvements and can continue to serve as a model for other programs. Watershed planning teams at once exemplify the merits of an interdisciplinary approach and call attention to problems involving communication between disciplines that still need to be worked on. Issues are being faced regarding community participation. When development occurs in an area whose resources are already heavily utilized, a vexing knot of economic, attitudinal, organizational, and legal strictures may be encountered. These will continue to be challenging as national growth leads to more and more pressures for resource development involving group action.

In order to examine the problems just mentioned, representatives of public agencies and universities assembled at Knoxville, Tennessee, in June, 1959, for the Symposium on the Economics of Watershed Planning. This book contains the proceedings of the Symposium.

v

The Symposium was sponsored by the Southeast Land Tenure Research Committee, the Farm Foundation, and the Tennessee Valley Authority. A major activity of the Farm Foundation is to encourage research in different fields of agricultural economics and in rural sociology through sponsorship of regional committees of college and government researchers. One of the first committees sponsored by the Farm Foundation was the Southeast Land Tenure Research Committee. The SELTRC is composed of agricultural economists from the seven southeastern land-grant college experiment stations, the Tennessee Valley Authority, and the Farm Economics Research Division and State Experiment Stations Division of the United States Department of Agriculture. Since its organization in 1946, members of the SELTRC have devoted their energies to a variety of problems concerned with the tenure status of farmers as it is related to land and water utilization.

The Tennessee Valley Authority has a continuing interest in the use of water resources in the smaller tributary drainage areas of the Tennessee Valley. With nearly complete control of the main stem of the Tennessee River an accomplished fact, TVA is expanding its research and developmental activities in these smaller tributary watersheds.

The land-grant institutions in the Southeast and the Land and Water Research Branch, Farm Economics Research Division, United States Department of Agriculture, cooperated with the sponsors. The Symposium was planned and carried out by the Water Resources Subcommittee of the SELTRC. The subcommittee membership included: George S. Tolley, North Carolina State College, *Chairman;* Harold H. Ellis, Farm Economics Research Division, USDA; William L. Gibson, Virginia Polytechnic Institute; John R. Greenman, University of Florida; Milton S. Heath, University of North Carolina; Fletcher E. Riggs, Tennessee Valley Authority; Max M. Tharp, Farm Economics Research Division, USDA.

Acknowledgment is appreciatively extended to the Tennessee Valley Authority and to the Iowa State University Press, through whose joint cooperation publication has been possible. Special acknowledgment is extended to Mrs. Dorothy Wilcox for her diligence in maintaining grammatical consistency throughout and for other invaluable editorial aid, and to Mrs. Lis Verbeck for typing and related help.

BEN T. LANHAM
  Auburn University
  Chairman, Southeast Land Tenure
  Research Committee, 1957-59

HOWARD G. DIESSLIN
  Associate Managing Director,
  Farm Foundation

E. L. BAUM
  Chief, Agricultural Economics Branch,
  Tennessee Valley Authority

Table of Contents

S. V. Ciriacy-Wantrup is Professor of Agricultural Economics at the University of California, at Berkeley.

Chapter 1

S. V. CIRIACY-WANTRUP

Philosophy and Objectives of Watershed Policy

THE WATERSHED AS A UNIT IN THE SOCIAL SCIENCES

HAVING NO CLAIMS to the status of philosopher — being a mere economist — I have puzzled a little about my assignment. I propose to focus on some of the essential concepts and principles that underlie the economics of watershed development and that need to be considered in public policy. Consequently, a number of topics are touched upon which will be treated more thoroughly in subsequent parts of this volume.

A watershed has clear conceptual unity in hydrology, physical geography, and other natural sciences.[1] It is not self-evident that, as a corollary, a watershed is a logical unit in a social-science context. There are many examples when rivers and swampy valleys have been barriers to social intercourse rather than arteries of communication. Frequently the upstream part of a watershed is occupied by a social group different from the one occupying the downstream part, and political boundaries bisect watersheds at the piedmont zone. In some parts of the world, the struggle between lowland people and mountain people has continued for centuries.

---

[1] Sometimes only the dividing ridges are defined as the watershed. This narrow definition is now generally replaced by a definition that includes the whole area between dividing ridges.

1

As a proposition, one may submit that the watershed has emerged rather recently in the social sciences as a unit of understanding and policy-making. This emergence appears connected with technological change and with shifting demands for the main products of a watershed in the course of economic development.

A most significant technological change was the discovery of large-scale uses for electric energy and of the role of falling water in producing such energy. A second change was the invention — or, possibly, rediscovery — of concrete and of its reinforcement through steel rods. These two changes made high dams both technologically possible and economically feasible. The experience with the construction of high concrete dams, together with the development of large earth-moving machines, led to the use of high earth-filled dams where they were cheaper or more suitable — for example, in earthquake areas — than concrete dams. All these technological changes took place during the last quarter of the nineteenth and the first quarter of the twentieth centuries. During the same period the demand for the main products of a watershed — hydroelectric power, water, timber, livestock, agricultural crops, and recreation — increased greatly. This increase in turn gave new significance to the control of floods, to soil erosion, to sedimentation of reservoirs and canals, to salinity, and to drainage — in other words, to the pervasive problems of water-quality, in contrast to water-quantity, management. Water-quality management becomes increasingly important as the demand for products of watersheds increases. This is a special case of the over-all problem of waste disposal when a population of organisms increases in size and density. The atomic age will pose this problem on a gigantic scale. These physical and economic interrelations force consideration of the watershed as a unit in economic understanding and policy.

From this sketch of the emergence of the watershed as a concept in the social sciences, two conclusions may be drawn.

First, the physical and economic interrelations that make the watershed a unit in the social sciences operate largely on the side of production and not on the side of consumption. Consumption of the products of a watershed may largely take place outside of it, and such consumption need not be interrelated. To regard a watershed as a unit in consumption is not required by the physical and economic interrelations just observed. Policies based on this misconception may hinder rather than facilitate watershed development. Let me give a few illustrations.

Important parts of water law implicitly regard the watershed as a unit in the use and consumption of water. The riparian doctrine, in contrast to the appropriation doctrine, is generally opposed to water export from the watershed in which the water originates. Ground-water laws in many states and the areas- and counties-of-origin laws in California permit water export only as long as it can be regarded as "surplus" water. The California laws require reservation of all potential future water requirements for the watershed.[2] Sometimes it is claimed

---

[2] For details on these laws, see S. V. Ciriacy-Wantrup, "Some Economic Issues in Water Rights," *Jour. Farm Econ.*, Vol. XXXVII, No. 5, Dec., 1955, pp. 875-85.

that the watershed should have the first rights to the hydroelectric energy that is produced within its boundaries.

My second conclusion is that a watershed as a helpful conceptual unit in the social sciences is not immutable. It is a concept of economic dynamics and not of statics. By dynamics I do not mean reference to time merely by dating, but an explicit consideration of changes in technology, preferences, and institutions. In the same way that the concept of a watershed has emerged in the social sciences in the course of technological and general economic change, so its significance may well be affected by similar changes in the future. A presently foreseeable technological change that may have such results is artificial modification of precipitation. In weather-making, a single watershed may not be an appropriate unit for understanding and policy-making. The boundaries of individual watersheds, which may be different for surface and ground water, change over time through geologic forces and drastic action by man.

It may be objected that the self-sufficient irrigation cultures that have existed during long periods of history prove the watershed concept to be of early origin, to be static over time, and to include interrelations in consumption as well as production. However, existing knowledge about the early irrigation cultures tends to confirm my proposition and conclusions. In these cultures the modern watershed concept did not exist, and this absence may well be related to some of the difficulties they encountered.

The early irrigation cultures were located in the alluvial plains of major river basins. They relied on periodic flooding and low diversion dams. While levees and water distribution systems were highly developed, high storage dams and upstream water management — especially quality management such as silt control, salinity control, and drainage — were absent. Physical difficulties caused by this absence were not the only ones. The actual destruction of some irrigation cultures was caused by military attack from outside. But such an attack came generally from the less civilized people, the "barbarians," in the upper watershed, attracted by relatively high economic development downstream. In this sense, one may regard the attacks as a consequence of the absence of economic and political unity in the watershed.

WATERSHED POLICY AND WATERSHED PROJECTS

When tracing the emergence of the watershed as a unit in the social sciences, I referred to public policy rather than public projects. The difference between watershed policy and watershed projects is not merely semantic. The economics of watershed projects, including benefit-cost analysis and other quantitative techniques for evaluating projects, comprises only a segment — and sometimes only a small segment — of the economics of watershed policy. In such project analyses, significant aspects of watershed policy are mentioned, if at all, as "institutional constraints." I submit that variation of the constraints should be one of the most important parts of the economics of watershed development. In other words, are the constraints to be *means to* or *obstacles to* social welfare?

In modern Western society, watershed development is accomplished largely through decentralized decision-making of many individual agents, both private and public. The public agents are, for example, flood control, drainage, irrigation, and conservation districts; municipalities; also federal and state forests. The private agents range from small subsistence farms to large commercial forest holdings, public utilities, and industrial corporations. These agents are subsectors in organizing and operating Western economies.

The "rules of the game" under which subsectors make decisions become operational largely through property institutions and the price system. These two systems are, therefore, of special interest in the social sciences. The ground rules and their continuous adjustment are the domain of policy decisions. Individual public watershed projects may be regarded as subsectors subject to ground rules not greatly different in principle from those applying to other subsectors.

OBJECTIVES AND CRITERIA OF WATERSHED POLICY

In proceeding to the objectives of watershed policy, one encounters a problem of unity of social objectives and criteria. The objectives of watershed policy cannot be divorced from those of other economic policies. Such objectives are interrelated. Social welfare criteria are no different in watershed policy than anywhere else.

Since Pareto,[3] economists have taken a special interest in optimizing social welfare and in the criteria for such optimizing. Optima of social welfare and formal criteria for optimizing are constructs in the sense of useful scientific fictions.[4] Optimizing is not and cannot be an actual policy objective. These fictional constructs are useful as organizing principles for the variables and relations that must be considered in welfare economics — to decide which ones to bring into the analysis explicitly, which ones to neglect, which ones to combine with others, and which ones to take into account as constraints. Information

---

[3] Vilfredo Pareto, *Cours d'Economique Politique* (Lausanne: F. Rouge, Libraire-Editeur, 1897).

[4] "A fiction is permissible in science if its character is clearly understood. A fiction is deliberate, conscious deviation from reality. A fiction, however, is not a hypothesis or theory. By itself, a fiction is not intended to be validated by testing with empirical evidence. But a scientific fiction should be useful as a stimulus for or as part of hypotheses and theories which *can* be so tested. That means the test of a scientific fiction is its conceptual usefulness, its expediency, in understanding, explaining, and predicting reality. A fiction becomes mere dogma and, therefore, unscientific if its two characteristics — consciousness of its fictional nature and conceptual usefulness — are obliterated. There are many examples in the history of science of fictions changing into dogma." S. V. Ciriacy-Wantrup, "Policy Considerations in Farm Management Research in the Decade Ahead," *Jour. Farm Econ.*, Vol. XXXVIII, No. 5, Dec., 1956, pp. 1301-11.

about variables and relations is insufficient for projecting an optimum expansion path of social welfare over time in a dynamic framework. The actual objective of policy decisions involves successive incremental improvements of the existing state of welfare, considering a limited number of alternatives. The Pareto criterion, likewise, is suited only for appraising whether an increase of social welfare results, but not for projecting an optimum.

For policy decisions of more limited scope — for example, evaluating individual watershed projects — incremental improvements in social welfare can be determined cardinally. This may be done by comparing hypothetical changes in income that can be attributed to projects. For policy decisions of broader scope, incremental improvements in social welfare can be appraised only ordinally in terms of *direction* of changes, the relative *speed* of changes, and their *sequence in time*. The issues involved in optimizing versus incrementally improving social welfare will be taken up in more detail later when quantitative analytic techniques are considered as an aid in watershed policy.

Having stressed the unity of objectives and criteria in public policies, I must now make a suggestion which may appear at first sight inconsistent: In natural resource economics, and particularly in watershed development, there tend to be characteristic divergencies in the actual welfare performance of the economy from the fictional welfare optima.

The conditions leading to these divergencies may be systematized in a number of ways. In what follows I shall try to systematize them in a way that brings out the relation of watershed development to the market economy and the price system.[5] It is frequently argued that market prices provide the signalling system that steers Western economies toward the social welfare optimum. An examination of the extent to which the price system fulfills this function helps to reveal conditions where public policy may need to find substitute or supplementary or countermanding systems.

WATERSHED POLICY AND THE PRICE SYSTEM

Three major types of breakdown and malfunctioning of the price system may be mentioned. The first two are of special significance in watershed policy:

1. Price signals do not exist.
2. Price signals are not received by the agent who makes decisions but are received by others.
3. Price signals are "distorted."

---

[5] An alternative way of systematizing is to differentiate between various classes of benefits and costs — explaining why their allocation to decision-making agents and the incidence among members of a social group lead to characteristic divergencies from a social welfare optimum. See S. V. Ciriacy-Wantrup, *Resource Conservation: Economics and Policies* (Berkeley: University of California Press, 1952), especially Chaps. 16-18.

Price signals do not exist for that part of benefits and costs of watershed development which I call "extramarket." Some of them are collective benefits in the sense that they are not divisible in consumption. The scenic values of a watershed unmarred by soil erosion, destructive logging, billboards, and slums are an example. Collective costs are the damage by floods, and the risk therefrom, to the general economy of a watershed rather than to individual properties, and threats to public health, such as malaria, related to drainage conditions.

Some benefits of watershed development, on the other hand, are divisible in consumption. In other words, a price could be charged for their enjoyment by individuals. Many of these goods, however, are free or nearly free institutionally. Recreational facilities offered by public reservoirs and public hunting and fishing are examples of extramarket benefits that are divisible in consumption but are public goods institutionally.

For some time, resource economists have been emphasizing the importance of extramarket benefits and costs without reference to particular stages of economic development. Recently, John Kenneth Galbraith has called special attention to them with reference to affluent societies.[6] Great emphasis is given the increasing lack of what is called "social balance" between the products supplied by the market economy and products such as education, defense, parks, and playgrounds, which are publicly supplied and financed by general taxation rather than sale. Galbraith reasons that the supply of extramarket goods has an inherent tendency to lag behind the supply of market goods because modern advertising and emulation, which are largely responsible for demand shifts in affluent societies, operate in favor of market goods.

While in substantial agreement on these points, I should like to note that the problem of social balance between market and extramarket goods is not confined to affluent societies. Furthermore, there are many examples of societies — not excluding contemporary ones — for which social balance might be regarded as threatened by the preponderance of public-supplied goods.

The historical fact of a great many ratios between the supply of market and extramarket goods raises the question of what is the criterion of an optimum social balance. Galbraith rejects the traditional criterion, namely, that the utility from a marginal increment of productive services devoted to the production of extramarket goods should be equal to the utility of the same increment devoted to the production of market goods. This criterion is rejected because the utility of market goods is what is called "synthesized," whereas utility from extramarket goods is not. A precise optimum in the social balance is regarded as unimportant. The direction in which policy should move to correct this condition is regarded as plain and the distance to be traversed considerable.

It has been suggested above that direction is frequently an acceptable

---

[6] J. K. Galbraith, *The Affluent Society* (Boston: Houghton Mifflin Co., 1958).

criterion for incremental improvements in social welfare through policy decisions of broad scope. For individual watershed projects, one may well consider going further. Whether the economist likes it or not, evaluation of extramarket benefits and costs — and also dismissal of such evaluation — is already a part of the political process. Reports of fish and game departments and other public agencies illustrate these attempts at evaluation. One may have professional doubt about some of the procedures used. Still, the economist may well take an interest in them in order to develop better substitutes. Otherwise, the arguments of well-organized groups interested in market values alone, who dismiss extramarket benefits and costs as "intangible," might receive disproportionate attention in policy decisions.

This is not to suggest that *all* benefits of recreational resources could be evaluated. In connection with many such resources, however, market values can be used indirectly — for example, through analyzing data on fees, leases, and real estate transactions. In other cases, measurement in terms of physical units of use — for example, mandays — can be accomplished fairly easily. Values of additional units of use can be approached through questionnaires and the study of behavior in other experimental choice situations. Even such crude and partial measurement is more useful than disregarding these values altogether, or substituting for them some figure based on the expenditures of users for transportation, room and board, guns, fishing tackle, and similar items.

Proceeding now to the second major type of breakdown or malfunction of the price system, what is meant by "price signals are not received by the decision-making agent but by others"? In traditional economics these problems appear as external economies and diseconomies. In watershed economics these externalities are discussed largely under the labels "offsite" and "indirect" benefits and costs.

External economies and diseconomies are of many kinds. They may be market or extramarket, pecuniary or nonpecuniary, static or dynamic, reversible or irreversible. In spite of an early article by Ellis and Fellner,[7] there is still much confusion between externalities that are merely transfer items in an international, national, regional, or local framework and those that are not. By some authors the terms "pecuniary" and "nonpecuniary" are employed in order to differentiate between transfer and nontransfer items. This is confusing because externalities may be either market or extramarket benefits and costs. If there are multiple decision levels in the same firm, price signals may affect these levels differently. In farming, for example, the tenant may be affected but not the landlord, or vice versa. The term "externality" becomes inapplicable, although the breakdown of the price system is of the same type as in other kinds of externality. For public policy it is necessary to ascertain in each particular case what kind of externality

---

[7] H. S. Ellis and William Fellner, "External Economics and Diseconomics," *Amer. Econ. Rev.*, Vol. XXXIII, No. 3, Sept., 1943.

is involved. The term itself is of little help for understanding and
policy-making.

The origin and the incidence of off-site benefits and costs can be
influenced through property institutions — especially resources law and
taxation. Taxation is used here in a broad sense as including "negative
taxation," that is, tax bonuses. Such bonuses may consist of depletion
or depreciation allowances, reduction of taxes, or outright supports and
subsidies. Tax bonuses may be made dependent on fulfillment by the
taxpayer of certain requirements regarding his use of resources.

Public districts can be employed effectively to make the influence
of resources law and taxation operational. This is a vital area for cooperative research between economics and other social sciences, especially law and public administration. The last part of this volume considers this area. When supplemental and countermanding systems were
mentioned previously, I had in mind especially resources law and taxation. It is difficult to see, for example, how the relations between upstream and downstream interests and upland- and bottom-land landowners could be adequately taken into account by the price system.

The problems of indirect benefits and costs in watershed policy have
been analyzed elsewhere.[8] It may be mentioned, however, that transfer
items deserve consideration in benefit-cost analysis. For example,
they are relevant to project repayment, interpreted broadly as including
cost-sharing and financing. This may be in an international, national,
regional, or local framework. Transfer items are also relevant to
project evaluations, provided the transfer is "out of" the framework
considered.

Turning now to distortions of the price system, the first difficulty is
to define "distortions." Most economists may agree that, for the following four basic reasons, distortion exists. However, few would deny that
value judgments are involved and that some qualification is needed with
respect to degree of distortion.

The first distortion was indicated earlier when the synthetic nature
of market demand in affluent societies was mentioned. That is the problem of the interpretation of and divergencies from consumer sovereignty.
Consumer sovereignty is a basic assumption in any attempt to employ
market prices in an economic analysis of alternative states of social
welfare.

The second distortion is more often explicitly considered in welfare
economics than the first. It occurs when the income distribution that
generated the market prices employed in welfare statements diverges
from an income distribution regarded as the "ideal."

The third distortion occurs in the absence of the necessary conditions regarding market organization which must be fulfilled if the price
system is to steer the economy toward a welfare optimum. The effects

---

[8] S. V. Ciriacy-Wantrup, "Cost Allocation in Relation to Western Water Policies," *Jour.
Farm Econ.*, Vol. XXXVI, No. 1, Feb., 1954, pp. 108-29; and by the same author, "Benefit-
Cost Analysis and Public Resource Development," *Jour. Farm Econ.*, Vol. XXXVII, No. 4,
Nov., 1955, pp. 676-89.

of monopoly, duopoly, oligopoly, and other divergencies from pure competition have been discussed by economists over the last several decades.

Last and not least, the price system may be called distorted if social institutions have lost the identity of "concept" and "structure," to use Sumner's terms.[9] Social institutions affect market prices not merely through income distribution and market organization, but in many other ways, both on the side of demand and on that of supply. It was noted previously that social institutions are brought into welfare economics as constraints. Usually, no attempt is made to ascertain whether they have lost identity of concept and structure.

Watershed policy is concerned with all these distortions, but no more so than other public policies. Watershed policy can work in the direction of correcting for these distortions. On the other hand, existence of these distortions suggests caution when market prices are used in quantitative economic analysis.

These points lead me to the last part of my assignment, namely, to appraise the merits and limitations of benefit-cost analysis for evaluating public investment in watershed development projects.

BENEFIT-COST ANALYSIS AND WATERSHED POLICY

The literature on benefit-cost analysis and related techniques has increased by leaps and bounds. At one time the professional contributions in this field consisted of a few articles. Now contributions are counted in books. In 1958 alone, three such books were published.[10] This literature is widely quoted and a flattering review article has appeared.[11] A careful and critical stock-taking will soon become necessary in order to ascertain where we stand and in what direction we should push forward. This is not the occasion for a detailed critique, but a few comments are called for by my assignment.

The claim of the "new" benefit-cost analysis is that evaluation of public investment in water resources projects is viewed for the first time as a problem of optimizing social welfare under budgetary constraints. Much space is devoted to formulating criteria for optimizing and to stressing the insufficiency of traditional benefit-cost ratios as such a criterion.

There is little awareness in this literature that economists in governments and universities who have worked critically with benefit-cost

---

[9] William G. Sumner and Albert G. Keller, *The Science of Society* (New Haven: Yale University Press, 1927), 4 Vols.

[10] Otto Eckstein, *Water-Resource Development: the Economics of Project Evaluation* (Cambridge: Harvard University Press, 1958); John V. Krutilla and Otto Eckstein, *Multiple Purpose River Development: Studies in Applied Economic Analysis* (Baltimore: Johns Hopkins Press, 1958); Roland N. McKean, *Efficiency in Government Through Systems Analysis with Emphasis on Water Resources Development* (New York: John Wiley and Sons, 1958).

[11] Julius Margolis, "The Economic Evaluation of Federal Water Resource Development: A Review Article," *Amer. Econ. Rev.*, Vol. IL, No. 1, Mar., 1959, pp. 96-111.

analysis over many years have frequently pointed out the insufficiency of benefit-cost ratios as an optimizing criterion. This insufficiency is rather obvious. Why, then, was use of these ratios not opposed more vigorously? There are several reasons.

First, to those familiar with the operational aspects of benefit-cost analysis, it seems naive to identify optimizing of social welfare, as a useful fictional construct in the sense explained above, with actual policy objectives. In time and uncertainty economics, such objectives must be formulated, as we know, in terms of incremental improvements in social welfare. The "new" benefit-cost analysis gives much attention to the numerical value of interest rates and uncertainty allowances that should be used in optimizing. But the real challenge of time and uncertainty economics — namely, how changes of technology, preferences, and institutions are to be taken into account through formulation of objectives and identification of variables and constraints — receives little consideration.

Second, even if optimizing of social welfare is assumed an operational policy objective, the shortcomings of the traditional ratios as a criterion for this purpose may well be regarded as of the second order of significance when considering other shortcomings of benefit-cost analysis. These other shortcomings are connected with the reliance on market prices in evaluating benefit and cost streams. The new benefit-cost analysis is little concerned with these other shortcomings. In other words, there is no progress in the treatment of extramarket values, offsite and indirect benefits and costs, consumer sovereignty, income distribution, market organization, and institutional influences. More is needed here than translating economics into the jargon of operations research or renaming externalities "spillover effects" or substituting a multiplicity of opportunity cost rates of interest for a multiplicity of market rates.

Third, the particular budgetary constraint that is emphasized by the new benefit-cost analysis, namely, that a water resources budget must be assumed as "given," is by no means the only one that can be selected. This constraint is merely similar to the one imposed by the present federal administration. Theoretically, optimizing of social welfare for the budget as a whole — not item by item — and relating investment expenditure to other expenditure and taxation is desirable. Operationally, especially in terms of political decision-making in the legislative branches of federal and state governments, it would seem more relevant to assume that water resources appropriations are actually made project by project, and that the total water resources budget is to some extent dependent on the size and number of projects that can muster the necessary political support in the legislatures. Under this assumption, benefit-cost analysis has the more modest but still highly important functions of ruling out, or at least stigmatizing, projects that do not make an incremental contribution to social welfare, and of selecting for each project, not necessarily the best alternative, but at least one of the better ones. For these purposes, ratios can serve.

Project selection is only one of three areas in which benefit-cost analysis may be useful. The other two areas comprise the broad problems of repayment of project costs, including problems of cost sharing and financing, and the related problems of pricing those products that are sold. The new benefit-cost analysis pays little attention to the problems of repayment and pricing. This is in accordance with the emphasis on optimizing and optimizing criteria. One may submit that the contribution of economics as an operationally significant policy science is potentially greater in the areas of repayment and pricing than in that of evaluation. My reason for this proposition is that problems of repayment and pricing remain important after a project has been selected and constructed. This means that benefit-cost analysis can operate in the areas of repayment and pricing with a more complete and better identified set of conditions that can be assumed as "given."

Present trends are toward substitution of linear programming for benefit-cost analysis. The programming techniques presently in use are static even though dating may be employed. The basic mathematics of dynamic programming have been known for some time. They have been used in the conceptual clarification of conservation economics.[12] As yet, no operational applications of dynamic programming are available in watershed economics. It will be interesting to see, when actual results become available, whether the particular advantages of the technique are sufficient to overcome its particular limitations.

Benefit-cost analysis is essentially an informal but flexible programming technique. The informal technique leaves considerable latitude to the user in exercising judgment, professional competence, and integrity — or absence of these qualities — in selecting and stating his assumptions. In formal programming, the assumptions are largely "built in" and concealed from those who are not familiar with the technique — like most legislators. Formal programming is superior to benefit-cost analysis in the sense that it can determine cheaply and precisely an *optimum optimorum*. As already implied, the significance of this superiority in time and uncertainty economics is at least doubtful. The numerical precision in determining optima may actually become harmful if it induces greater confidence in them. Calculation must be projected for fifteen to twenty years in the future. Such a gestation period is unavoidable between the planning stage and operation. The subsequent pay-out period cannot well be set at less than forty years. Programming for subsectors in the above sense necessitates great detail in "activities" and "processes." While the conceptual defects of optimizing for subsectors are less than for broader policy decisions, the problems posed by the availability of data for smaller statistical aggregates are usually greater.

Turning now to policies of broader scope, we noted that they can often be appraised only ordinally and in terms of direction of changes,

---

[12] S. V. Ciriacy-Wantrup, "Private Enterprise and Conservation," *Jour. Farm Econ.*, Vol. XXIV, No. 1, Feb., 1942, pp. 75-96.

the relative speed of changes, and their sequence in time. Before concluding, one aspect of such an appraisal may be mentioned because it is of particular interest to watershed policy.

It is important for public policy to know whether a change sets in motion corrective counterchanges tending over time toward a balance of the initial change, or whether it sets in motion other changes that are circular and cumulative and tend to reinforce the initial change.[13]

For example, there is evidence that in the United States during the first half of the twentieth century relations between prices of land, prices of agricultural inputs other than land, and technological change in agriculture can be regarded as a corrective system.[14]   On the other hand, Myrdal's well-known thesis about the nature of economic change is an example of a circular and cumulative system.[15]   There is also evidence that the relation between soil erosion, income, population, and technology is frequently such a system.[16]   Such a system, if operating in the upstream portion of watersheds, has physical and economic consequences downstream which have circular and cumulative effects upon the whole watershed.

Watershed policy may make allowance for the risks involved in this circular and cumulative system, but it cannot be made by adding a few percent to the interest rate used in benefit-cost analysis. Rather, the approach is that of establishing minimum standards in resource use through a variety of institutional approaches. In this way, allowance for uncertainty is built into the formulation of policy objectives itself.[17]

This is merely an illustration for the generalization suggested above that objectives of policy of broader scope may well focus on conditions that cause characteristic divergencies in the actual welfare performance of the economy from fictional welfare optima. For the pursuit of these objectives, benefit-cost analysis and related quantitative techniques must be supplemented by a type of analysis that takes cognizance of research in economic history, in the sociology of value systems, and in the change of social institutions, especially the law. This type of analysis relies heavily on theory, but not on economic theory alone. It focuses on time and uncertainty economics, but not necessarily through increasing the number of variables and equations in optimizing.

---

[13] The common terms, "equilibrium" and "disequilibrium," are not too well suited for describing these two systems. A corrective system has at best only a tendency toward equilibrium. A cumulative system, under some conditions, is more likely to realize and maintain equilibrium.

[14] S. V. Ciriacy-Wantrup, *Conceptual Problems in Projecting the Demand for Land and Water*. Presented before the Land Economics Institute, University of Illinois, June 24, 1958. Giannini Foundation Paper No. 176, Berkeley, California, May, 1959 (Processed).

[15] Gunnar Myrdal, *Rich Lands and Poor* ("World Perspectives," Vol. XVI [New York: Harper and Brothers, 1957]).

[16] S. V. Ciriacy-Wantrup, "Resource Conservation and Economic Stability," *Quart. Jour. Econ.*, Vol. XL, May, 1946, pp. 412-52.

[17] *Ibid.*, Chap. 18.

EMANUEL L. BAUM

LELAND G. ALLBAUGH

Comment

AN IMPORTANT PART of the purpose implied by the title of his chapter has been fulfilled by Dr. Wantrup. He rightly emphasizes that certain objectives of watershed development are not expressed adequately through the market mechanism. Accordingly, the basis for planning and the final selection of watershed projects do not always neatly fit into the calculus that consumers can apply in well-defined markets, or that economists can employ in empirical research in other problem areas. He properly suggests that more thought be given to changes in institutions to help achieve the objectives of watershed programs.

This is a positive approach in contrast to the belief frequently expressed that certain institutions are given or that institutional restraints prevent the achievement of particular objectives. However, value considerations that underlie existing institutions need to be critically evaluated before progress can be made in altering these institutions. While the social scientist should not try to impose values on the community, he can provide information so that policy-makers are better able to formulate their goals. For example, the economist can indicate the economic consequences of alternative courses of action that may be adopted in the political arena. This is particularly important since conflicts in values and political acceptability are great for water resources programs.

Wantrup correctly emphasizes that the watershed is unique largely as a producing unit. However, as a producing unit *per se*, it requires no procedures not applicable to other resources and producing units. Perhaps the most unusual characteristic of watershed resources is their immobility. But the same characteristics apply to other natural resources, and the same principles and analytical procedures are appropriate. This is also true for extra market values.

Hence a more positive approach might systematically examine the extent to which research procedures connected with resource use in other areas can be applied to watersheds. This would include more attention to: basic principles, analytical procedures, cooperative efforts among various scientific disciplines, and institutional arrangements in other areas of resource use.

While Wantrup favors use of traditional benefit-cost analysis, he lacks enthusiasm for other quantitative techniques, including linear programming and the operations research approach. He apparently feels

Emanuel L. Baum is Chief of the Agricultural Economics Branch of TVA. After receiving his doctorate from Iowa State University in 1949 he was agricultural economist at Washington State College until joining the staff of TVA. Leland G. Allbaugh is the Director of the Division of Agricultural Relations of TVA. He was formerly Associate Director of the Extension Service at Iowa State University and has held other government positions.

that they are not adapted for watershed planning, but does not specify a systematic framework for watershed planning to replace them. It is difficult to accept the apparent de-emphasis of the quantitative approaches that either have been long used or that appear on the horizon.

Wantrup does not distinguish between considerations for river basin and small watershed programs. In the development of land and water resources heretofore, greater emphasis has been placed on the farm unit and multipurpose river basin development programs. More recently, attention has been directed toward small watershed development projects because the other two types of programs were not accomplishing the objectives of land and water conservation and use in small watersheds. Small watershed programs are geared toward local flood control, more efficient use of water in the relatively small drainage area, and attaining desirable land use changes that would make possible better hydrologic conditions. River basin projects are largely concerned with hydroelectric power, navigation, recreation, main channel flood control, municipal and industrial water supplies, as well as agricultural development. Distinction should be made between these two major types of resource development programs, and planning procedures should be developed to fit the objectives of the particular program. In each case, however, similar economic principles and quantitative approaches are applicable.

Watershed planning is progressing, even though it is imperfect. Wantrup might have been more helpful if he had presented a comprehensive framework for watershed development within which the various professional efforts such as found in this volume might be related to public decisions more systematically than in the past. Watershed planning need not be a "guesstimation affair," devoid of systematic principles and procedures. We believe that a relevant economic framework for watershed development does exist even though it is less than perfect — as is true for many other areas of public planning and resource use.

It is our conviction that many major problems in watershed planning are quantitative in nature. Quantitative research in the physical sciences in this area is difficult because relevant small-scale experiments with replications of watersheds are either impossible or very costly. It is even more difficult in the social sciences because census and other basic data are not collected separately for watersheds. Also, the relevant economic relationships are either difficult to measure or are not independent of other economic sectors. The pricing mechanism operates imperfectly in this area. The economist working closely with the engineers and agricultural production scientists must use judgment in placing values on costs and benefits.

The needed improvements in watershed planning will require a substantial development of data. Research activities, including economic evaluations of existing projects, should precede new policies. By placing more emphasis on economic evaluations of watershed projects, future planning will be improved.

We wish to emphasize that the watershed approach is sound if properly used, and it should play an important role in the development of our land and water resources.

Gladwin E. Young is Deputy Administrator of the Soil Conservation Service. He was with the Natural Resources Planning Board and the Resettlement Administration, and joined the Bureau of Agricultural Economics in the 1930's. From 1947-52 he was a member of the Missouri River Basin Inter-Agency Committee.

Chapter 2

GLADWIN E. YOUNG

Where Does Watershed Development Fit Into the Total Picture of Resource Development?

THE WATERSHED PROGRAM is off to a good start, and we can expect many improvements that will come from studies and appraisals of actions that can be taken administratively under present authorizations. Other improvements will come by bringing about a more widespread understanding of interrelationships that must be taken into account in policies set by executives and legislators as they deal with the total resource development programs in the United States.

The contribution of economists to resources development, it seems to me, has not yet made much of a dent in the public consciousness. It is true that the influence of economists is reflected in the fact that a benefit-cost ratio is required in project reports submitted to the Congress. This requirement in law, and its reinforcement by the Bureau of the Budget, is recognition that economic consideration should be applied in setting minimum limits for project approval. But benefit-cost ratios cannot always serve as an acceptable guide for making choices. Choices between irrigation and drainage, between power and flood damage reduction, or between navigation and recreation are examples. To try to use benefit-cost ratios to select between these purposes holds no more promise than to try to use the same device for making decisions between public education and national defense, or between highways and hospitals.

15

The point I am making is that the contribution of economists should not be limited to getting bugs out of the benefit-cost calculations, even though this is one major task.

I make no pretense of trying to outline what the additional contributions can be. I feel sure, however, that they will be of increasing value as economists join hands with other social scientists, with engineers, and with physical scientists. Our traditional efforts have been directed toward breaking down the problem and isolating its molecules and atoms. From now on in the social sciences, and especially in the field of resource development, the largest effort must be in the direction of interrelation, not isolation.

LAND AND WATER RESOURCE DEVELOPMENT

To provide a setting for watershed development as a part of total resource development, this chapter deals with land and water resources and their interrelationships. I include as land and water resources those associated resources such as forests, range, fish and wildlife, and recreational opportunities.

Up to this time relatively little of the total land and water resource development has been done by government. Although most of the productive land in the United States was once owned by the federal and state governments, practically no development took place until it passed into private ownership. Most of the nation's productive land resource is now in private ownership, and most of the usable water resource is being used under rights of private ownership or controls. Almost all land clearing and drainage has been done by private effort. A large portion of forest resources is in private ownership. Only about one-fourth of present irrigated land is in federal projects, and only 45.5 percent of the hydroelectric power is, at the present time, developed in public projects.[1]

This suggests that the most important function of government in the resource field is in *conservation*. Through our conservation programs, public assistance is made available for acceptance on a voluntary basis to those who use our land and water resources. The developments that can take place to expand the resource base of land and water under public control are small indeed compared to those resources already developed by private effort. For this country to direct its efforts toward public *resource development projects*, to the exclusion or neglect of *resource conservation programs* aimed at maintaining and protecting the productivity of resources already developed, could not be a defensible policy.

At the same time, the opportunities for resource development through public works projects carried out by the federal government should not

---

[1] From statement by Francis L. Adams, Chief, Bureau of Power, Federal Power Commission, at meeting of Interagency Committee on Water Resources, Apr. 14, 1959.

be overlooked or neglected. The federal government already has moved into the field of developing projects where the costs are too great or returns too delayed or intermittent to attract private capital. This is generally accepted as a proper function of government, even though there remain major policy questions of balance and of priority in its relation to other proper functions of government.

To amplify for the purpose of this discussion, the programs of the federal government are listed in three general categories:

1. Conservation programs. Through these the federal government helps private ownership protect productive resources against decline and at the same time make profitable uses of them. Here is where the greatest public interest should lie because here is where most of our resources are. In this category I would include all the efforts that contribute to improving and maintaining land and water resources in private ownership, including organized educational efforts, research, credit, conservation cost-sharing, conservation technical assistance, and other assistance in improved technologies, engineering, and sciences.

A total of approximately $370 million is available for 1959, and $375 million is in the budget for the federal government for 1960 for work in this category.

2. Local projects. In these the federal government participates with organized local efforts in planning and further developing land and water resources. This includes watershed programs, special credit for small irrigation projects, water conservation loans, pollution abatement, grants-in-aid for fish and wildlife conservation programs, river basin planning and similar assistance extended on a cooperative, or joint participation, basis to state governments, units of state governments, or other organized groups. These projects involve private land and individual water rights almost exclusively.

Funds appropriated by the Congress for local projects falling in this category include approximately $125 million for 1959 and $84 million in the budget for 1960. Of this amount, $25.5 million was appropriated for 1959 and $20 million is in the budget for 1960 for the Watershed Protection and Flood Prevention Act (Public Law 566).

3. Federal projects. These include flood control, irrigation, power, navigation, recreation, fish and wildlife, and water supplies where costs are so great or where benefits are so delayed, uncertain, intermittent, or of a nature that private capital and management is not attracted.

Funds available for projects in this category amount to $1,100 million for each of the fiscal years 1959 and 1960.

These comparisons of funds from federal appropriations are given to show the relative emphasis placed on the three categories of federal programs. These programs are constantly re-examined by the general public and by the legislative and executive branches of government in light of national objectives and public interest. Economists have an important role in providing a basis for such continuing appraisals of public interest in resource development.

The tremendous increase in agricultural production during the 1940's and 1950's has been referred to as one of the bad national problems — a sort of blight on the farmers of the nation who, through improved use of soil and water resources and application of new technologies, have produced beyond our capacity to consume at favorable prices. Because of the perspective of nonagricultural people generally, farmers are looked upon as having contributed to some kind of national deficit — some kind of millstone around the neck of the nation's economy.

There needs to be an understanding that the present peak reached by our nonagricultural economy could *not* have been attained if it had not been for the tremendous increase in agricultural efficiency and productivity. In 1900, 40 percent of the population of the United States was required to produce food for the other 60 percent. Now, 12 percent produce food for the other 88 percent. Improved use and development of land and water resources through science and technology have made this possible. The significance of this fact cannot be appreciated without answering the question: What is it worth to the nation to be able to have abundant agricultural production, by using for that purpose only 12 percent, or even less, of its population? If the same efficiency in the agricultural use of land and water resources prevailed in 1959 as in 1900, this nation now would be losing the productive work of almost 50 million persons.

If the nation's total economy is to grow to an estimated $2,000 billion gross national product by the year 2000, and if a population of 370 million is to be as well fed as at present, increased agricultural production must come essentially from land already in use. The amount of land brought into cultivation through irrigation and drainage is likely to be more than offset by the amount of farmland taken up by urban, recreation, and other nonagricultural uses.

With such an outlook, resource conservation and resource development must be given first priority. Productive land will become more important in our total economy. Those who would neglect the conservation of productive soils now in the hope that technological advancement in machinery, fertilizers, or biological improvements will make land relatively unimportant would indeed gamble with the nation's security.

WATERSHED PLANNING IN RELATION TO RIVER BASIN PLANNING

There have been no "comprehensive" river basin plans yet that serve as a blueprint for all water and land resource development. Experience strongly indicates that only plans of the broadest design should be attempted. The time lag between over-all planning and the installation of all the features provides one of many reasons for not attempting a complete plan. No one can foresee technical changes over a period of one to five decades — the period over which installation must be extended. It becomes obvious, therefore, that planning is a continuous job.

Interagency committees have helped immeasurably toward coordinating development of resources of river basins. The river basin interagency committees have served as forums at which administrators, technical staffs, and lay people have presented points of view and technical facts and have debated issues. This is a wholsome and necessary procedure. Coordination of opinions of the general public is just as much a part of the total process as is coordination of the policies and procedures of federal agencies. Public opinion itself becomes a most effective coordinating force and an important factor in planning river basins or watersheds.

When water was as free as the air, there was no need for committees or commissions to be concerned with river basins. But competition for the use of water now makes it an economic factor, often a limiting factor to economic development. Only when water supplies become unusable through pollution, or when there is too much water during flood season or too little during drouth, do communities become keenly aware of how critical the water problem can be.

A part of the responsibility for finding solutions with which to meet expanding water requirement rests on the federal government. The problem has become larger than the individual community and may involve many communities or many states. The interrelationship of developments, therefore, must be resolved in a climate of extreme competition for use of water. It is important that watershed projects contribute to solutions of problems within each watershed and thus contribute to solutions of problems within the river basins of which they are a part. River basin plans are as useful to guide watershed projects as they are to other resource projects, but it would not be desirable to delay watershed projects until plans for river basins are fully developed. River basin planning may in the future be extended and will become more useful as more experience is gained. Experience of communities and states in watershed planning gives promise of adding realism to river basin planning in the future.

WATERSHED DEVELOPMENT OBJECTIVES

The objective of the watershed program of the Department of Agriculture is to develop and improve the management of land and water resources in small watersheds through project-type undertakings, planned and carried out jointly by local, state, and federal agencies, with the full understanding and support of a large majority of the private landowners and operators involved.

The objectives of a watershed project are to provide the fullest protection, development, and management of the land and water resources to maximize the net economic return, consistent with those less tangible objectives and values that cannot be measured in economic terms. Included in the specific measures to attain these objectives are land stabilization, soil improvement, irrigation and drainage, flood prevention, development of municipal and industrial water supplies, pollution abatement, and enhancement of fish and wildlife and recreational opportunities.

Watershed protection and management is not a new concept. The relation of forest cover to streamflow has received public recognition for more than a century in the United States. The interrelationship between the use of land in the watershed and the behavior of runoff and streamflow has been apparent not only to hydrologists and engineers, but also to farm people in communities where soil conservation measures have been most widely applied. While these relationships have long been recognized, nothing very effective could be done without organized efforts of the majority of landowners and other interests in the watershed community. For this basic reason, therefore, significant progress in watershed protection and development on watersheds involving mostly privately owned land did not take place until special authorizations made it possible for the federal government to enter this problem in cooperation with organized watershed communities on a project-by-project basis.

WATERSHED PROJECTS REQUIRE LOCAL ORGANIZATION

The Watershed Protection and Flood Prevention Act places full responsibility for starting small watershed projects on local people acting through their own organizations. Only local organizations can initiate a project. Federal help cannot be given if a project is disapproved by the state government. The policy of the Department of Agriculture is to help only when the state takes affirmative action to approve an application for federal help.

Local organizations, to be eligible as legal sponsors, must have authority under state law to carry out, maintain, and operate works of improvement. They must finance their required share of costs of the project, including land, easements, and rights-of-way; must acquire any water rights required under state law; must agree to operate and maintain the structures and other improvements after the project is completed; must construct or let contracts for construction of works of improvement agreed upon in the workplan; must obtain agreements from owners of at least one-half of the land above each detention structure to plan and apply soil and water conservation measures; must comply with all state laws governing watershed improvements, water rights, or specifications for structures; and must submit a satisfactory plan for repayment of any loan or advancement obtained under this act.

At the outset of the watershed program under authority of Public Law 566, in 1954, conditions in very few states allowed local organizations to meet all these requirements. To 1959, 39 states had passed 98 separate pieces of legislation for the purpose of putting local organizations in a position to assume the required legal obligations. While there is still need for enabling legislation to meet minimum requirements in several states, and while much of the legislation already

enacted can undoubtedly be improved with amendments, nevertheless
the action taken to date demonstrates a phenomenal interest on the part
of state governments and local watershed communities in this new
approach.

One of the greatest opportunities for helping the watershed movement lies in the field of improving state enabling legislation and the
improvement in procedures and techniques of administration by local
organizations.

Delays in getting under way with installations of watershed projects
are caused more from failure of local organizations to carry forward
their required responsibilities than from any other cause. This situation will undoubtedly be improved as experience is gained, both by the
Soil Conservation Service and by the responsible state agency in each
state giving assistance to local organizations in carrying out their obligations.

Here is a field for rewarding effort for an agency in every state to
work with soil conservation districts and other watershed groups authorized under state law to act as legal sponsors.

To students attempting to appraise the progress of the watershed
development program still in its early stages in 1959, it should become
obvious that the potential benefits from this program can be realized
only through participation by local watershed communities. The fact
that watershed projects are partially paid for and entirely operated by
local watershed communities dictates that the project shall be fully acceptable to local sponsors, shall be designed within their financial and
legal limits, and shall meet the objectives they seek. I think anyone
studying this arrangement must recognize that in the last analysis, the
scope and purposes of each project will be acceptable to communities
only as they meet the needs they now know and understand. Planning
and development at this early stage are likely to be deficient when
measured by the possibilities under greater knowledge and comprehension. It seems quite certain, therefore, that watershed communities
sponsoring projects in 1959 will be seeking amendments in their projects by the year 1969 or 1979 as awareness of their needs increases or
as needs change in those communities. In recognition of this, some
have advocated that approval be withheld until it is certain that all future
needs can be fulfilled by the selection of the best possible alternative
combinations of measures which can be devised. In my opinion, the
watershed program must go forward, as have almost all other programs
carried out by human beings, on the basis of something a little short of
perfection.

EXTENT OF WATERSHED DEVELOPMENT

As of June 1, 1959, 172 watersheds had been given approval to proceed with the installation of the works of improvement provided for in
workplans. In addition to these 172 watersheds, there are 265 additional

watersheds on which project workplans are in various stages of development. Applications for planning assistance have been requested by an additional 679 watersheds and have received the endorsement and approval of the state governments in each case. New applications are being received at the rate of about 20 per month.

To finance the Watershed Protection and Flood Prevention Act and the pilot watersheds, the Congress appropriated as follows: fiscal year 1955, $7.25 million; 1956, $12 million; 1957, $17.5 million; 1958, $25.5 million; 1959, $25.5 million. For fiscal year 1960, the budget is for $20 million. Thus, in the five years 1955 to 1959, Congress has appropriated $107.8 million for watershed projects. Since these appropriations are available until expended, the sum of the five years' appropriation represents the total funds available for the watershed program to date.

REGIONAL CONCENTRATIONS OF WATERSHED PROJECTS

It now seems too early to draw any very reliable conclusions about the extent of concentrations that may eventually take place. The largest number of watersheds approved for operations in any one state on June 1, 1959, was 17 — in Texas. North Carolina, Oklahoma, New Mexico, and Georgia each have eight approved projects.

The dispersion of the 265 watershed projects now being planned, together with the experience of moving forward on the 172 already approved, indicates that while the program has potentialities for meeting definite needs in almost every state, it apparently will have greater adaptation in some areas than in others. For example, it is now apparent that the program is likely to find least application in the northeastern states. On the other hand, the southeastern states and the southern Great Plains states are apparently going to find greatest application for this program. Probably the next priority will be the central states or corn belt area. While the program has not yet found wide application in the western states, or subhumid area, we believe it will find a constructive place as a supplement to established irrigation projects; or in some instances to develop supplemental irrigation along with the other watershed development features.

KINDS OF PROBLEMS ATTACKED

The underlying philosophy of the watershed program is that it shall be multiple purpose in nature.

Basic to all watershed projects is the application of required soil conservation measures and farm conservation plans on the farms of the watershed, as well as minimum requirements for conservation practices on the forest lands and range lands, either public or private.

Another principal purpose, as set forth in the act, is flood prevention or the reduction of damages from flood and sediment in the flood plain. The reduction of flood damages is not confined to agricultural values alone. The protection of urban values is equally as important as the protection of agricultural values from flood damages. Since the Corps of Engineers also has authorization in this field, the Soil Conservation Service and the Corps of Engineers have recently developed a memorandum of understanding which provides a basis for cooperating with local organizations in carrying out projects that may involve urban protection.

A third principal purpose of the watershed program is the development of benefits from agricultural water management. This involves improvements which serve two or more farms. Drainage, irrigation, and measures to provide a more uniform supply and distribution of water may be included.

By amendment to Public Law 566 during the last session of Congress, the Fish and Wildlife Service in the Department of the Interior is given a special responsibility to provide technical and financial assistance to local organizations in the development of fish and wildlife resources.

Many measures not eligible for cost-sharing assistance from Public Law 566 funds are eligible to receive federal loans in the same way that all other purposes previously mentioned are eligible. Works of improvement for municipal or industrial water supply, recreation, power, pollution abatement by streamflow regulation, and salt water intrusion control may all be included in the watershed workplans, provided they are integral parts of the plan for protection and improvement of the entire watershed.

All of these purposes have been included in varying degrees in the approved watershed project plans.

WATERSHED RESEARCH, BASIC DATA, AND
ENGINEERING STANDARDS FOR WATERSHED PLANNING

A systematic procedure has been established to channel a report on research needs from all field offices of the Soil Conservation Service to the Agricultural Research Service and the state agricultural experiment stations. At the same time, procedures have been established to channel the results of research so that they will flow back to the field offices with necessary interpretations and instructions.

The report on research needs is available to anyone, and particularly to those who may have an opportunity to contribute to the fulfillment of these research needs. High on the list of research needs are problems now confronting watershed planners, and any researcher can be assured of a ready market for his product as soon as it is available.

In recent years the appropriation for soil and water research for the Agricultural Research Service has been substantially increased. For each of the fiscal years 1959 and 1960 the budget for this purpose is $6,975,000. This represents a substantial increase over past years.

Basic data available to the watershed program are essentially the same as basic data available to all agencies. Special efforts are made through interagency cooperation at the federal level to see that there is a systematic exchange of data and interpretations being used.

Engineering standards and criteria now in use in the watershed program are based on the best professional information now available. Engineering experience in the construction of small dams and other water control and conservation measures now extends over a period of a decade and a half in the Department of Agriculture. Thousands of structures have been built and have been tested by extreme storm conditions under a wide variety of hydrologic, geologic, and engineering conditions. I am sure that nowhere in the world is there greater experience and engineering competence in watershed development than can be found in the Soil Conservation Service, the Forest Service, and the Agricultural Research Service.

As we look to the future we can expect improvements to come through research, experience, and observations, and through improved basic data. We can go forward with confidence that the watershed program is soundly conceived and is supported as a continuing part of the nation's land and water resource program.

RAYMOND J. PENN | *Comment*

A GOOD CASE for the Soil Conservation Service watershed program has been presented by Gladwin Young, and he has hinted at a broader role for the social scientist in future resource development. It is difficult to find much with which to disagree.

I suspect his priority recommendations for federal resource development programs could touch off interesting arguments. He ranked conservation first, local projects (including watershed projects) second, and other federal projects third. However, I do not see much to be gained by opening old quarrels about how to develop the resources of an area. Rather, I want to suggest that in concentrating on what we do with *water*, we have overlooked much of the real significance of *watershed programs*. Why does a watershed organization exist? Not to control the runoff and use of water; instead, it permits a variety of economic

Raymond J. Penn is Professor of Agricultural Economics at the University of Wisconsin. He was chairman of the Department of Agricultural Economics from 1948-55. He served on the staff of South Dakota State College from 1935-40 and did regional research for the USDA in Nebraska, New Mexico, and Wisconsin from 1940-46.

groups to work together. Water is the critical resource and initially the main focus of attention, but inevitably a watershed organization finds itself considering other resources and all kinds of questions of community and economic development.

For these reasons I would like to emphasize the possibilities of the watershed organization as an action and planning unit for *economic development* as well as for *resource management*.

Fragmenting of economic interests and increasing hostility between economic groups seems unfortunately to be a trend of our times. Editorial policy of several national newspapers and magazines seems to be deliberately aimed at discrediting agriculture. My experience indicates that the conflicts between rural and urban people are increasing at an alarming rate. I have just finished grading over 130 term papers by seniors and graduate students on the subject, "Agricultural policies and programs I would suggest." Less than half of the group were majoring in agriculture. I was shocked at the amount of and also at the increase in antagonism toward agriculture on the part of this class as compared to a similar class a year ago.

Farm people are not too happy either. Food costs are up, and the farmer is blamed. Yet the farmer knows his returns are down. Expansion of urban uses into rural areas presents problems; the new highway to which the farmer has no access takes part of his farm. Rural government officials — often without adequate financing — must plan and build the schools, streets, water and sewage systems, and other services needed by a new subdivision in their districts.

A large proportion of decisions relating to economic development are group decisions. Both urban and rural people must be members of these groups. Since rural-urban relations seem to be growing increasingly strained, the problem of arriving at a reasonable group decision will require our best efforts.

The watershed organization may have a large part to play in these decisions. It is a local organization made up of all the people in the area, whether they are farmers or not. The organization usually has methods of raising funds and of cooperating with state and federal technicians. We have a wide range of watershed organizations in Wisconsin. In those I have observed, the people seem to be working together toward their objectives. A watershed organization should be judged not alone on the miles of stream bank improvement, or the rate of soil loss, or the structures built. Improvement of working relationships between people of an area is equally as important — especially their confidence in and their respect for each other.

Water allocation is becoming increasingly involved in intergroup conflicts. There are problems of how to protect the public interest, how to maintain sufficient security of water supplies to warrant individual investment, and how to maintain enough flexibility to allow changes in use as the economy develops.

In Wisconsin, as in most eastern states, we have only recently become aware of major water allocation problems. Our rules have grown up in the past when almost everyone had enough water. It was natural to tie water allocation to land. Whoever owned the land adjacent to a stream or lake could make any reasonable use of it so long as he did not pollute it or reduce the flow. It was assumed that what was diverted would be returned either directly or via the groundwater route. Land-owners also have the right to use all the water they can get from under their land.

New kinds of water use problems are developing in our modern economy that the old rules do not fit very well. Water is needed increasingly for domestic consumption in cities, for industry, for recreation, and for irrigation. If it is drawn from under the ground, the water table may go down and harm others using the same aquifer. Surface water may be most valuable for recreation, and no other use should be permitted. In another area it may be most needed for private use at some distance from the lake or stream on nonriparian land.

Conditions are so different in the several parts of Wisconsin that no one set of rules is likely to be uniformly satisfactory even for a single state. Priority of water use needs to be different in the populated areas around Milwaukee, in the recreation areas of northern Wisconsin, and in the primarily agricultural areas of central and western Wisconsin. Availability of water differs by area also.

Procedures are needed for balancing the interests of water users in view of the availability of water. Watershed organizations are already involved in flood water control. I am hoping they will give attention to other surface water problems and underground water as well.

I agree with Gladwin Young that economists have more to contribute to resources development than getting the bugs out of the benefit-cost calculations.

Erwin C. Ford is an agricultural economist with the Soil Conservation Service. He has been in the Agricultural Adjustment Administration, the Resettlement Administration, and the Bureau of Agricultural Economics. Elco L. Greenshields is Head, Water Development Programs Section, Land and Water Research Branch, Farm Economics Research Division of USDA. He has also served with the Farm Security Administration and the Food and Agriculture Organization of the United Nations. Fletcher E. Riggs is an agricultural economist in the Division of Agricultural Relations, TVA. George S. Tolley is Professor of Agricultural Economics at North Carolina State College.

Chapter 3

ERWIN C. FORD

ELCO L. GREENSHIELDS

FLETCHER E. RIGGS

GEORGE S. TOLLEY

The Benefits From Watershed Development [1]

THIS CHAPTER attempts to give perspective to benefit issues confronting planners. It concentrates on physical and economic factors conducive to different kinds of benefits. It also considers whether, in securing one type of benefit, the expense of securing other benefits is affected — or, in other words, whether complementarity or competitiveness exists between benefits. The chapter is based partly on benefit estimates taken from Public Law 566 watershed workplans.

For grouping the projects, the country was divided into 13 regions. These are shown in Figure 1. The regional breakdown conforms to physiographic and economic characteristics. It has been designed to contain the minimum number of regions necessary for reasonably homogeneous groupings of the projects.

The first part of the chapter describes the benefits with which the small watershed program is concerned under Public Law 566 and related laws. Results from project plans through time and by regions are presented. The second part concerns some hypotheses to help explain the geographic distribution of benefits. Finally, issues surrounding benefits in the planning process are considered.

[1] Journal paper No. 1145 of the North Carolina Agricultural Experiment Station.

KINDS OF BENEFITS FROM SMALL WATERSHED PROJECTS

The watershed protection and flood prevention program authorized in 1954 by Public Law 566 grew out of 18 years of effort by the U. S. Department of Agriculture in upstream flood prevention. The 1936 Omnibus Flood Control Act brought the department into the flood control activities of the federal government. From 1937 to 1953, the department was engaged in nationwide preliminary examinations and surveys. The Flood Control Act of December 22, 1944, authorized construction of works of improvement in 11 watershed areas. By appropriation for fiscal year 1954, the Congress directed the department to initiate some 60 pilot watershed projects. Throughout all this activity, the main emphasis was on flood control — the prevention of damage by inundation and sediment.

While the emphasis has been on flood prevention, the watershed protection program, even from its inception, has never been considered a single-purpose program. Land and water conservation measures were accepted in the initial planning effort as integral parts of a watershed program. Drainage, irrigation, nonagricultural water use, recreation, and fish and wildlife development are other major purposes for which the development is planned. In a few projects now authorized for construction, flood prevention is not a major purpose.

The purposes for which a watershed program is planned depend on a number of factors. The primary consideration naturally must be the physical potential of the watershed area for resource development. Another major factor is the ability and interest of local groups for carrying out potential resource development. From the standpoint of the authorizing legislation, the major consideration is the relative amount of federal cost-sharing. Cost-sharing under the original Public Law 566 required local organizations to furnish land, easements, and rights-of-way, and to assume such proportionate share of the cost of installing any works of improvement involving federal assistance as determined by the Secretary of Agriculture to be equitable in consideration of anticipated benefits from such improvements; provided, that no part of the construction cost for providing any capacity in structures for purposes other than flood prevention and features related thereto were to be borne by the federal government under the provisions of the Act.

In the administrative arrangements worked out by the Secretary under the above cost-sharing provisions, local organizations were expected to assume all construction costs for providing storage in any structure for purposes other than flood prevention and features related thereto. It was the policy that local organizations would be expected to assume that part of the cost of installing works of improvement, exclusive of federal costs of technical services such as planning, design, supervision, and economic analysis, which was equal to the ratio of local benefits to total benefits, and all construction costs for water distribution and other facilities for purposes other than flood prevention

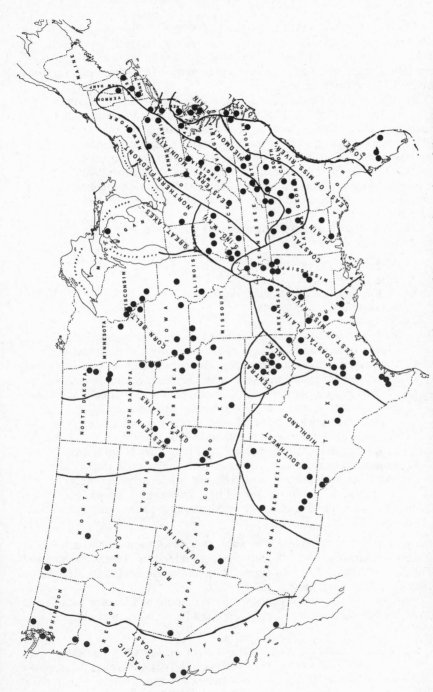

Figure 1. Location of 160 Public Law 566 watersheds by physiographic-economic regions of the United States.

and features related thereto. In addition to such costs as accrue to the federal government under the above provisions, the federal government could share a portion of the costs otherwise accruing to the local organization when justified in the workplan and when the reasons for so doing were set forth in detail.

In 1956 an amendment to the Act, Public Law 1018, authorized the federal government to: (1) include nonagricultural water management measures, (2) authorize federal credit assistance, (3) revise the watershed workplan approval procedure, and (4) bear the entire construction cost for flood prevention purposes in watershed projects.

The Act was further amended in 1958 by Public Law 85-865. This amendment permits the federal government to provide technical assistance and to participate in the sharing of the costs for fish and wildlife development.

The principal purposes that may be included in Public Law 566 projects are:

1. Watershed protection.
2. Flood prevention.
3. Agricultural water management.
   a. Irrigation.
   b. Drainage.
   c. Other agricultural water management measures, including the provision of a more uniform supply and distribution of water for agricultural use. Measures for the stabilization of annual streamflow, increasing the recharge of ground water reservoirs, and installing community water supply and distribution systems to provide water for livestock, orchard and crop spraying, rural community use, and other agricultural uses may be included in this category. Control of salt cedars and other phreatophytes may also be included.
4. Nonagricultural water management. Included in this category would be such purposes as fish and wildlife development, municipal or industrial water supply, recreation, power, pollution abatement by streamflow regulation, and saline water intrusion control.

As of May 1, 1959, some 436 watersheds had been authorized for planning assistance, and 172 had been authorized for actual operations as of June 8, 1959. For this paper, data are summarized for 160 watersheds approved as of May 1, 1958.

Examination of the distribution of the amount and kind of benefits at this stage can be considered only tentative for a number of obvious reasons:

1. Upland conservation benefits are not evaluated in monetary terms nor incorporated in the benefit-cost analysis tables contained in the Public Law 566 watershed workplans.
2. The basic law and the technical standards and criteria as established by administrative rules and regulations have been

undergoing change with respect to authorized purposes and the arrangements for cost-sharing.

3. The understanding on the part of local sponsoring groups of the potentials of watershed development is expected to continue to grow with experience in the program.

4. The location and the special interests of the sponsoring group of the initial projects cannot be considered as fully representing the kinds or amounts of benefits expected from future projects in many areas of the United States.

5. The watershed workplans which are the source of data on benefits were not prepared with the view of incorporating a full accounting of all types of anticipated benefits. For example, benefits of the so-called incidental categories are by intent not included in quantitative terms.

6. Many "extramarket values" have not been included in the data.

7. Since the Public Law 566 program is a joint undertaking among landowners, local districts, and state and federal agencies, the tendency is to incorporate in approved workplans only those purposes which local interests want at the particular time. As suggested above, additional purposes and broader interests on the part of local groups can be expected with more experience in the program.

Several kinds of benefits stem from the different purposes that are eligible for inclusion in small watershed projects. These are indicated in Table 1. One major group of benefits is the *reduction in floodwater damage* to crops, pasture, farm buildings and improvements, farm fences, stored crops; prevention of loss of livestock; and reduced flood damage to roads, bridges, railroads, power lines, utilities, and urban properties. Flood damage reduction benefits may also accrue downstream from or outside the boundary of a watershed. These are called downstream damage reduction benefits.

Control of water runoff and flood prevention also creates benefits through the prevention of sediment deposition on flood plain lands, in streams, and in reservoirs. Other benefits arise through the prevention of scouring of flood plain lands by floodwater, erosion of streambank channels, the headward cutting of gullies, and roadside erosion.

Restoration of former productivity, another floodwater damage reduction benefit, is possible on flood plain lands damaged from the deposition of sediment. Frequently, accelerated erosion from the uplands over the years has caused cropland to become swamped or poorly drained, and as a result unsuited for profitable crop production. Often such lands are idle or in poor pasture or brush. With an appropriate level of flood protection and some associated treatment such as drainage or clearing, these lands can often be restored to their former use.

Two other types of benefits — changed land use and more intensive use of land — are commonly found where flood plain lands are given flood protection. These occur under the following situations: As a result of the reduced flood hazard after protection is installed, areas of

Table 1. Types of Benefits by Resource Area for 160 Public Law 566 Watersheds Approved for Construction as of May 1, 1959

Type of Benefit	Lower Coastal Plain		Coastal Plain East of Miss. River		Piedmont		Eastern Mountains		Southern Indiana-Western Kentucky	
	Dollars (000)	Percent	Dollars (000)	Percent	Dollars (000)	Percent	Dollars (000)	Percent	Dollars (000)	Percent
Flood damage reduction benefits:										
Agricultural	54	10.8	419	42.0	172	30.3	370	45.3	220	37.6
Nonagricultural	8	1.6	38	3.8	22	3.8	232	28.4	51	8.7
Indirect and off-site	2	0.4	32	3.2	14	2.5	102	12.5	27	4.6
Restoration of former productivity	181	36.3	341	34.2	290	51.0	74	9.1	4	0.7
Changed land use	43	8.7	14	1.4	29	5.1	8	1.0	118	20.2
More intensive land use			97	9.8			4	0.5	64	11.0
Drainage	163	32.7	6	0.6			9	1.1	11	1.9
Irrigation	41	8.3	1	0.1	6	1.1				
Conservation benefits			45	4.5	31	5.4	8	1.0	64	11.0
Municipal and industrial water					5	0.8	4	0.5		
Recreation and wildlife			2	0.2			4	0.5	25	4.3
Other agricultural and nonagricultural	6	1.2	2	0.2			1	1.0		
Total	498	100.0	997	100.0	569	100.0	816	100.0	584	100.0

Table 1. (continued)

Type of Benefit	Corn Belt		Coastal Plain West of Miss. River		Central Oklahoma		Southwest Highlands		Western Great Plains	
	Dollars (000)	Percent	Dollars (000)	Percent	Dollars (000)	Percent	Dollars (000)	Percent	Dollars (000)	Percent
Flood damage reduction benefits:										
Agricultural	485	41.7	1211	58.6	527	56.3	142	34.1	103	65.2
Nonagricultural	88	7.5	127	6.1	76	8.1	207	49.7	44	27.8
Indirect and off-site	52	4.5	187	9.1	69	7.3	52	12.5	4	2.6
Restoration of former productivity	43	3.7	264	12.8	140	14.9	1	0.2		
Changed land use	248	21.3	86	4.2	42	4.5	1	0.2		
More intensive land use	15	1.3	26	1.2	83	8.9	10	2.4	6	3.8
Drainage	168	14.4	145	7.0						
Irrigation							3	0.7		
Conservation benefits	62	5.3	11	0.5			1	0.2	1	0.6
Municipal and industrial water			2	0.1						
Recreation and wildlife										
Other agricultural and nonagricultural	4	0.3	8	0.4						
Total	1165	100.0	2067	100.0	937	100.0	417	100.0	158	100.0

[33]

Table 1. (continued)

Type of Benefit	Rocky Mountains		Pacific Coast		Great Lakes–Northern Piedmont		Total	
	Dollars (000)	Percent	Dollars (000)	Percent	Dollars (000)	Percent	Dollars (000)	Percent
Flood damage reduction benefits:								
Agricultural	45	21.6	151	13.0	95	28.1	3994	40.4
Nonagricultural	82	39.4	692	59.9	92	27.3	1759	17.8
Indirect and off-site	26	12.5	136	11.8	24	7.2	727	7.3
Restoration of former productivity							1338	13.5
Changed land use			20	1.7	19	5.7	628	6.3
More intensive land use	26	12.5	55	4.8	40	12.0	426	4.3
Drainage			88	7.6	65	19.4	655	6.6
Irrigation	29	14.0					80	0.8
Conservation benefits			8	0.7	1	0.3	232	2.3
Municipal and industrial water							11	0.1
Recreation and wildlife							31	0.3
Other agricultural and nonagricultural			5	0.5			26	0.3
Total	208	100.0	1155	100.0	336	100.0	9907	100.0

flood plain land that are in native timber or pasture can be converted to crop production. For simplicity this conversion is called *changed land use* in Public Law 566 watershed reports. The elimination or reduction of the flood hazard may permit a *more intensive use of land* without change of use in the flood plain. The reduction of the flood hazard may encourage the operator to use the land more intensively. For example, he might shift land presently in small grain to alfalfa. Or he might use fertilizer and seed to improve low-producing pasture.

Agricultural water management benefits resulting from drainage and irrigation are the increased net incomes arising from the areas affected.

Municipal and industrial water and *fish and wildlife benefits* are self explanatory.

Certain other types of benefits such as pollution abatement, regulation of streamflow, recharging of ground water reservoirs, and the provision of water for livestock, for rural communities, and for orchard and crop spraying create direct benefits where such purposes are included in projects.

Secondary benefits of the project also occur as an increase in net incomes, or other beneficial effects, in activities stemming from or induced by the project. These benefits are values added over and above the immediate products or services created by the project. These benefits are not used in the determination of benefit-cost ratios, but may be considered for cost-sharing purposes. Certain *indirect benefits* also accrue as a result of flood prevention work. These may include prevention of delays or rerouting of traffic, of loss of business in urban areas, and of disease; also, elimination of sanitation hazards and of the need for caring for flood victims.

Other intangible or nonmonetary benefits may also occur. Examples would be the prevention of loss of life and a reduction in the fear of possible flood losses on the part of individuals.

Early flood control work of the Department of Agriculture, and thus many of the initial Public Law 566 watershed workplans, emphasized flood prevention and drainage. Until the passage of the amendment, Public Law 1018, in 1956, none of the workplans contained measures that would bring about nonagricultural water management benefits (Table 2). Since the passage of the 1956 amendment a few plans have been developed that include storage for municipal and industrial water, and the trend seems to favor more of these developments in the future. A few projects include provisions for supplemental irrigation. Indications are that the number of these will increase. Since amendment by Public Law 85-865, more Public Law 566 watersheds include fish and wildlife development. Thus, it appears that amendments to the Act will lead to the inclusion of all important types of benefits from the development of small watersheds.

A summary of the types of benefits by resource areas and for the United States as a whole, for the 160 watersheds, reveals some significant points. First, over 75 percent of all benefits are agricultural

Table 2. Trend in Distribution of Benefits by Type, Watershed Plans Completed to May 1, 1959

Type of Benefit	1955		1956		1957		1958		Jan.-May 1959		Total	
	No. of Water-sheds	Percent of $ Benefits	No. of Water-sheds	Percent of $ Benefits	No. of Water-sheds	Percent of $ Benefits	No. of Water-sheds	Percent of $ Benefits	No. of Water-sheds	Percent of $ Benefits	No. of Water-sheds	Percent of $ Benefits
Flood damage reduction	16	77.2	22	55.4	52	69.4	47	70.3	22	60.5	159	67.8
Land use enhancement	7	19.6	17	27.8	40	25.2	31	21.1	12	29.5	107	24.1
Drainage	1	3.0	6	16.8	11	3.9	7	5.6	3	9.7	28	6.6
Irrigation	1	0.2			1	-[a]	3	2.3			5	0.8
Other agricultural management					3	0.5	6	0.4			9	0.3
Municipal water					2	0.2	1	-[a]			3	0.1
Fish and wildlife					3	0.8	1	0.3			4	0.3
Other nonagricultural uses					1	-[a]			1	0.3	2	-[a]
All types	17	100.0	22	100.0	52	100.0	47	100.0	22	100.0	160	100.0

[a] Less than 0.1 percent.

(Table 1). The most important agricultural benefit is the reduction in floodwater damages. This constitutes some 40 percent of the total of all benefits. The next most important benefit is restoration of former productivity, followed by drainage and changed land use, respectively.

For the country as a whole, nonagricultural benefits constitute less than 25 percent of the total. Here again, a reduction in flood damages is the most significant type of benefit. This item accounts for 17.8 percent of all benefits. By resource areas, nonagricultural benefits are highest in the Pacific Coast area, where they account for approximately 60 percent of the total. Some of the other resource areas, namely the Eastern Mountains, Southwest Highlands, Western Great Plains, Rocky Mountains, and the area called Great Lakes-Northern Piedmont also had substantial nonagricultural benefits. Due to the small number of cases, with the possible exception of the Eastern Mountains and the Great Lakes-Northern Piedmont, the figures for most of these areas do not appear significant. When classified by purpose, benefits from these watershed projects would be ranked in the following order of importance:

1. Flood prevention
2. Drainage
3. Irrigation
4. Recreation and wildlife
5. Municipal and industrial water

The distribution of some of the less important benefits seems to be accounted for in a small number of projects. For example, only 4 out of the 160 summarized reports contained benefits from fish and wildlife; 5 were designed to provide irrigation benefits; and only 2 projects provided for other nonagricultural benefits.

On the other hand, 28 out of the 160 provided for drainage benefits. All 7 of the projects in the Lower Coastal Plain contained drainage benefits, and 4 out of 15 in the Upper Coastal Plain. Five projects out of 19 in the Coastal Plain west of the Mississippi River area provided for drainage benefits.

REGIONAL DISTRIBUTION OF BENEFITS

It must be emphasized that the following ideas on why benefits vary between regions are tentative (Figure 1). They are included to call attention to regional differences that have been revealed so far in small watershed projects. This may help in judging the representativeness of specific watersheds that are analyzed later in this volume. It may also suggest how planning procedures need to be varied to suit regional needs.

The fact that drainage benefits are relatively more important in the Lower Coastal Plain may be due to the fact that it is flat and near sea level. In areas of greater elevation and rougher topography, flood protection may be effective in reducing wetness, but in the Lower Coastal Plain high watertable rather than flooding may be the primary cause of wetness. The land is productive, a consideration making for profitability of drainage.

In the Coastal Plain east of the Mississippi River area the sandy, friable, loose soils are responsible for sediment damages. This helps to explain why sediment damages are relatively great in this area.

The heavy concentration of watershed projects in the southeastern Piedmont may indicate that it has conditions particularly favorable to flood protection through small structures. For the region as a whole, the land is not highly productive, as evidenced by generally low land values. But alluvial bottom land often has economically desirable characteristics. Moreover, annual flooding may be the rule. In other words, there is the potential of high production in flood plains, and it appears that flooding may be a principal hindrance to production.

In the Eastern Mountains, flood plains are relatively small, and many of them are already intensively utilized. In some mountainous farming areas the flood plain is the only land that is cropped. There is frequent flooding. These facts help explain the high benefits in this region from reduction of agricultural flood damages. On the other hand, the relatively low benefits from changed flood-plain agriculture[2] are consistent with the fact that many flood plains are already intensively utilized. High benefits from reduction of nonagricultural damages reflect urban influences. As we shall see, this urban influence is significant in every mountainous region.

In Southern Indiana-Western Kentucky, if we separate out two non-typical projects having large fire prevention and recreation and wildlife benefits, the six remaining projects appear to have the flood protection benefits one would expect from a predominantly agricultural region. These include significant benefits from both reduced agricultural flood damages and changed flood plain agriculture.

The Corn Belt also has significant benefits from reduced agricultural flood damages and changed flood plain agriculture. In addition, it has relatively high drainage and gully benefits. A partial explanation of the drainage benefits is that some of the projects are clustered along the Mississippi River where there are drainage problems. Another group of projects is clustered along the Missouri River in the Windblown soil area. This area has productive deep loess soils which are subject to gullying and so give rise to the gully benefits.

One of the areas where there is a high concentration of projects is the Coastal Plain west of Mississippi River. The favorable circumstances here include high rainfall and a productive agriculture. Low cost of dams may be another factor. Earth movers have experience from earlier water resource projects in the area. Open country may

---

[2] For simplicity in this section, we put three types of benefits together: restoration of former productivity, changed land use, and more intensive use of land. We lump these and refer to them as "changed flood-plain agriculture."

be conducive to low earth-moving costs. The rolling plain may favor good dam sites, while in many other sections of the country gradients may be so steep that even if there is a good site for the face of a dam, the storage capacity is limited.

Central Oklahoma is a region of relatively high crop value per acre and sufficient rainfall to permit a fairly diverse agriculture. Hence, with flood protection there may be opportunity to turn to intensive cropping in flood plains. These considerations help to explain why Central Oklahoma has high benefits both from reduction of agricultural flood damages and from changed flood-plain agriculture.

Common to the Southwest Highlands, the Western Great Plains, and the Rocky Mountains are climatic and soil conditions conducive to the production of sediment. These include erodable soils and storms of high intensity. In these three regions sediment benefits approach 15 percent of total benefits.

Differences between the regions mentioned in the preceding paragraph may also be noted. In the Rocky Mountains, if we take out one project having pronounced irrigation benefits, we find that benefits are predominantly from reduction of nonagricultural flood damages. The potential for benefits in connection with irrigation in this region may be high. Other than this, the value per acre of the produce of the land in this region tends to be low. This may leave urban sites as a main additional source of benefits.

Both the Southwest Highlands and the Western Great Plains have benefits from reduction of agricultural flood damages, but there is a relative lack of benefits from change in flood-plain agriculture. This may be because there are few crop alternatives. In these regions land is often used for wheat, or for grain sorghum, or for grazing — and in each case for little else. Due to limited crop alternatives, there may be little possibility of changing cropping patterns in response to flood protection.

In projects approved so far for the Pacific Coast there is a tendency, also noted for other mountainous regions, to have high benefits from nonagricultural flood damage reduction. The projects are located on the Pacific Ocean slope protecting urban property. Tentatively, it may be said that the Pacific Coast region's lack of projects inland is related to the fact that, inland, water is scarce and highly productive in agriculture. Much of the water runoff is caught and stored for irrigation — a practice that helps to minimize flooding. In view of water scarcity in some areas of the West, there may be a potential for watershed projects that emphasize irrigation and other supplemental water uses.

The Great Lakes-Northern Piedmont area is a large region encompassing much of the Northeast. It has few projects, and they cover many kinds of benefits. Much of the area is characterized by high population and low-intensity agriculture. The main positive hypothesis that might be offered is that, so far, costs of development have been high in this region. This may be associated both with terrain and with high cost rates for labor and other items.

PLANNING FOR MAXIMUM NET BENEFITS

The objective of the watershed planning process is to seek the greatest possible benefits (e.g., flood protection, irrigation, recreation) through combinations of appropriate measures (e.g., vegetative measures, channel improvement, big dams, little dams). The benefits may be likened to a preference function, and the measures to production possibilities. This volume is concerned for the most part with problems involved in achieving the general objective just stated.

Complementarity or competitiveness between benefits underlies many of the issues in watershed planning. A motivation for obtaining many kinds of benefits from one structure, or one project lies in the fact that, if the benefits are obtained in concert, they can be obtained at less expense than if measures were undertaken separately for each benefit. For example, if it is most economic to serve flood prevention and irrigation from the same dam, the costs of a dam of the necessary capacity must be less than the sum of the costs of other measures aimed at securing the benefits separately. Often, of course, there is only one dam site available and if multiple purposes are to be obtained the only way is to build a multiple purpose structure.

A special case of complementarity occurs when a single measure inevitably leads to more than one kind of benefit. An instance of this was indicated earlier in this chapter when downstream benefits were mentioned. Flood protection *within* a watershed usually gives some protection downstream. Another example is land treatment measures for conservation which in themselves help to reduce flooding and sediment damage. The degree of automatic complementarity will vary with the kinds of measures considered. Flood protection through detention structures will automatically provide some drainage benefits. However, the same degree of flood protection obtained through channel enlargement would provide greater drainage benefits.

There is a large degree of competitiveness involved in certain water resource developments. That is, one set of measures may preclude another set. Sometimes this goes so far as to be a physical preclusion, such as when alternative structures would occupy the same site or when a big dam would flood out a little dam. Sometimes the preclusion is less extreme and occurs because alternative measures are aimed at the same benefits. Complementarity or competitiveness at the planning level may vary from that existing in an operating project. For example, flood control and irrigation may be complementary elements in the planning of a multiple purpose dam. After the dam is in place, all water storage for irrigation will compete with storage space for flood protection.

Perhaps the most important point is that *at the margin* in planning there ought to be competition between benefits. Planning at the margin — that is, contemplating the addition or subtraction of increments of benefits — may be done consciously or unconsciously. It determines the total of each kind of benefit that will be included. To illustrate the point that there ought to be competition between benefits, suppose an initial project plan is contemplated securing flood protection benefits by means of a structure only. *Then,* suppose that the possibility is considered of adding land treatment measures for watershed protection that will secure benefits from reduced gullying and erosion. The cover crops and other measures to do this will also retard water runoff, giving flood protection benefits. Hence, the same flood protection benefits for the project could now be secured with a lower dam. If the costs saved by having a lower dam are more than the costs of the land treatment measures assignable to flood control, no further comparisons need to be made to conclude that the plan for having a structure only is inefficient. More benefits could be secured at the same cost with the alternative plan. The general proposition is that if — for a given project expenditure — it is possible to obtain additional benefits without giving up others, this fact is evidence that the project has not been planned to give maximum benefits. In the present example, the planner should contemplate adding more land treatment measures. Eventually, land treatment possibilities would tend to reach the point of saturation, so that added costs on them would permit less and less cost savings on the structure. When added erosion and gully control benefits would require reduced flood control benefits for a given project expenditure, the planner would know he had reached the range that might be efficient. Once he was in this range of competition between benefits, the planner might start varying project expenditures to find the best size of project. It might be desirable to increase project cost by adding still more land treatment measures. Even if the cost savings on the dam were less than the costs of added land treatment, it would be efficient to add the latter, provided gully and erosion benefits exceeded the cost difference.

We close with two conjectures about optimizing. There is little disagreement that maximum benefits are difficult to attain and are seldom, if ever, reached. To use economics to advantage in watershed planning, it is not necessary to ask economics to point out the absolute maximum. Economics will have made a significant contribution if it succeeds in screening projects so that those chosen will have positive net benefits.

A final conjecture is suggested by the geographical groupings of projects discussed earlier in the chapter. It seems important that there be sufficient flexibility in water resources development to allow for regional differences. The optimal institutional arrangements, laws, and planning procedures for one region may not be optimal for another.

Morris L. Weinberger is in charge of the Watershed Unit of the Land and Water Research Branch, Farm Economics Research Division, USDA. Formerly he was an agricultural economist with the Soil Conservation Service and the Bureau of Agricultural Economics of USDA.

Chapter 4

MORRIS L. WEINBERGER

Potential Investment in Small Watersheds[1]

IF PAST TRENDS are an indication, expected population growth and economic expansion in the United States will make insistent demands on water resources. Water use increased from approximately 40 billion gallons per day in 1900 to more than 260 billion gallons per day in 1955.[2] Distribution in 1955 by major uses was 45.7 percent for irrigation; 45.7 percent for industry, including steam electric power; 6.5 percent for public water supply; and 2.1 percent for farms and other residences not connected with public water supplies. The increased use of water between 1900 and 1955 represented a change in daily use per capita from 526 gallons to 1,573 gallons. With an estimated population of 370 million by 2010, little vision is required to foresee the need for vast increases in investments in water resources.

Estimates of the potential outlay of resources for watershed

[1] Many of the data in this paper are from a study under way by the Soil Conservation Service and the Agricultural Research Service. They are tentative and subject to revision. The views expressed are those of the author and do not necessarily reflect official views. Assistance in the statistical analysis by Dean Jansma, Farm Economics Research Division, is gratefully acknowledged.

[2] Use for hydroelectric power is excluded. See Walter L. Picton, "Summary of Information on Water Use in the United States, 1900-1975," BSB-136, Business and Defense Services Administration, U.S. Dept. of Commerce, Jan., 1956.

improvements can provide perspective for evaluating our present efforts in this direction. A projection is developed in this paper based in
part on watersheds approved for operations as of January 1, 1959, under the Flood Prevention and Watershed Protection Act. These watersheds are a small and not necessarily representative sample of the
total potential for watershed improvement. At the beginning of 1959,
they included only about four-tenths of 1 percent of the land area of
the United States. It should be emphasized that the projection of potential investment is subject to many uncertainties.

In the present study the United States has been subdivided into
physiographic regions as shown in Figure 1. The percentage of all
lands in approved watersheds ranged from 0.12 percent in the Western
Mountains and Pacific Coast to 0.72 percent in the Atlantic and Gulf
Coastal Plain. The percentages by regions are shown in Table 1.

Table 1. Number and Area of Watersheds Authorized for Operations
as of January 1, 1959, by Physiographic Regions

Physiographic Region	Number of Watersheds	Watershed Area	
		Acreage	Percentage of Region
		(Thousand Acres)	(Percent)
Atlantic and Gulf Coastal Plain	36	2,001	0.72
Appalachian-Ozark Highlands	39	1,541	.52
Central Basin	23	1,307	.46
Great Plains	18	1,967	.49
Western Mountains and Pacific Coast	23	748	.12
Total	139	7,564	0.40

Under the present program, measures for flood prevention fall into
three categories — structural, land treatment primarily for flood prevention, and land treatment for both flood prevention and watershed
protection. Amounts that have so far been recommended in approved
workplans for investment in these and other measures are shown in
Table 2.

Of the total of approximately $154 million, 96.5 percent is for flood
prevention. Structural measures account for about 61 percent of the
investment for flood prevention, land treatment for watershed protection for 38 percent, and land treatment for flood prevention for 1 percent. The 3.5 percent of the total investment for purposes other than
flood prevention includes drainage, irrigation, municipal water, and
recreation.

While these data appear usable as a base for estimating the potential investment for flood prevention and watershed protection, they are
less adequate for investments for other purposes. Recent experience

Table 2. Investment in Works of Improvement Recommended
in 139 Watershed Workplans Authorized for Operations
as of January 1, 1959, by Physiographic Regions

Measures	Physiographic Regions[a]					Total
	A	B	C	D	E	
	(Thousand dollars)					
Flood prevention:						
Structural	26,520	16,149	10,531	16,497	21,169	90,866
Land treatment for flood prevention	873	606	0	0	145	1,624
Land treatment for watershed protection	20,821	14,864	8,304	10,097	1,800	55,886
Total	48,214	31,619	18,835	26,594	23,114	148,376
Other:						
Drainage	2,643	362	251	0	56	3,312
Irrigation	391	62	0	0	610	1,063
Other agricultural water management	0	0	31	0	53	84
Municipal water supply	72	269	0	0	0	341
Fish and wildlife	38	411	164	0	0	613
Other nonagricultural water management	0	10	0	0	0	10
Total	3,144	1,114	446	0	719	5,423
All measures	51,358	32,733	19,281	26,594	23,833	153,799

[a]A - Atlantic and Gulf Coastal Plain, B - Appalachian-Ozark Highlands, C - Central Basin, D - Great Plains, E - Western Mountains and Pacific Coast.

indicates a growing demand for assistance for purposes in addition to flood prevention. But estimates of potential investments for drainage, irrigation, water supplies, fish, wildlife, and recreation would require analyses of river-basin surveys in which account was taken of all major uses of water. To go over existing survey data systematically was not deemed promising enough to attempt in this study. Hence the consideration here of purposes other than flood prevention is brief and subjective.

FLOOD PREVENTION

Estimates of utlimate investment in watershed improvements for flood prevention are based on annual floodwater damages in the United States. Other characteristics that might have been used are area of land subject to overflow, major land use, and value of land improvements and buildings. But use of these latter characteristics has two major weaknesses — their relation to works of improvement for flood prevention is indirect, and their numerical appraisal is difficult.

Erwin C. Ford in 1953 estimated average annual upstream

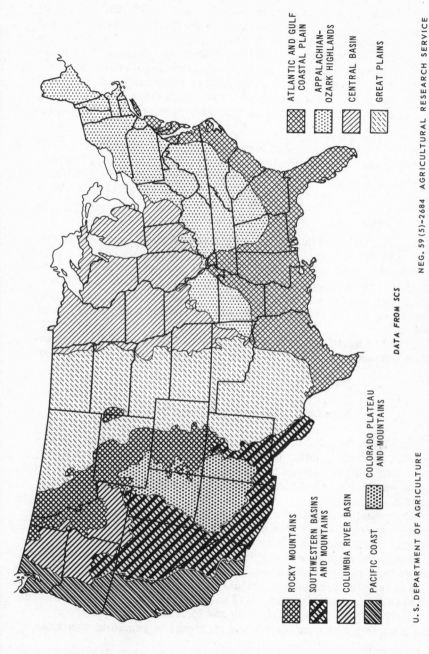

ATLANTIC AND GULF
COASTAL PLAIN

APPALACHIAN-
OZARK HIGHLANDS

CENTRAL BASIN

GREAT PLAINS

ROCKY MOUNTAINS

SOUTHWESTERN BASINS
AND MOUNTAINS

COLUMBIA RIVER BASIN

PACIFIC COAST

COLORADO PLATEAU
AND MOUNTAINS

DATA FROM SCS

NEG. 59 (5)-2684   AGRICULTURAL RESEARCH SERVICE

U.S. DEPARTMENT OF AGRICULTURE

Figure 1.   Physiographic regions of the United States.

floodwater damages in the United States to be $545,122,000.[3] His estimates were made for seven different groups of states and were based on prices prevailing for the year ending July 31, 1952. I have adjusted these estimates to conform to the physiographic regions of this study. A further adjustment was made to reflect projected levels of prices used by the U. S. Department of Agriculture for benefit and cost analyses of land and water resource projects. With these revisions, average annual floodwater damages in upstream watersheds are estimated as follows:

Atlantic and Gulf Coastal Plain	$128,590,000
Appalachian-Ozark Highlands	137,745,000
Central Basin	94,622,000
Great Plains	104,039,000
Western Mountains and Pacific Coast	51,908,000
Total	$516,904,000

It should be noted that these estimates are based on data collected prior to 1953, including pre-World War II studies. Methods of computing damages have changed since 1953. For example, in present damage surveys, "restoration of former productivity" is included as a flood damage, whereas it was not included formerly. This pertains to loss in net income from changes in land use induced by adverse effects of flooding.[4]

A further qualification is that development of flood plains may increase damages in the future, although zoning may be a partial deterrent.

Structural Measures for Flood Prevention

Data from the sample of watershed workplans were used in a regression analysis relating the cost of structural measures for flood prevention to flood damage in the watershed. The correlation for each region was highly significant, as shown in the summary of results in Table 3.

The potential investment for flood protection was estimated by applying these equations to the estimates given above of annual flood damages occurring in the regions.

It definitely appears that a projection of potential costs should take into account regional influences. Costs of structural measures for flood prevention per dollar of annual floodwater damage shown in Table 3 ranged from approximately $6.12 in the Appalachian-Ozark Highlands to $16.60 in the Western Mountains and Pacific Coast. One factor producing this variation may be the efficiency of remedial measures.

---

[3] Erwin C. Ford, "Upstream Floodwater Damages," *Jour. of Soil and Water Conservation*, Vol. 8, No. 5, Sept., 1953.

[4] Soil Conservation Service, *Economics Guide for Watershed and Flood Prevention*, USDA, Dec., 1958, Chap. 4.

Table 3. Selected Statistics for Establishment of Relationship of Structural Costs
of Flood Prevention to Average Annual Flood Damages
in Approved Watersheds by Physiographic Regions

Physiographic Region	Selected Statistics				
	n	r	r^2	t_{n-2}[a]	$\hat{y} = a + bx$
Atlantic and Gulf Coastal Plain[b]	35	0.9566	0.9151	18.95	$\hat{y} = -39.74 + 8.304x$
Appalachian-Ozark Highlands	39	.7196	.5178	6.30	$\hat{y} = 109.56 + 6.118x$
Central Basin	23	.8189	.6706	6.54	$\hat{y} = 147.59 + 7.626x$
Great Plains	18	.8739	.7635	7.19	$\hat{y} = 297.94 + 6.376x$
Western Mountains and Pacific Coast	23	.9959	.9918	50.38	$\hat{y} = -54.78 + 16.600x$
Total	138	0.8888	0.7900	22.62	$\hat{y} = -37.60 + 10.290x$

[a]All t values significant at 1 percent level.
[b]There is one less watershed in this table than in Table 1, owing to the combination of Upper Brushy and Lower Brushy Creek watersheds, Texas, in the Atlantic and Gulf Coastal Plain.

Another may be the degree of flood protection afforded by the flood prevention measures.

Land Treatment Measures for Both Flood Prevention and Watershed Protection

Under present watershed planning procedures, land treatment measures for watershed protection may include any measures that are ordinarily included in a soil and water conservation program. They are, however, limited to those which have a measurable influence on reduction of flood and sediment damages. They are also limited to those reasonably expected to be installed by farmers during the recommended period of installation. This period is usually five to ten years.

Future investment in land treatment measures, in view of potential national requirements, could be tremendous. Land treatment measures include many farm and ranch management practices that conserve soil and retard runoff. Many of these practices, such as rotation changes, liming, and fertilizing, to a large degree also increase agricultural production. Application of land treatment measures will play an important part in meeting future needs for greater production of food, fiber, and woodland products.

The potential investment in land treatment measures on public lands and forest lands is not indicated by the volume of such measures recommended in the sample watersheds. Many watersheds containing large acreages of forest lands or public lands will have economic need for land treatment measures, but benefits from water control and management may be of minor importance. Attainment of the potential investments for land treatment measures in such areas may be accomplished through programs of a nonproject type.

Potential investment in land treatment measures for watershed protection developed in this paper are predicated upon the quantities needed for flood prevention. They do not reflect the needs for other conservation purposes. The U. S. Department of Agriculture is making a nationwide survey to determine needs for soil and water conservation measures and practices, but the estimates indicated herein are not intended to be comparable with the results of that study.

The estimated investment in land treatment measures for potential watershed improvement were based on the ratio of costs of such measures to the costs of structural measures for flood prevention as found in the sample workplans. An alternate approach would have involved application of the cost of land treatment per acre of open land to the total area of open land. This method, however, would give a cost of land treatment nearly four times as large as that obtained by the former method. Results of the two procedures vary least in the Atlantic and Gulf Coastal Plain Region and most in the Western Mountains and Pacific Coast Region. It appears that use of the ratio of open land in sample watersheds to total open land in the problem areas for projection would overemphasize investment in land treatment measures associated with flood prevention. This is probably because flood problems are inconsequential in many watersheds. As pointed out earlier, investment in land treatment measures may be made in such watersheds, but not primarily for flood prevention or watershed protection.

Land Treatment Measures Primarily for Flood Prevention

Potential investments in land treatment measures primarily for flood prevention were also estimated by the ratio of such costs in sample workplans to the cost of structural measures for flood prevention. Measures in this category include planting of critically eroded areas to grass, shrubs, or trees, minor erosion control structures, roadside planting, and protection from forest fires. Although minor for any region as a whole, costs of these improvements are substantial in local areas where erosion has reduced land productivity to the level where remedial measures are not profitable from a private viewpoint.

Potential Investment in all Measures for Flood Prevention

It is estimated that the potential investment for flood prevention in the United States as a whole includes 61.2 percent for structural measures, 1.1 percent for land treatment measures primarily for flood prevention, and 37.7 percent for land treatment measures for watershed protection. These percentages by physiographic regions are shown in Table 4.

Table 4. Potential Investment in Watershed Improvement for Flood Prevention, by Kinds of Measures, by Physiographic Regions

Physiographic Region	Structural Measures	Land Treatment Primarily for Flood Prevention	Land Treatment for Watershed Protection	All Flood Prevention Measures
		(Percent)		
Atlantic and Gulf Coastal Plain	55.0	1.8	43.2	100.0
Appalachian-Ozark Highlands	51.1	1.9	47.0	100.0
Central Basin	55.9	0	44.1	100.0
Great Plains	62.0	0	38.0	100.0
Western Mountains and Pacific Coast	91.6	.6	7.8	100.0
Total	61.2	1.1	37.7	100.0

Estimated potential investments in flood prevention by region, computed by the methods described above, are as follows:

	Million dollars
Atlantic and Gulf Coastal Plain	1,941
Appalachian-Ozark Highlands	1,650
Central Basin	1,291
Great Plains	1,070
Western Mountains and Pacific Coast	941
Total	6,893

If the $6.9 billion of investments were carried out evenly over fifty years, the yearly investment would be about $138 million and would require great expansion of the present program. On the assumption that the potential watershed improvement for flood prevention would require the same investment per unit of land treated as in the sample watersheds, it is possible to estimate the area of land involved. If the further assumption is made that in the future watersheds will average the same size as the sample group, the number of watersheds to be treated may also be estimated. These calculations are indicated by physiographic regions in Table 5.

The potential investment for flood prevention decreases by physiographic regions proceeding from the East to the West. The projected costs per square mile of all land range from $4,460 in the Atlantic and Gulf Coastal Plain Region to $960 in the Western Mountains and Pacific Coast Region. The costs per square mile of watershed treated show considerable variation. To some degree these variations in cost reflect differences in amounts of damageable values. In the western

Table 5. Potential Area of Land, Number of Watersheds, and Investment
for Flood Prevention by Physiographic Regions

Physiographic Region	Area of Land To Be Treated in Region		Cost Per Sq. Mile of Region	Cost Per Sq. Mile Treated	Number of Watersheds
	(Square miles)	(Percent)	(Dollars)		(Number)
Atlantic and Gulf Coastal Plain	125,890	29.0	4,460	15,420	1,450
Appalachian-Ozark Highlands	125,680	27.1	3,560	13,130	2,040
Central Basin	140,010	31.3	2,880	9,220	1,580
Great Plains	123,680	19.7	1,700	8,650	720
Western Mountains and Pacific Coast	47,590	4.9	960	19,770	940
Total	562,850	19.0	2,330	12,560	6,730

region where urban damages are high, the cost of flood prevention is
$19,770 per square mile treated, in contrast to $8,650 per square mile
in the Great Plains.

The low proportion of land area to be treated in the Western Mountains and Pacific Coast Region undoubtedly is due to the large areas of
wild and waste lands. Even in the regions to the east, no more than
about a third of the land area would be included in watershed projects.

Several factors not accounted for may influence the magnitude of
the potential investment for flood prevention in small watersheds.
Among these is the estimate of flood damage itself. As stated earlier,
the estimated average annual flood damages of about $517 million
probably do not include losses that result from loss of former productivity of flood plains. Inclusion of this damage would increase the investment in feasible flood prevention measures by 12.2 percent. On-
site land damage from gully erosion is currently classified as a flood
damage, but it is probable that flood damage estimates made in 1953,
upon which projected improvements are based, did not include these
losses. In the Central Basin or Corn Belt, such losses account for 10
percent of the total damage. Their inclusion would increase estimated
flood prevention investments by 1.3 percent.

Downstream major river damages were not included in the national
damage estimates cited. These losses are estimated by the Soil Conservation Service to be in excess of $500 million annually. To date,
approved watershed workplans claim no benefits from reducing flood
damages on major rivers. Current hydrologic studies indicate that
upstream measures in some situations may produce a consequential
reduction in downstream damages or they may lower the storage requirements of major-sized structures. If $50 million of the down-
stream damages are added to the average annual upstream damages to

account for this potential benefit investment in upstream flood prevention, improvements might be increased another 10 percent.

Allowance might be made for increased future settlement of flood plains. Future settlement might precede the need for flood prevention, or flood prevention measures might be installed to permit more intensive settlement. In either event, a 10-percent increase in potential flood prevention is probably a conservative estimate.

If account is taken of all of the foregoing factors, the total projected investment would be increased by a third, bringing the total to approximately $9.2 billion.

Other potential investments for flood prevention in small watersheds are not estimated quantitatively in this paper. Pooling arrangements administered by the Agricultural Conservation Program Service for construction of improvements that have flood prevention values were not projected in estimating future investments. Still other investments, although possibly of minor importance, include improvements for flood protection installed without federal assistance by states, local governments, and private landowners.

Nature of Potential Investments in Flood Prevention Measures

Floodwater-retarding structures may be regarded as the backbone of the national flood prevention program. These structures, along with stream-channel enlargement and improvement, account for 60 and 34 percent, respectively, of the investment in structural measures. Based on relationships to date, in a national flood prevention program of $6.9 billion, 42,600 floodwater-retarding structures and 74,400 miles of stream-channel improvement would be constructed. Additional structures totaling 8,300 miles would be installed for grade stabilization and prevention of major gully erosion.

Within regions, there is considerable variation with respect to the relative importance of different kinds of structural measures. In the Atlantic and Gulf Coastal Plain Region and in the Appalachian-Ozark Highlands Region, the proportionate investment in structural measures for floodwater-retarding structures and stream-channel improvement is about the same as the national average. In the Central Basin, the relative potential investment in floodwater-retarding structures is lower than the national average, but structures for grade stabilization would compensate. Floodwater-retarding structures in the Great Plains accounted for 95 percent of the potential investment in structural measures. In the western region, however, the corresponding proportion is 35 percent. In this region, stream-channel improvement represents 55 percent of the investment in all structural measures.

The estimated outlay for potential structural measures for flood prevention includes 66 percent for construction; 19 percent for installation services; 14 percent for lands, easements, and rights-of-way; and 1 percent for administration of contracts. Looking toward the achievement of potential improvement, we should expect the relative cost of lands, easements, and rights-of-way to increase. Factors operating in this direction will be more intensive use and occupancy of flood plains, the tendency to construct dual- or multiple-purpose structures with the attendant need for public ownership or control of the site, and the achievement of the program itself.

The $6.9 billion potential flood prevention program does not account for associated costs required to achieve the expected benefits. In watersheds in which changes in use of flood plains will result from reduction of flood hazards, land improvements such as clearing, fencing, and drainage may be needed. In planning, these investments are deducted from the estimated flood prevention benefits.

Based on estimates of planned watersheds, operation and maintenance of the potential flood prevention program, exclusive of land treatment for watershed protection, would cost about $33 million annually. These costs are based on brief experience only, and they may prove to be more or less than adequate. Comparable costs were not estimated for land treatment measures for watershed protection.

Land treatment for watershed protection accounts for about 38 percent of the cost of the potential flood prevention program. Approximately 90 percent of this cost would be for construction or application and the remainder for provision of technical assistance by public agencies. The latter cost is estimated at approximately $271,592,000, of which about one-fourth would normally be included in going programs of public agencies.

EFFECTS OF POTENTIAL IMPROVEMENT ON NATIONAL INCOME

Flood prevention benefits of sample watersheds include reductions in several types of flood and sediment damage, increased intensity of flood-plain use, and other incidental effects. Projection of these benefits to regional totals was based on the ratio of costs of flood prevention measures in the sample watersheds to the projected costs, the results being shown in Table 6. Only primary benefits, both direct and indirect, are shown in this table. [5]

For the United States as a whole, annual benefits from potential flood prevention totaled $389.7 million, of which about 10 percent would occur to land, 63 percent to crops and pasture, 4 percent to agricultural improvements, and 23 percent to nonagricultural property. Nearly all of these benefits would result from protection of flood plain lands and other property located therein.

On-site effects of land treatment measures for watershed protection are not evaluated in watershed workplans. A rough approximation of these benefits may be gained from planning experience of the pilot watershed program initiated by the U. S. Department of Agriculture in

---

[5] *Ibid.*, Chap. 3, for a definition of these benefits.

Table 6. Benefits Attributable to Potential Flood Prevention Improvements,
by Physiographic Regions

Physiographic Region	Land	Crops and Pasture	Agricultural Improvements	Non-agricultural Improvements	Total
		(Thousand dollars)			
Atlantic and Gulf Coastal Plain	13,689	98,441	5,194	6,643	123,967
Appalachian-Ozark Highlands	4,436	60,384	3,236	20,458	88,514
Central Basin	7,470	40,574	1,782	9,869	59,695
Great Plains	7,603	33,712	3,983	15,488	60,786
Western Mountains and Pacific Coast	5,129	14,083	814	36,714	56,740
Total	38,327	247,194	15,009	89,172	389,702

1953. *Ex ante* evaluation of net returns from land treatment measures
recommended in the pilot program indicated an annual net benefit of
$2.50 per acre,[6] but land treatment measures in current projects are
recommended in smaller quantities than they were in earlier years. If
we assume that the net benefit from land treatment measures as currently planned is $1.25 per acre, the potential benefit in the area to be
treated for flood prevention would be $450,280,000. Including this re-
turn, total net returns creditable to the potential investments for flood
prevention measures would be nearly $840 million annually.

Of the potential total increase in income, approximately 89 percent
would be to agriculture. In consideration of greater supplies of agricultural products that will be required for a larger population during
the next 50 years, this increase in net agricultural income of $751 mil-
lion does not seem unreasonable.

WATERSHED INVESTMENT FOR PURPOSES OTHER THAN FLOOD PREVENTION

The Watershed Protection and Flood Prevention Act as amended is
broad in scope with respect to land and water resource developments.
Thus far, flood prevention has been the major type of development requested by local agencies. However, in the Atlantic and Gulf Coastal
Plain, 10 percent of the cost of structural measures planned in the
sample watersheds was for drainage. In the Western Mountains and

---

[6]M. L. Weinberger and Erwin C. Ford, "Protecting Watersheds — Ways and Whys," in
Land, The Yearbook of Agriculture, 1958, USDA (Washington, D. C.: Government Printing
Office).

Pacific Coast Region, 3 percent of the cost of planned structural measures has been for irrigation.

Approximately 20.7 million acres of potentially drainable undeveloped land could be made suitable for agricultural production.[7] About 17 million acres of this land is outside existing organized drainage enterprises. Most of it is located in the southeastern states, including the Southern Plains. As the need arises for improving these lands, it is probable that much of the drainage work can be accomplished through watershed improvement authorized by Public Law 566. Other watershed improvements for drainage purposes may be undertaken on a large scale in areas presently organized for drainage enterprises. There were about 98.6 million acres of land in such enterprises in 1950.[8] Already these drainage districts are sponsors of some of the sample watersheds.

Irrigated land in 1954 totaled 29.6 million acres — 27 million acres in the 17 western states and 2.6 million acres in the 31 eastern states. Compared with acreage irrigated five years earlier, this represented increases of 10 percent in the West and 70 percent in the East. Some authorities have stated that the greatest potential of irrigation in the United States lies in correcting the seasonal deficiencies of moisture in the nonarid regions.[9]

The precise role to be taken by watershed programs in achieving potential investments for irrigation is difficult to predict. It is reasonable to expect, however, that fulfillment of this potential development would involve construction of structures for water storage and other improvements included in the purposes of the Watershed Protection and Flood Prevention Act. In the western states, important aspects of watershed investments for irrigation are improved efficiency of water use and construction of additional storage facilities.

Studies in pilot watersheds show the increasing importance of recreational services and water supply derived from water storage in the pool areas of floodwater-retarding structures reserved for sediment.[10] As the watershed program develops, local governments will become more aware of the features that may be economically incorporated with flood prevention structures. We might reasonably expect to encounter far greater interest in planning mutliple-purpose structures.

---

[7] Hugh H. Wooten and James R. Anderson, "Agricultural Land Resources," Agr. Info. Bul. 140, USDA, June, 1955.

[8] U.S. Census of Agriculture, U.S. Bureau of the Census, 1950.

[9] Elco L. Greenshields and William I. Palmer, "Some New Jobs for Irrigation," in *Land, The Yearbook of Agriculture, 1958*, USDA (Washington, D.C.: Government Printing Office).

[10] "Watershed Program Evaluation, Six Mile Creek, Arkansas," Interim Progress Report, Agr. Res. Serv., USDA, ARS 43-51, July, 1957; and Morris L. Weinberger, "Watershed Program Evaluation, Plum Creek, Kentucky," Interim Progress Report, Agr. Res. Serv., USDA, ARS 43-85, Jan., 1959.

ATTAINMENT OF POTENTIAL INVESTMENT IN
SMALL WATERSHEDS

In summary, the estimated investment in potential watershed improvement for flood prevention as projected in this paper is approximately $6.9 billion. In accordance with present law and policy with respect to cost-sharing, the federal cost would be approximately $3.8 billion over and above expenditures for other related going programs. Even though a large part of the first cost of flood prevention is at federal expense, farmers may bear substantial associated costs for land improvement in those instances in which restoration of former productivity or changed land use of flood plains is involved.

In addition to the problems of financing potential investments, there is the problem of providing technicians able to plan and supervise construction of watershed improvements. Requirements for technical service to attain even limited potential levels within fifty years or so would represent about a fourfold increase over present efforts.

There might also need to be prodigious efforts, not dealt with in this paper, to overcome legal and organizational problems — particularly at the local level.

W. BURL BACK | *Comment*

THE STORY is told that the government of India is very keen on amassing statistics. The process includes collecting estimates from village watchmen, raising these estimates to the nth power, and taking the cube root of the result.[1] Weinberger also expanded some estimates, but he failed to take the cube root. I would have been happier with his results had he done so. On the other hand, one may consider Weinberger's effort a process in operations research, where "Operations research is the art of giving bad answers to problems to which otherwise worse answers are given."[2]

I shall divide my discussion of Weinberger's paper into two parts: First, I will present a criticism of his procedure, but assume the Soil

[1] P. K. Mukherjee, *Economic Surveys in Under-Developed Countries* (New York: Asia Publishing House, 1959), p. 3.

[2] Thomas L. Saaty, *Mathematical Methods of Operations Research* (New York: McGraw-Hill Book Company, Inc., 1959), p. 3.

W. Burl Back is Professor of Agricultural Economics at Oklahoma State University, having previously been Assistant Professor at Oregon State College and Assistant in Farm Management at the University of Kentucky.

Conservation Service estimates of costs and benefits which he used are
relevant for estimating the potential investments in small watersheds.
Second, I will present a brief criticism of the Soil Conservation Service estimates of costs and benefits with particular reference to use of
these in estimating future national or regional net benefits from small
watershed development.

The basic data for Weinberger's analysis were Ford's estimates of
annual flood damage as revised by application of U. S. Department of
Agriculture projections of prices and costs, and the Soil Conservation
Service estimates of benefits and costs in currently approved watershed projects. The procedure for deriving the estimated potentials for
works of improvement reported in the paper can be reduced to the following:

1. Define the potential benefits as the revised annual flood damage
    adjusted by proportion of flood damage not removed by cur-
    rently approved projects.
2. Define the potential number of watersheds as the potential ben-
    efits divided by the benefits per watershed in approved projects.
3. Define the potential investment as investment per watershed in
    approved projects times potential number of watersheds.

Weinberger assumed the acres in watersheds with potential for development would average the same as the acreage in presently approved
watersheds. Thus,

4. Total potential acreage is the number of potential watersheds
    times the acres per watershed in approved projects, and
5. Potential investment per acre is the potential investment di-
    vided by number of acres.

Weinberger chose a slightly different sequence of steps in procedure.
In particular, he fused steps 1, 2, and 3 by use of the cumbersome
method of linear regression for averaging simple benefit-cost ratio
estimates. Having performed the regression analysis, he failed to take
advantage of the opportunity to place confidence limits on the coefficients in order to estimate ranges in his totals.

The main justification for the procedure rests upon an assumption
that works of improvement of watershed projects presently approved
can be projected to other similar watersheds. Implicit in his procedure is the assumption that the benefit-cost ratio remains constant as
numbers of watersheds increase to the maximum for exhausting the
potential benefits. The assumption also is implied that the annual flood
damage is included completely in the watersheds with the estimated
potential for development. My own belief is that the benefit-cost ratio
decreases with increase in numbers of watersheds. Furthermore, I
suspect Ford's flood damage estimates were meant to apply to a
greater area than the 19 percent, nationally, reported as having potential for development. The alternative assumption of a decreasing
benefit-cost ratio with increases in numbers of watersheds would

result in lower potential benefits, although not necessarily smaller numbers of potential watersheds and lower potential investment, than Weinberger obtained.

I shall now tread on "holy ground" with a brief criticism of the foundations for Weinberger's analyses — the Soil Conservation Service estimates of flood damages, benefits and costs. Upon examination of several workplans for Oklahoma watersheds, I concluded that our Soil Conservation Service accountants have mastered the art of double-counting of benefits in nonobvious fashion. Some workplans included both "restoration of productivity" and "change in land use" listed as benefits. All of the plans I examined projected both reduction in crop damage and preventing reduced flood-plain soil productivity as future benefits. It is conceivable, of course, that, in any given year, or for any given flood, both flood-plain soil damage and crop damage can occur. However, such soil losses reduce future productivity and, consequently, the amount of crops subject to damage by future floods. If such soil losses do not affect the amount of crops subject to damage by future floods, why be concerned about soil erosion at all in watershed planning? Surely some double accounting occurs when these benefits are listed separately and projected in the future. Ford's estimates of annual flood damage, when projected, contain this element of double-counting.

A second major weakness I suspect in both Ford's estimates of damages and in the Soil Conservation Service accounts of benefits is the failure to consider decreasing intensity in total flood-plain land use associated with changing demand for farm products, technological progress, and with other factors independent of flooding. Indirectly, Weinberger presented a defense for this neglect with his discussion of population increases and the implied future need for more intensive use of flood-plain land. He was bold indeed to state a "conservative" estimate of 10-percent increase in potential benefits, over those accounted for by Ford, to provide for increased future settlement of flood plains. For several decades we have experienced a farm population decline in small watersheds accompanying national population increases. Population projections for several decades in the future include a continuation of these past trends. Accompanying the farm population decline in Oklahoma has been a marked shift in land use from field and row crops to grass and forage production, both statewide and in the watersheds, and estimates of upstream flood damages to crops for the state applicable prior to 1953 now would be obsolete.

Many economists have criticized the use of long-term government bond interest rates for projecting costs of public resource development projects. The government borrowing rate of 2.5 percent takes no account of the risk associated with investments in watershed projects. Krutilla and Eckstein estimate the social cost of publicly financed projects to be 5 to 6 percent, as contrasted with the currently used 2.5

percent.[3] If a 5.5-percent rate were applied in projecting costs of improvements in watersheds, the estimated federal share of the cost would about double. This would make considerable reductions in the net benefits, regionally and nationally, implied in Weinberger's estimates.

It is possible, as Weinberger points out, that many benefits to upstream watershed development are not included in present accounting. For example, the downstream flood prevention benefits may be underestimated. However, if increasing monetary national income is our objective, I believe the need is urgent to allocate the restricted annual expenditure on small watershed development more efficiently. If present accounting methods are continued, watersheds with the highest benefit-cost ratios, rather than any with a ratio greater than one, should receive priority in order to maximize public benefits. Furthermore, from the standpoint of economic efficiency, the appropriate criterion for adding increments of investment to individual watersheds is the cut-off ratio for each year, not the 1:1 ratio of current practice.[4]

[3] John V. Krutilla and Otto Eckstein, *Multiple Purpose River Development* (Baltimore: Johns Hopkins Press, 1958), Chap. 4.

[4] Otto Eckstein, *Water Resource Development, The Economics of Project Evaluation* (Cambridge: Harvard University Press, 1958), Chap. 3.

Fletcher E. Riggs is an agricultural economist in the Division of Agricultural Relations of TVA. He was formerly Assistant Professor of Agricultural Economics at Kansas State University and Research Associate in Economics at Vanderbilt University.

Chapter 5

FLETCHER E. RIGGS

The Watershed As an Entity for Planning

HISTORICALLY, watershed planning has been primarily concerned with the somewhat narrow purpose of land and water resources development. In a few instances the objectives have been broader. The Tennessee River watershed, or river basin,[1] has provided the geographic context for a broad program of regional economic development.[2] However, the focus in this paper is on the usefulness of the watershed in planning for the development of land and water resources.

---

[1] The distinction between watershed and river basin has traditionally been one of size only. In many cases the same drainage area has been referred to as both a watershed and a river basin. A sharp distinction is not attempted in this paper. Reference to watersheds will be to small drainage areas, and the larger drainages will be referred to as river basins. If a distinction between watershed and river basin were attempted, it might be based on function or purpose in development. For example, hydroelectric power generation and navigation are usually confined to the large drainage area or river basin, whereas flood control and drainage can be accomplished in the smaller drainage areas as well as the large basins.

[2] This concept has been carried over to TVA's Tributary Watersheds Program, where the emphasis is on area economic development, with water and the watershed providing the focus for developmental activity.

PHYSICAL CHARACTERISTICS OF THE WATERSHED

Timmons has stated, "The only unique physical characteristic of a watershed is that it is a hydrologic unit of space composed of an inter-related drainage area with a common movement of water including all the consequential implications for land and water use."[3] In other words, the watershed is a natural drainage area. It is tied together physically by an interrelated stream and drainage pattern.

Figure 1 illustrates the drainage pattern of a watershed. Precipitation falling at point A either soaks into the ground or moves overland to a field ditch or drainage course. From there it goes to the small streams and on to point B, and thence to point C, continuing to be fed by other small and intermediate-sized streams such as D, E, and F. Within a particular drainage area, the farther one gets downstream, the larger the available supply of stream water and the larger the capacity of the stream channel to carry it. The significance of this is that there may be a small drainage area problem without there being a problem in the larger drainage area.

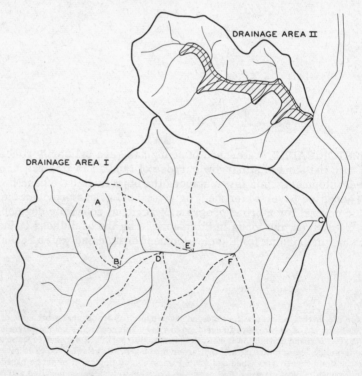

Figure 1. Map of hypothetical drainage areas.

[3]John F. Timmons, "Economic Framework for Watershed Development," *Jour. Farm Econ.*, Vol. XXXVI, No. 5, Dec., 1954, pp. 1171-72.

Several additional characteristics of the drainage area need to be considered. First, the physical conditions found in a natural drainage area are dependent on happenings upstream but relatively independent of happenings downstream. Thus, physical conditions in drainage area B can affect conditions at point C, but the reverse is not true. Second, two otherwise independent drainage areas may be interdependent when considered as parts of a larger drainage area. Thus, drainage areas B and D are physically independent when considering happenings within either drainage area, but they are interdependent when considering the larger drainage area of which they are an integral part.

These characteristics can be illustrated by reference to drainage areas I and II in Figure 1. Assume that a serious flood problem exists in the hatched area of area II. No measure in area I could provide flood control in area II. The two areas are not hydrologically related through a common stream or drainage pattern *at the location of the flood problem.*

Equally obvious is the fact that a structure completely stopping the runoff from area D would have almost no effect on a flood problem within area B, which is upstream. Conversely, completely stopping water flow from area B could have an effect on a flood problem within area D, depending on the size of area B in relation to the total drainage area above point D. In any case, the effect would be minor, extending only the distance upstream in area D affected by backwater from the major stream to which drainage areas B and D both contribute. However, there is a more significant interrelationship between these two drainage areas resulting from the fact that both contribute to streamflow downstream from point D, and therefore the flood plain below this point is common to both drainage areas.

The physical characteristics of the drainage area are also of significance for development purposes other than flood control. For example, a proposal for draining wet lands in area B could not be effectuated by corrective measures in area D, and vice versa. However, both areas could be involved in a drainage proposal for the larger stream to which they contribute waterflow.

A proposal for irrigating lands in area B from stored surface water would probably require that water be impounded in area B near the land to be irrigated, in view of the high cost of transporting water from other drainage areas. Here again, conditions (surface-water storage) in area D would be independent of conditions (need for irrigation water) in area B. Irrigation in area B is not wholly dependent on its own surface-water storage conditions, however, since irrigation water could be obtained from wells drawing on the ground water supply.[4]

The high value placed on water for municipal and industrial use may make it economically feasible to store surface water in one

---

[4] The supply of ground water available to a given drainage area, while related to some extent, may be fairly independent of the surface water supply and other conditions on the drainage area surface.

drainage area and transport it for use in another, thus overcoming the natural hydrologic independence of the two drainage areas. Ground water is also a source of municipal and industrial water supply. This reinforces the independence of municipal and industrial water supply from the drainage area as such.

The supply of recreation services can be expanded independently of the drainage area, since (1) non-water-based recreation can be developed, or (2) users can transport themselves from one drainage area to another to consume recreation services, thus solving the recreation problem outside the drainage area context.

The land and water development purposes that have been discussed fall into two broad categories. First, there are those for which consideration of the physical characteristics of the drainage area is *necessary*, e.g., flood control, drainage, and to some extent irrigation. Second, there are those for which consideration of the physical characteristics of the drainage area may be *desirable* but not necessary, e.g., municipal and industrial water supply and recreation. However, the complementarity of many land and water development purposes and the economies associated with multiple-purpose development, particularly in relation to reservoirs, may make it desirable to plan development purposes in the second category along with those in the first. This will tie the development of all land and water resources more closely to the drainage area and enhance its usefulness as an entity for planning.

The importance can hardly be overstressed of planning land and water resources development to take advantage of multiple-purpose opportunities rather than planning for only flood control or drainage or some other single-purpose development.[5]

WATERSHED PROBLEMS

The foregoing discussion should not be construed to imply that solutions for all land and water problems must be planned in relation to the watershed.

A first guidepost as to whether to consider a problem on a watershed basis is that it is significantly related to the hydrology of the drainage area. Involved here may be transportation, power, recreation, and stored water supplies for various uses, or the reduction of negative products such as accelerated erosion, flooding, scouring, siltation, poor drainage, and pollution. On the other hand, low incomes, reforestation, tenure and lease improvements, capital and credit problems, and others would be considered in watershed planning only if materially related to the hydrology of the watershed.

For example, low per capita incomes in a watershed may be a problem, but not necessarily a watershed problem. Low incomes might be raised with either no effect, a beneficial effect, or a detrimental effect on the hydrology of the watershed.

[5] See references cited in footnote 14.

Not even all land and water problems are watershed problems in the sense that their alleviation is best planned on a watershed basis. Conservation and improvement of land result from measures carried out primarily by individual landowners. They can go forward in most cases without the benefit of investments commonly incorporated in a watershed development program. It is true that terraces, contour cultivation, sod waterways, and long rotations may have beneficial effects over the entire watershed, but these latter effects appear relatively small.[6] For example, in eight Public Law 566 watersheds in the Tennessee Valley and adjacent areas for which the Soil Conservation Service has completed plans, land treatment for watershed protection reduced total floodwater damages by 0.1 to 15.2 percent, an average of 6 percent per watershed. In these eight plans, sediment/damages averaged only 5.4 percent of total damage. The benefits for reducing sediment damages that were credited to land treatment, both for watershed protection and flood prevention, were 33 percent of sediment damages and 2 percent of all damages. Total benefits attributed to land treatment in these eight watersheds were only 11 percent of all benefits.

The point is that land treatment as a watershed measure may not weigh heavily in the total planned investment for correcting hydrologic problems, but it may nevertheless play a critical role.[7] The bulk of the benefits in these eight plans was attributed to measures better called land development or water development, i.e., measures that prevent damages to present uses or make possible more intensive use and development of water and land resources, particularly of flood plain lands.

A second guidepost to identifying watershed problems is that there is disassociation[8] of costs and benefits. This can be illustrated for hypothetical drainage area I described previously. The movement of water from higher to lower portions of the drainage area may result in damages to upper and lower parts of the drainage area, but usually the latter. When measures are taken to reduce these damages, costs must often be incurred in the *upper part* of the area that result in benefits to the *lower part*. We have disassociation of benefits and costs *when these two parts are under different ownership*.

Leopold and Maddock have succinctly described this conflict between owners of upland versus bottom land in commenting on the Army Engineers' Tuttle Creek Project in Kansas. This project, designed primarily for protection downstream of urban sites, will inundate much productive agricultural land.

---

[6] Luna B. Leopold and Thomas Maddock, Jr., *The Flood Control Controversy* (New York: Ronald Press Co., 1954). The authors present strong supporting evidence for this conclusion in Chap. 11.

[7] Drainage projects in west Tennessee and many other areas which have gone defunct primarily due to sedimentation of the drainage ditches are nagging testimony to the critical role that good land cover, or proper maintenance, can play in the success of water development projects. See Bernard H. Zellner, "A Study of the Hydrology of Cane Creek Watershed," (unpublished Master's thesis, University of Tennessee, 1952).

[8] Timmons, *op. cit.*, pp. 1170-83.

"Other problems resulting from present trends are those arising where the areas damaged by the flood control program are geographically separated from the areas benefited. The area flooded by reservoirs must be purchased either by agreement or condemnation. This procedure is usually objected to by the local community. When the area being acquired is some distance away from the protected area, there is no mutual interest between the two groups, and strong opposition to the Corps program develops in many locations. This is the situation in the famous Tuttle Creek Dam controversy. The local communities on Big Blue River have no concern in flood control for the downstream cities and can see no reason why the federal government, being essentially the only party with a direct financial interest, should injure them to confer benefits on cities downstream. These cities, not being interested either in the cost of the Corps program or in the upstream communities, and being interested only in such benefits as the program may provide to them, consider all those who oppose flood control as obstructionists to progress. So are conflicts made."[9]

In trying to reduce this type of conflict, one could attempt to bring beneficiaries into closer association with the costs involved in flood control by selection of measures that tended to orient costs toward beneficiaries. Such measures are available. Channel improvement — clearing, straightening, or enlarging — designed to take care of flood flows by increasing the capacity of the stream channel directs the costs at the flood plain rather than upland areas, as is the case with detention dams.[10]

The riparian owner in the flood plain of the small watershed, who usually has most to gain from flood control, would bear most of the inconvenience involved in the channel improvement. *His* land would be taken for a larger channel and for the disposal of the spoil from channel work.

The appropriate procedure might be to consider as alternative plans different amounts of channel enlargement in combination with different detention basins and other measures. The results of each plan would be presented to sponsors of the project for the selection best fitting their needs and associating costs with benefits to the extent desired.

A system having close association of costs and benefits, e.g., channel improvement, might yield a smaller total net benefit than a plan not having this association, but it might still be preferred because of the close association of costs with benefits, conversely, a plan having

---

[9] Leopold and Maddock, *op. cit.*, p. 154.

[10] Leopold and Maddock, *op. cit.*, Chap. 4. The authors have presented the hydrologic aspects of flood control by engineering or structural measures which substantiate this point. The following statements are made: (1) Engineering measures for control of floodwaters may be levees, floodways, channel improvements, or reservoirs. (2) Levees, floodways, and, to a major extent, channel improvements have the advantage of providing protection in the very areas where protection is most needed. (3) Because protected areas are near the protective works, control is exerted on all floods up to the design flood. (4) The beneficiaries of these works are near by and easily identified.

substantial disassociation of costs and benefits, e.g., detention reservoirs, might be preferred if its features are considered desirable enough to compensate for the difficulties caused by the disassociation of costs and benefits.

This approach might eliminate some of the conflict between upland and bottom land landowners in the development of small watersheds.

THE ENTITY FOR LAND AND WATER RESOURCES PLANNING

Engineering works for flood control — dams, levees, floodways, and channel improvement — can be installed in small watersheds as well as in larger basins. When installed in small watersheds, these works *can* be effective in the areas in which they are installed, but they will be only partially effective in alleviating downstream flood problems.[11] The physical interrelationships in a natural drainage area suggest that even though it is physically and economically feasible to develop the small drainage area, some other unit might be more appropriate. In other words, to take account of all relevant effects,[12] the individual watershed might best be fitted into the larger basin of which it is a part, or into a region, trade area, or some other larger geographic or developmental unit.

Whether or not the unit of development will turn out in practice to be the small watershed depends to some extent on local people. If there is interest in the small watershed but not in the larger basin — the most likely situation — and a national program of technical and financial assistance is available to the small watershed but not to the larger basin, it is not difficult to visualize the small watershed as the major vehicle for future land and water resources development in this country. Two dangers are inherent in this. First, development on a small watershed basis could preclude the development of the larger river basins for purposes not possible in small watersheds. Power, navigation, and downstream flood control are examples. Second, the development of the different areas of the country in a small watershed context may not contribute most to the economic growth of these areas.

Assume that landowners in the larger river basin decide they want flood protection for the downstream area and that this requires a large structure in the protected area of an already developed small watershed. The investment in the small watershed may raise the costs of acquiring structure and reservoir sites for the basin program to the point where that program would not be economically feasible. This is not an uncommon type of occurrence. It is treated in the literature of

---

[11] Leopold and Maddock, *op. cit.*, p. 33. "Reservoir storage is effective in reducing flood peaks in the reach of streams immediately below the dam, but this effect diminishes rapidly with distance downstream."

[12] About 28 percent of the Tennessee River drainage area is in relatively independent drainage areas of less than 400 square miles, and 72 percent is in larger basins of more than 400 square miles.

economics as external economies or diseconomies and more recently as "spillover effects."[13]

An example of such spillover effects is in the Upper French Broad River Basin near Asheville, North Carolina. A Tennessee Valley Authority proposal providing flood protection for main stem agricultural lands and the city of Asheville would include seven medium-sized detention structures plus channel improvement. The Soil Conservation Service proposes to provide flood protection for the flood plain of Mud Creek, a small watershed tributary to the French Broad, through a series of small dams and channel improvement. The Tennessee Valley Authority proposal would inundate a portion of the Mud Creek flood plain to be protected by the proposed Soil Conservation Service development. The construction of either one of the two proposals would raise the costs and/or reduce the effectiveness of the other.

Prior construction of the river basin proposal would probably reduce the benefited area of the Mud Creek flood plain to the point where the small watershed proposal would be noneconomic. Prior construction of the small watershed proposal would increase the costs of land and easement acquisition for the basin program. If all the small watersheds of the basin were developed along the lines of the Mud Creek proposal, the basin proposal would be noneconomic.

This is a problem to be resolved by the political process. However, the best solution in the long-run interests of the Upper French Broad area is more likely to be arrived at if as complete information as possible on alternative courses of action is available. Both the Tennessee Valley Authority and Soil Conservation Service proposals need to be evaluated in this context.

After consideration of the physical characteristics of the drainage area, the nature of watershed problems, and the existence of spillover effects, the following conclusions are offered regarding the appropriate entity for planning land and water resources development: (1) The large drainage area or river basin is the appropriate entity for planning land and water resources development. (2) Where plans for the river basin have been accurately and appropriately formulated, proposals for small watershed development should fit into the broader plan. (3) Where the small watershed is not an integral part of a larger drainage area, development can be planned for the small watershed. (4) It may also be suggested that where plans for the comprehensive development of the resources of the river basin do not exist, they should be formulated.[14]

---

[13]Roland N. McKean, *Efficiency in Government Through Systems Analysis* (New York: John Wiley and Sons, Inc., 1958), p. 134.

[14]Opinion is not unanimous on this point, however. Wantrup argues, to the contrary, that land and water resources development will be more effectively planned and carried out through the states or through groups of states which he calls federal regions. However, other writers, the President's Water Resources Policy Commission, the Hoover Commission, a bill in Congress, and the highly successful experience of TVA argue for the river-basin or large watershed approach to planning. See S. V. Ciriacy-Wantrup, *Resource Conservation: Economics and Policies* (Berkeley and Los Angeles: University of California

If the river basin is to be the unit for planning, who will have the responsibility for this planning? Local groups are not going to push for over-all river basin planning. Their lack of interest and organized leadership on behalf of the basin approach and the high proportion of federal cost-sharing on most water resources projects suggest that the federal government should assume primary responsibility for basin planning.

OTHER ENTITIES FOR LAND AND WATER RESOURCES PLANNING

It has been argued above that the drainage area is the appropriate physical entity for planning and that the large drainage area or river basin should be favored. When the small drainage area is not an integral part of a larger basin, it can be used as the physical entity for planning.

An addendum is that there are entities other than the drainage area important in land and water resources development, even though they may not be appropriate physical units for planning. One scheme for their classification is as follows: (1) established units of government at different levels — township, county, state; (2) special governmental units — drainage or conservancy districts, federal regions;[15] and (3) nongovernmental units — community, trade area.

These entities can help to set the goals, establish the broad economic and social context within which planning takes place, assist in financing, and take responsibility for decisions.

Established units of government are especially well qualified to serve in these capacities. They can be expected to exist throughout the life of a project. They have custody of the public purse with which to help finance projects and to bear continuing economic responsibilities. Their major contribution is in providing institutional machinery for getting the job done, rather than serving as the physical entity for planning.

Press, 1952), Chap. 21; Arthur Smithies, *The Budgetary Process in the United States* (New York: McGraw-Hill Book Co., 1955), p. 348; Report of the President's Water Resources Policy Commission, *A Water Policy for the American People* (Washington, D.C.: Government Printing Office, 1950), Vol. I, pp. 3-5, 9, and generally throughout Chap. 3; *Task Force Report on Natural Resources* (Appendix L), prepared for The Commission on Organization of the Executive Branch of the Government (Washington, D.C.: Government Printing Office, Jan., 1949); House of Representatives bill under consideration, "The Water Resources Policy Act of 1959."

[15] Ciriacy-Wantrup, *op. cit.*, Chap. 21.

JOHN C. REDMAN | *Comment*

THE CONCLUSION reached by Dr. Riggs is that the watershed, largely because it is a hydrological unit, is a desirable unit for planning land and water resources. Further, the degree of desirability depends upon the goals of planning, with flood control being one of the more important goals. Nearly all would agree that some form of organization for basin-wide planning and for unification of activities in the watershed would be desirable, but there is a wide difference of opinion as to what that form should be. Riggs expressed the opinion that it should be a river basin type.

The question of determining the optimum-size watershed was left unanswered. His argument against small watershed development rests on the fact that capital already expended might render larger projects uneconomic. A decision to move from a small watershed to a large one should require cost estimates that are essentially incremental, while costs already sunk are irrelevant to the decision. Often the most important incremental cost is the opportunity lost by not making a change. The costs that will be incurred in the future by making the change are the relevant ones. To follow Riggs' argument, a two-lane highway should never be built, since someday hence it may be decided to build an eight-lane and this would include the costs of building the two-lane.

It would have been interesting if he had examined the hypothesis that as watersheds become larger, they lose (or gain) some claim as the appropriate entity for planning. As watersheds increase in size, social, political, and economic institutions may become more important. If so, more concern should be expressed for other entities, such as a trade or market area. Using the trade area would permit several small watersheds to be planned jointly. A good stable market is essential for products produced in the watershed, and this can exist only if there is sufficient volume and quality. Watershed plans must be coordinated with market plans; often, they must be planned simultaneously. This can be done through long term contracts between the producers and the market firm. Such an arrangement brings together a group, with similar backgrounds and problems, who have common goals. These similarities make the educational process easier. The whole community should understand the proposal if the project is to be effective. Not only should the residents feel they have a common interest in the administrative organization of the watershed; they must be taught appropriate farm management to obtain the expected return from the newly

John C. Redman is Professor of Agricultural Economics at the University of Kentucky. Prior to joining the staff there in 1950, he was with Western State College, Kentucky, and Mississippi State University.

developed physical resources. They must be given guidance in social and political aspects of community development. In this respect the smaller watersheds could have a tremendous advantage over the large river basin. However, the large river basin, as an entity, can have sub-entities built around some common bond.

The larger the watershed becomes, the greater will be the level of organizational hierarchy. This is not generally desired by the rural resident, who will probably respond very differently to a stimulus placed before him by a group representing a large river basin than one by a smaller group from the small watershed in which he has a part.

It would have been appropriate for Riggs to mention the influence of purpose and the level of desired flood protection. Often, for agricultural purposes, the level of flood protection desired is lower than for cities downstream. Because of the difficulty of obtaining simultaneous development and coordination of all small watersheds, a larger watershed with larger structures than those permitted under Public Law 566 may be desirable for the very high level of protection desired for cities. It seems logical that the Public Law 566 projects combined with less expensive proposals for large basins can give the protection desired at less cost than a single basin proposal. In other words, both approaches can be used advantageously to provide the maximum net benefits. The Public Law 566 projects can be multiple purpose in scope, and they are usually placed where the Corps of Engineers have not been able or authorized to operate. More harmonious relationships between agencies can serve to do the job more economically.

To minimize the disassociation of costs and benefits, Riggs appropriately suggested more emphasis on channeling and levee building. While disassociation of benefits and costs should not be completely ignored, Riggs' procedure may conflict with the idea that plans should attempt to give a desired level of protection at the lowest cost. Achieving least cost involves consideration of all possible on-site improvements such as proper rotations, reforestation and terraces, and off-site improvements such as water retarding structures, sediment basins, and levees.

While Riggs accepted the watershed as the appropriate entity for planning because it is a hydrological unit, I am inclined to add more to the entity than merely physical resources. Like Riggs, I favor river basin type of development — but only under special conditions. Because of organizational problems, I am inclined to think that the small watershed has more to contribute than he indicated.

Ayers Brinser is Professor of Economics at the University of Colorado, and was formerly Director of the Land Use and Conservation Seminar in the Graduate School of Public Administration and Lecturer in Economics at Harvard University. He has been an editor with *Time, Fortune, Every Week,* and with Harper Brothers. From 1941-49 he served with the National Resources Planning Board, the Office of Price Administration, and the Federal Reserve Bank of Boston.

Chapter 6

AYERS BRINSER*

Meshing Watershed Development With River Basin Development

ORIGINALLY a watershed was simply a physical feature of the landscape — a drainage area bounded by a divide. For a variety of reasons, a watershed has become a community, an administrative unit, a political subdivision, a planning area, and an economic tributary to a much larger unit, the river basin. The focus of attention has ceased to be the boundary of the area, a fixed topographic feature. It has shifted to the flow of water from the hillsides, a plastic resource to be managed. And as its identity has undergone this metamorphosis, the functions to be managed have taken on a new array of characteristics. Some of these derived definitions conceive of a watershed as an independent unit, while others place it in the role of a dependent subsidiary, not only to some larger scheme of water resource development, but also to various political, social, and economic patterns orientated to many different centers of power and interest. This ambivalence creates a large measure of the difficulty in designing a resource

*In preparing this paper I have had the benefit of the criticisms of the members of the Land Use and Conservation Seminar at the Harvard Graduate School of Public Administration, and of my colleagues, Professors John Gaus, Hugh Raup, and Dr. Ernest Gould. What is written here is, of course, wholly my responsibility.

management policy that will provide for an efficient meshing of watershed development with river basin development.

An accepted solution to these issues is the doctrine that the proper unit for designing a water resource development program is the river basin. River basin development is by assumption, if not by definition, a program of investment that will enhance the economic productivity of an integrated river system. The river is the key resource to be manipulated for that purpose. It follows from this that in the design of a basin development program, the water in the watersheds should be managed to make the greatest possible contribution to the net benefits earned by the basin as a whole. The limit to development is reached when the net marginal returns from watershed investments equal those of other planned investments in the basin, and the funds assigned to the system are exhausted.

If watersheds were no more than a source of water supply for a river system, that formula would provide an adequate answer for both watershed and river basin development. The previously cited definitions, however, imply that within watersheds there are many interdependent interests, some complementary, some conflicting with the optimum development of the main stream. These can be reduced to insignificance insofar as water resource development is concerned if the objective of investment is restricted to an agreed-upon level of returns to water resource use in the basin as a whole, and if the model for the program design is based on the hypothesis of a frictionless economy and society. This requires, in effect, that the functional identity of the watershed be absorbed in that of the basin.

It is not to deny validity to this approach to ask the question: Would the criteria of an efficient water resource use program be different if the functions within the watersheds were permitted to keep their unique identities in the analysis of alternatives for river basin development? By definition, both economic and engineering analysis, supported by the necessary facts, deny that the sum of the parts could be greater or less than the whole. Thus, the question arises first from the possibility that all of the necessary facts are not available. A second justification for the question is that the confining assumptions of the frictionless model into which the facts are fitted ignore important real issues of decision. Admittedly, there are disparities between the real world and the model. The point is, how significant are they in comparison with the technical difficulties of measuring identifiable costs and benefits within the terms of the model? This brings the reason for asking such a question down to this: Would an approach to program and policy design incorporating an analysis of watersheds as units in their own right be useful as a basis for inquiry into these issues? If there is an affirmative answer to this question, there is some point in considering the meshing of watershed and river basin development as a substantive problem; otherwise there is no real issue, since the criteria for river basin development infer that the full integration of watershed investment is a necessary consequence of an over-all basin design.

It should be obvious that watershed planning cannot take the place of integrated river basin planning. The issue raised here is rather that in watershed development there are problems of adjusting conflicts of interest that are merely reflected in the economic calculus of river basin planning. In the alternative possibilities facing watersheds the points of emphasis may be distributed differently from those of the basin. Perhaps most important, the process of policy formulation and decision-making is usually not the same as that of the river basin. This is to argue that a watershed has a functional integrity, and also that an analysis of these characteristics in their own terms can be useful in constructing a river basin program. The meshing of the two would then be a matter of setting up a process of relating development rather than merely one of integrating the watershed into the river basin.

For the sake of brevity, the problems of relating watershed development to the requirements of an optimum design for a river basin are here divided into two general categories: (1) The kind of economic adjustments necessary in watershed planning to adapt the development of such units to an optimum for the river basin. That optimum is accepted as the overriding objective of river basin planning, but it is assumed that it should not be achieved at the expense of uncompensated loss to the component parts such as the watershed. (2) The planning process by which these economic objectives can be fitted into a policy and program that is feasible and consistent with emerging political and social objectives. Here these are regarded not as discrete problems but rather as a progressive statement of the issues embedded in a program of "meshing watershed development with river basin development."

Under the rubric of the first statement the generally accepted requirement is a plan to adjust the complementary and competing relationships of the physical resources to yield a desired net return to given investment. This kind of planning requires a clear-cut objective for the whole basin. From this plan should emerge a set of designs for an integrated group of structures which will produce predictable amounts and quality of water at given times and places. Just which structures will be built and where, of course, will depend on the calculation of net marginal gain from each. The schedule for their construction will be ordered to maximize the net returns to the whole development program. This brief recapitulation of the obvious is not to gloss over the fact that the technical problems of making such a calculation for a major river basin are formidable indeed.

Planning short of this mandarin ideal opens the way for a misallocation of investment funds and something less than optimum returns. In a society dedicated to the idea of economic rationality, the shortage of good agricultural land in Vermont's West River Valley is not a valid argument against inundating that valley behind a flood control dam to allay flood damage downstream on the Connecticut River at Springfield, Massachusetts, and Hartford, Connecticut. To be sure, in the real world of political compromise Vermont farmers had some difficulty in seeing that the value of their land to them was less than the value of the opportunity to exploit real estate investment in Connecticut. They persisted in this unbelief even though the benefit-cost ratio in the rational language of dollars was heavily in favor of Connecticut and Massachusetts. An interesting point passed over by the favorable benefit-cost ratio was the alternative calculus of costs and returns from a downstream program of flood plain zoning.[1]

Perhaps this friction can be put down to cultural lag. The fact that the benefit-cost ratio is a somewhat less sensitive measure of the values of the people in a rural watershed than it is of the investment calculations of real estate operators in the case cited, at least, has ceased to be a cause of open discontent.[2] The farmers are leaving the valley to New Yorkers who build summer and retirement homes. These newcomers can understand the anxieties of the citizens of Hartford a great deal better than those of the displaced farmers who were rapidly becoming an anachronism anyway.[3]

A related problem, but of a different order, in constructing a schedule for river basin development is the question of equality of opportunity, not only for a watershed vis-a-vis the river basin, but also among the watersheds. The fact that such opportunities may be discrete can create conflicts.

Issues such as this can arise even in an integrated river basin program in which the budgetary constraints are progressively relaxed as the agency in control expands its investment horizon. The efficient meshing of watershed with river basin development would seem to depend in part on a basin plan in which a wide range of possible alternative investments for the various units is placed in the schedule for decision-making. The justification for assuming this greater burden of planning cost is that the feasibility of reaching given levels of development and the probability of changes in the schedules are themselves part of the criteria for relating watershed with river basin development. Before the final program decisions are made, these considerations are as much elements of the alternatives as of the constraints.

The argument comes down to this general point: The decision as to how to gear the timing of watershed development with basin development rests as much on the pragmatic facts of the situation as on the imperatives of doctrinal consistency. The point has been adequately

---

[1] Cf. William Edward Leuchtenburg, *Flood Control Politics* (Cambridge: Harvard University Press, 1953), Chap. 10.

[2] For a discussion of a solution to this type of conflict, cf. G. S. Tolley, "Analytical Techniques in Relation to Watershed Development," *Jour. Farm Econ.*, Vol. XL, No. 3, Aug., 1958, pp. 661-63. Tolley asks the question, "Does not equity suggest that we lean in the direction of ensuring that flooded out people do not lose, even if it may mean that they might sometimes gain quite a bit?"

[3] A similar point for a different location is made by Henry Hart. "It is a condition of the occupation of semi-arid lands in an urban-industrial civilization that the plainsman make his peace with nature and the planners of the economy, even if they reside no nearer to his floods and droughts than Chicago, Boston, or New York." Henry C. Hart, *The Dark Missouri* (Madison: University of Wisconsin Press, 1957), p. 50.

established that economic efficiency requires integrated river basin
planning, an over-all design, but this does not rule out constructing the
design step by step in those cases where the interdependence of water
resources is considered to be less significant than some other physical,
social, or economic aspect of the planning landscape. It would follow
from this that there is allowable latitude in watershed planning. The
criterion of whether, or how much, freedom is desirable is in a large
measure the unique importance of water management now and in the
predictable future to the welfare of the basin, and the possibility of serious conflict between watersheds and basin design.

A different and what is becoming an increasingly obvious aspect of
this issue arises when technology redefines the comprehensive role of
the water as a critical resource. Atomic energy may soon have considerable influence on the desirable levels of integration and development in river basins. For example, new techniques of accumulating
and storing water for the uses that may arise with the development of
atomic energy can shift drastically the pattern of complementary and
competing alignments between river basin and watershed development.
One of the most disturbing prospects for river basin development programs is weather control. Even if one has limited faith in human in-
genuity, enough is now known about weather control to suggest massive
change in the contours of optimum river basin design.

These various points could be subsumed under the general heading
of uncertainty. Economic analysis has been reasonably useful in estimating the present cost of alternative strategies to compensate for the
imponderables that lie on the planning horizon. This calculation becomes a critical factor in setting the budgetary constraint within which
the river basin development program must operate. It is translated to
the watershed by the allowable marginal increment determining the
last investment in that area. The general problem, of which the preceding discussion singles out merely a few examples, is what happens
to integrated basin planning and to the investment opportunities of the
watersheds when the basin development constraint is changed. This
may not be merely a matter of political shift and maneuver, although
that in itself is both a necessary and justifiable cause of uncertainty.
Budgets have a habit of being revised. Specific areas of public programs are singled out for expansion or reduction, institutional changes
are stimulated by agency assignments. These in fact change the con-
straining budgetary limits which in turn determine the proportions and
nature of investment in basin development. Thus the virtue of integrating watershed development with that of the basin in terms of a set basin
optimum is somewhat less than perfect. There is a sufficient certainty
that there will be changes in the constraints to justify something less
than inflexible rectitude.

Even within those limits of the future that are reduced to a kind of
certainty by a discount rate, the problem of meshing watershed and
river basin development is not wholly removed. To return to the definition of optimum development, one condition of that optimum is that

the present value of a stream of investment for that development within the given planning period meet the predetermined level of return. In his discussion of Krutilla's and Eckstein's[4] use of the discount rate in watershed project evaluation, Margolis makes the point, "The discount rate appropriate to this transformation (the rate of substitution of a dollar in year t to a dollar in year t + 1) need not be the same as the one necessary for any other pair of years. Though no general remarks are possible about how to find the discount rates appropriate for the many pairs of future years we should be cautious about a procedure which neglects the problem."[5] This question of the applicability of the discount rate to the particular situation in which it is used is a significant issue when watershed and river basin development are combined under a generalized optimum. For a variety of reasons the planning horizon within a watershed, the level of investment, especially if that involves the use of private funds, and the incidence of the stream of income may be based on a different set of values than is the case in the river basin. Because of the level of income and the type of investment in many watersheds immediate benefits often have a higher value than those which are postponed. Security may weigh more heavily than opportunity. These and many other factors may create a significant difference between time preference in the watershed and that in the river basin. An integrated development program in which the decision of what investment to select rests on the benefit-cost ratio calculated with a given rate of social interest may be a distorted reflection of values in the watershed. To the degree that watershed projects have a higher time preference, a calculation of benefits based on a maximum growth of assets as McKean suggests may be the more fruitful method of choosing among alternatives available to the people living in the watershed.[6]

The dictates of reason would not permit aberrant watersheds to reduce the returns to river basin projects. On the other hand, to force a watershed development decision into a benefit-cost ratio which is less favorable to the watershed because of differences in time preferences which are not compensated for may hide real costs of the project. Sometimes such costs are recognized and paid in the form of a subsidy. It is not a distinction worth pausing over here, but there is, from the point of view of the recipient at least, a difference in the value of income paid as a direct earning in contrast with one derived from a subsidy.

As the scope of watershed and river basin development is expanded to include economic development, and it seems to be difficult to

[4]John V. Krutilla and Otto Eckstein, *Multiple Purpose River Development* (Baltimore: Johns Hopkins Press, 1958); Otto Eckstein, *Water Resources Development* (Cambridge: Harvard University Press, 1958).

[5]Julius Margolis, "The Economic Evaluation of Federal Water Resource Development," *Amer. Econ. Rev.*, Vol. IL, No. 1, Mar., 1959, p. 102.

[6]Roland N. McKean, *Efficiency in Government Through Systems Analysis with Emphasis on Water Resource Development* (New York: John Wiley and Sons, 1958), especially Chaps. 5 and 7.

justify holding development to direct investment in water resource
management alone, the area of the conflict of interest between river
basin design and that of the watershed increases. For example, a program such as that of the Tennessee Valley Authority creates new patterns of economic activity, and new schedules of opportunity. To predict the responses of the watershed units to these changes as they
develop requires something more than the evidence of the justifying
benefit-cost ratio. Obviously, water resource development cannot wait
for a complete answer that can be accepted with perfect confidence.
On the other hand, this ambiguity suggests that a chosen program
should have a sufficiently high rate of return to pay the costs of flexibility and adjustment within the basin.

The issues that have been sketched here fall for the most part in
the area of market economy decisions. Economic analysis is the best
source of straightforward, specific criteria for designing a program of
river basin development that will satisfy postulated levels of market
efficiency. These criteria are in essence that external diseconomies
will be avoided and internal economies will be distributed equitably and
within the dictates of an agreed-upon time distribution of the rate of
resource use.

While accepting this as the basis for rational resource allocation
decisions, economists are practically unanimous in disclaiming responsibility for determining what that level of efficiency should be beyond indicating the money cost of relaxing standards of maximum efficiency, however defined. Whether this efficiency is an absolute of
value implicit in the models economists construct to conduct their
analysis is a relevant question, but an aside to the present discussion.

An economic analysis of river basin development is a systematic
method of resolving the issues created by relating watershed development to program projection for a river basin. To say that the method
of analysis at hand is the most effective is not to claim that it is perfect. It is an explanation, not an excuse to claim that the flaws in the
method that interfere with the projections of economic planning stem
from the intransigency of the data and the consequent uncertainty of
prediction. This leads to the conclusion that the way to overcome this
limitation is to refine the analytical techniques. The meshing of watershed with river basin development from the point of view of economic analysis is thus mainly a technological, not a substantive, problem — one of establishing greater degrees of certainty of the data and
of constructing a more consistent order of priority in the light of both
physical and institutional possibilities.

To describe these issues as technological rather than substantive
is clearly not the same as saying that they are inconsequential. Recent
studies have done much to establish economics as a powerful tool in
defining the issues from which to project alternative policy decisions
about river basin development. They have not only buttressed the base
of the analysis, they have also increased its breadth. The application
of welfare criteria to the problems of water resource development has

indicated the possibility of manipulating the economic data to reveal the real policy alternatives as distinguished from a perfect market idealization. At the same time they have increased the range within which the data can be useful. The benefit-cost ratio has been made a better instrument of judgment by a more precise definition of its component parts and its organic connection with such concepts as opportunity cost and rate of return. The question of relating watershed management to the general problem of economic growth has been stated in quantifiable terms by the application of a social rate of interest, even if a wholly acceptable level remains an open question. The critical investigation of the composition and incidence of the stream of investment in multiple purpose river basin projects has indicated specific means to achieve greater economic efficiency as a corollary of welfare.

It is not to decry these achievements to ask the question: Is it true that the making of better investment decisions for the development of river basins must wait only for the further refinement of economic techniques for quantifying costs and returns in the real world? To put it another way, is there any point in discussing the meshing of watershed development and river basin development as an issue involving anything more than economic analysis? Most simply, does the benefit-cost ratio or its economic alternatives provide both the necessary and sufficient criteria for river basin development policy? Someone less sympathetic to the therapeutic powers of economic analysis might put the question this way: Has the definition of the issues in economic terms evaded the substantive questions for decision?

In an essay discussing the general problem of natural resource management, Edward Mason has written, "An analysis of the conditions under which the price system does not assure an effective comparison of present and future costs and benefits, and of various types of public action designed to prevent or rectify these failures, is an important part of the political economy of natural resource use."[7] From the title of his essay as well as the content, it is clear that Professor Mason's choice of the term "political economy" rather than "economics" is deliberate.

No useful purpose would be served by attempting to establish here a distinction between economics, political economy, and politics. All three take as their point of departure for policy analysis the physical data of the landscape and the technologic possibilities. Their differences are primarily matters of emphasis and methods of interpreting human behavior. The nature of the economic approach to river basins has been referred to. Recent books like that of Ackerman and Löf indicate the growing interest in the wedding of technical data to the

---

[7] Edward S. Mason, "The Political Economy of Resource Use," in *Perspectives on Conservation* (Baltimore: Johns Hopkins Press, 1958), p. 185.

decision-making process. [8] On the score of political and institutional analysis there are many studies such as those of Charles McKinley, Arthur Maass, Gilbert White *et al.*, William Edward Leuchtenburg, and David Lilienthal. [9] If the canon is deficient, it is in the synthetic area of political economy.

Henry Hart's *The Dark Missouri* fits this last category. It is concerned with the process of policy formation and decision making. The objective is to relate data revealed by economic analysis and engineering investigations to the process of creating and executing a public policy decision. For the purposes of this discussion that may be taken as a description of political economy. The questions to which political economy must address itself in river basin development are: Why should a program be undertaken? What should its objectives be? And, providing the political content to both of these is the question: Who should pay the costs and who should receive the benefits? Mark Regan's distinction between evaluation and cost-sharing may be forced into service here to indicate the role of political economy. [10] Regan writes, "Efficiency in producing services is the controlling consideration in evaluation; in cost sharing, emphasis is on the equitable distribution arrangements." He continues, "The chief type of considerations that warrant attention in devising arrangements for sharing financial responsibility are: (1) the objectives to be served; and (2) the merits and limitations of alternative basic approaches for apportioning charges or assessments. Attention must also be given to adjustments and modifications necessitated by problems of practical application and acceptability." [11]

The major concern of economics is evaluation of alternatives in terms of efficiency; political economy as it is used here is directed to combine this evaluation with an allocation of costs and benefits within the limitations set by "practical application and acceptability."

The benefit-cost issue is not resolved merely by a schedule of monetary rewards to a group of individuals here and now. Returns and expenses are also distributed to future generations and over a population that may include the whole nation. What is more, these payments are not confined to some form of currency; they may be enhanced

---

[8] Edward A. Ackerman and George O. G. Löf, *Technology in American Water Development* (Baltimore: Johns Hopkins Press, 1959). Also such earlier studies as W. G. Hoyt and W. B. Langbein, *Floods* (Princeton: Princeton University Press, 1955); and Luna B. Leopold and Thomas Maddock, Jr., *The Flood Control Controversy* (New York: The Ronald Press Co., 1954).

[9] Charles McKinley, *Uncle Sam in the Pacific Northwest* (Berkeley: University of California Press, 1952); Arthur A. Maass, *Muddy Waters* (Cambridge: Harvard University Press, 1951); Gilbert F. White *et. al.*, *Changes in the Urban Occupance of Flood Plains in the United States*, University of Chicago, Department of Geography Research Paper No. 57, 1958; Leuchtenburg, *op. cit.*; David Lilienthal, *TVA — Democracy on the March* (New York: Harper and Brothers, 1945). In this connection, it would be unfair to slight the pioneer work of Harlow S. Person, *Little Waters* (Washington, D.C.: Government Printing Office, 1936).

[10] Mark M. Regan, "Sharing Financial Responsibility of River Basin Development," *Jour. Farm Econ.*, Vol. XL, No. 5, Dec., 1958, p. 1690.

[11] *Ibid.*, p. 1692.

security, political power, greater or less economic certainty. Perhaps
most important in this connection is the fact that development decided
upon today will affect the terms and criteria of desirability of future
development, and in ways that cannot easily be predicted.

The process of fitting economic data into a structure for political
decision requires that the test of relevance of the data shall be how and
where it fits into the structure, not the elegance of the data itself. This
is not to descend to that wholly indefensible level of pragmatism that
would pervert the data to fit the pattern in which it would be used, certainly a regrettable, but not wholly unfamiliar, practice in river basin
development planning. The first step of planning under this description
of political economy is the assignment of the responsibility for land
planning and the identification of the area to be developed, with the
reasons for such development. Next is the exploration and testing of
alternative solutions, the selection of the immediate alternative, and
the delegation of authority for the execution of that alternative. Finally,
it becomes necessary to provide for measuring the progress of development and for making adjustments in the program as it is extended
into the future.

The problem of defining the area in which a development program
shall be established is in the first instance one of defining the problem.
In the case of a watershed this can be done as a first approximation by
identifying the felt and expressed need. Thus, the starting point becomes an awareness of a cost to someone, and/or the opportunity to
achieve a benefit. The problem of cost and benefit, not project evaluation, is what sets the process of planned development in motion.

If a watershed has any relevance to a planning program, it can be
presumed that the management of the water resource is identified as the
solution to the expressed need. This may take the form of a request for
protection from floods, the need for irrigation or recreation development, or some aspect of the watershed's contribution to the water resources of the basin. It should be obvious that the management of the
water resource is considered to be sufficiently independent of the other
aspects of the economic and political life of the area so that it can become the focal point for a program of planned action.

As a stage in the planning process, the expression of the felt need
in a given area invites the attention of public or private agencies interested or assigned to meet this need. When the need is related to the
management of water resources, the watersheds become the center of
attention because of the physical distribution of the water resource.
This leads to an investigation of the present level of use of the water
resources and an assessment of the alternative possibilities for investment in development. Depending on the contours of the watershed,
its situation and its relation to the river basin, management of the water resource has a varying significance to the actual needs of the area.
In some watersheds in which the felt and expressed need inviting attention is flood control, it may soon develop that the necessary solution to
this problem is to raise the level of income and provide for its more
equitable distribution as the necessary condition to establish

water-retaining land-use practices. To do this, however, may demand
the assistance of a new agency. The relevant area in which to locate
the improvement program may then become the county rather than the
watershed, if the jurisdiction of the new agency is based on county organization. A question then arises whether the focal point of attack
shall be flood control or higher or more efficiently distributed income.
Usually there are more direct ways of doing the latter than by manipulating the water resources of the area.

If income level or distribution is the point at issue, there is no
reason to confine the planning area to a watershed. The effective answer to what has now been defined as the critical problem, the solution
for which a felt need has been evoked, depends on redefining the planning area and programming in a way that is consistent with the available instruments of control. Finally, the area must be a homogeneous
one in which the defined problem is recognized as significant.

Whether the correct planning area or the most efficient planning
area is finally delimited depends on the process of investigation, not on
the precision of the technical tools of analysis. Merely to derive a
perfectly calculated benefit-cost ratio for a water program will not reveal this process. On the other hand, if the benefit-cost ratio is pre-
ceded by an investigation of alternative means to solve the general
rather than the initial felt needs of the area, planning would lead into
the process of developing new strategies of attack. This greater vision
is one of the assumed advantages of beginning with a river basin as the
planning area. But if an integrated system is really going to integrate
resource development within the framework of an evolving rather than
static economy, the integrated system has to be adapted to the needs of
its units just as much as they in turn must make their contribution to
the integrated system. In the end, this seems to leave the basic requirement pretty much as it was in the beginning, step-developments
involving the decisions and commitments of the watersheds.

To recapitulate the issues, if the constraints within which a river
basin development will be carried out can be only imperfectly predicted, and if the overriding objective is the economic development of
an area rather than the maximizing of returns from water resources
isolated from other factors of production, there is no overwhelming
reason for gearing watershed development absolutely to river basin
development. Furthermore, except in terms of interdependent effects
of the water in the watershed with that of the river basin, there is no
necessity to define a watershed as a planning area. Finally, a benefit-
cost ratio calculated to show the interrelationships between water resource investment opportunities in a river basin may or may not indicate an optimum development program for a watershed. These are
areas of ambiguity which require economic data to provide more satisfactory answers, but these data have to be made available discretely
and in that pattern of order that the planning process will require, not
as a single answer according to an economic concept of efficient river
basin development.

Successful watershed management depends on introducing rational economic calculation into the complex pattern of the planning process as one of the criteria to be weighed in making decisions. In the formulation presented here, this is a schedule of investigations beginning with the defined felt need, proceeding to an investigation of alternative solutions to that need, and following through to an identification of the most important recognized need within the range of solution by the means at hand. In this process, the problem changes, the designated agencies for working out the solution are changed, and the boundaries of the planning area expand or contract as the selected alternative solution may require. Within this area of change there can be no final solution, but rather an emerging solution as development in its progress creates new definitions of ends and means.

The crux of the planning process becomes education, with the responsible agencies preparing comparisons as precise as possible of the predictable consequences from alternative investment programs. The basic tool in this educational process is the series of budgets that are constructed in evaluating alternatives.[12] The content of these budgets reveals in concrete terms the points at which political and social values must be weighed, and the economic consequences of those weights. The final benefit-cost ratio then becomes the summation of these decisions, the justification for the decisions that were made in evaluating the alternatives. This is not to oppose what goes for "grass roots" thinking as an alternative to rigorous calculation. The intention rather is to provide a structure for relating economic analysis to the necessary, if disorderly, process of creating a policy and program out of the complex of values, political power, and economic prediction.

When the project area is a vast domain such as the Missouri Basin, the planning process becomes indeed complex. But as Hart's study has shown, out of this complexity and the faltering efforts to develop the basin there has come a growing awareness of what the possibilities are. That this process had to begin with Major Powell's *Report of the Arid Land of the United States* and the putting down of the incurable optimists like Gilpin is perhaps not too high a price to pay for achieving consensus by conviction. This process of education has continued into the present without a positive solution. The serious limitation has been that while education has proceeded at a snail's pace, the problem has grown at an ever-accelerating rate. Hart's study might be described as an attempt to show how this process of understanding what is necessary and how to do it can be brought up to date with the problem, and kept there. What is to be accelerated is not so much decision-making, but rather achieving a basis for consensus among the people to be affected and who will in the end shape the course of development.

---

[12] S. V. Ciriacy-Wantrup has stated a not dissimilar point of view. "One may argue, therefore, that the mere necessity of quantifying makes benefit-cost analysis worthwhile *because of its stimulating effects in expanding scientific understanding of the physical as well as social problems in public resource development.*" S. V. Ciriacy-Wantrup, "Benefit-cost Analysis and Resource Development," *Jour. Farm Econ.*, Vol. XXXVII, No. 4, Nov., 1955, p. 678.

In a large measure this education has begun to catch up with the problem in the small watersheds where the people are directly touched by Missouri water. They may not see all of the issues, or even the most relevant ones, but they do have a concrete interest. With this interest in the problem of the watershed has come a series of investment programs — some consistent with one scheme of basin development, some consistent with another, but many of them consistent with only limited local objectives. Inefficient as this may seem to be at any moment in time, nevertheless what has happened has been a gradual redefinition of Missouri Basin development, one that would require a major revision in optimum basin design that might have been made twenty-five years ago. The objectives that are emerging today may be going back to what Major Powell prescribed in the 1890's, but the context within which they are relevant is wholly different.[13]

Warning was given at the outset that this discussion is orientated to watershed development. The point of departure is not a river basin development in being such as the Tennessee Valley, nor does it presuppose that future basin development will be a proliferation of basin authorities. If the experience in the case of the Missouri is any guide, the probability would seem to be that river basin development is still in the formative stage and that the emphasis of concrete action is still on watershed development programs. The design of watershed planning programs may therefore still serve usefully as test areas for what may become basin programs. In any event, there is the real possibility that many future basin programs will grow out of watershed development.

One reason for the strength of watershed programs is the fact that there is a felt and expressed need for watershed management. Agencies and programs have been created to meet that need. As these programs have been applied the area of concern has increased from a simple one of flood control toward complete water resource development as a focal point for economic growth. Where water is the critical resource in economic development in a river basin, there is a strong motivation to make an ultimate definition of the planning area as the basin. Today there is no single agency of government in a position to take over the planning of such basins. Rather, there is a collection of agencies with specific program obligations which, in the context of basin development, often represent competing interests rather than an integrated approach to basin problems.[14] Thus far the solution has been to propose coordinated effort by such agencies to be achieved largely through enforcing standard techniques of measuring costs and benefits.[15] The results of this effort, like so many attempts at coordination and integration of government programs, have not been remarkably successful largely because what is to be integrated has not in fact

---

[13] Cf. John Wesley Powell, *The Report on the Arid Regions of the United States* (Second edition; Washington, D.C.: Government Printing Office, 1879, p. 8).

[14] Second Hoover Commission, *Task Force Report on Water Resources and Power* (Washington, D.C.: Government Printing Office, 1953-55).

[15] U.S. Bureau of the Budget, Revised Circular, A - 47.

been defined by a concrete policy, nor is it related to any specific conceptual framework.

An examination of watershed programs suggests that in some cases this may be the wrong approach to developing a program for river basin development. As an alternative, the solution may lie rather in recognizing the fact first that each basin is in an essential way unique. In each, water resource management may have quite different roles, in some as the primary means for economic development, in others as a secondary factor. Until there is what might be called a basin public which is prepared to express a consensus of need and to engage in a planning process, river basin development lacks a firm base. To be sure, in some instances this consensus and authority can be imposed from outside the basin area, but so far this kind of planning and development has been successful in only extraordinary situations, as, for example, to support an anti-depression public works program.

This argument brings up the possibility that the problem of achieving an optimum plan for river basin development in the future is not so much one of finding ways to mesh watershed with basin development as it is to set in motion a process that will relate watershed development and basin programs and will satisfy an optimum yet to be defined for each of the planning areas. Economic analysis of the alternatives must play a critical role in this evolution, but ultimate decision of what to do and how to do it depends on knowing how to use the data provided by such an analysis in the planning process. A close examination of the development of watersheds may provide some useful answers to this question.

CONCLUSION

The problem of adjusting watershed development to river basin development can be greatly reduced by the continued refinement of the tools for measuring the input-output relationships in water resource management. These in turn will help to reduce the area of uncertainty and support investment decisions. To be useful, however, in developing an optimum basin program, the economic data have to be fitted into a planning process that will relate predictable economic consequences to political and social values. This assumes that the optimum is an emerging objective that is approached by contingent solutions sufficiently flexible to respond to change.

Programs for river basin development are still in their formative stage. The fact that each basin has its own range of possibilities suggests that there may be no one program for such development. For these reasons, a close scrutiny of going watershed programs that are early stages in basin development may provide a useful insight into the essential planning process by which water resource management may be guided toward social objectives as time and circumstances define them.

LYLE E. CRAINE | *Comment*

I AM in substantial agreement with Dr. Brinser's principal themes and am therefore less inclined to challenge than to be challenged by the several doors he has opened. I turn to one, not because it is necessarily most important, but because it appeals to me.

THE DRAINAGE BASIN AS A PLANNING AREA

Brinser deals not only with meshing development in the watershed with that in the river basin, but also with the question of whether a drainage area (watershed or river basin) is an adequate planning unit. This is proper because, in my judgment, we will never understand the "meshing" problem until we have a more definitive concept of the role of drainage basin development in planning generally.

The extent to which a watershed or a river basin is a necessary and/or sufficient unit for planning purposes may differ with each drainage subject to development. Certain combinations of physical, economic, social, and institutional factors may make one drainage area an adequate planning jurisdiction, while other combinations may entirely disqualify another area. This suggests that an understanding of the co-actions of these conditioning factors is fundamental. Brinser has suggested some of these conditioning factors.

For example, he suggests that the relevance of a hydrologic unit to a planning program is directly proportional to the extent that water development is identified as the solution to the expressed need. The crux of the matter is "the expressed need." If the need is to have more usable water or to keep floodwaters in the channel, the drainage basin is sufficient to the planning problem. But if the expressed need is to reduce flood losses, other possible solutions than water management appear, and different planning jurisdictions are involved. The same distinctions can be made by using navigation, irrigation, hydroelectric power, or water recreation as an example. Each of these is only a segment of a larger, nonwater orbit of public concern, i.e., transportation, agriculture, energy supply, and recreation.

When regional social-economic growth becomes the expressed need, the relevant economic and social groupings are rarely coterminous with drainage areas. The dilemma of harmonizing planning for the Great Plains and the Missouri Basin, and for metropolitan regions

Lyle E. Craine is Professor in the Department of Conservation, School of Natural Resources, University of Michigan. Formerly he was Assistant Director of Program Staff of the U. S. Department of the Interior and Director of Organization Planning for the War Production Board.

and the drainage basins they dominate are familiar and forceful examples. The drainage basin does not appear sufficient for the planning of economic growth and stability in these situations. Still, it is sometimes called upon to serve as such.

The reasons why water development planning has become the vehicle for regional economic development are complex. Probably most of them are related to the historical evolution of governmental involvement in water development, and to the fact that planning explicitly for economic development has always been anathema to our concept of free enterprise. At the same time, the expansion of multiple-purpose and basin-wide development has directed increased attention to the measurement of relative benefits and to the impact of water development upon the social-economic complex of the region. White comments that "regional effects in water development planning became intimated but not planned, then enjoyed but not managed."[1]

As interest increasingly focuses upon the planning of regional effects, water development becomes a means rather than an end in itself. Critical planning decisions must then be made by jurisdictions other than drainage areas. Watershed and river basin development play mixed roles in this end-means schema. This blurs our view of the relation of drainage basin development to planning. Recognition of these mixed roles and a conscious attempt to define the place of water development in any given situation are first steps in bringing our problem into focus.

GUIDING IDEAS

With this brief discussion as a general setting, Brinser's presentation suggests to me several specific concepts which may provide guides in designing relationships between watershed development, river basin development, and planning.

First, the integrity of the drainage basin as a development unit is inviolate only if the basin is viewed as a production facility for water services. Using an analogy from industry: The drainage basin is the manufacturing plant, and the social-economic region is the market. Drainage basins have their importance as "production units" rather than as "marketing units," and if we keep this in mind, we have some ground rules for constructing planning relationships.

Second, the problem is to determine the extent and methods of articulating water production planning with comprehensive planning, rather than to force one to absorb the other. As Hart says, "What the basin needs is not integration but relationship, not identity but articulation, not a plan but a variety of planning for known interdependencies."[2]

---

[1] Gilbert White, "A Perspective of River Basin Development," *Law and Contemporary Problems*, Vol. XXII, No. 2, Spring, 1957, p. 173.

[2] Henry C. Hart, *The Dark Missouri* (Madison: University of Wisconsin Press, 1957), p. 213.

Third, the extent and method of this articulation will differ in different situations, and a major determinant will be the expressed need that motivates a drainage basin development. We may postulate type situations. If water, or some combination of water services, is the extent of the expressed need, the articulation of water development with comprehensive planning may be relatively simple. In areas where regional development is the expressed need, and water is the key to development, plans for the production of water services and for regional development may be integrated within a drainage basin. In other areas, the planning jurisdiction may dominate and overlap the drainage basin. Here articulation becomes critical, and a sharp distinction of the drainage basin as a production facility is important to this articulation. This situation will become increasingly frequent in burgeoning metropolitan areas where urban planning and water development promise to develop intricate interdependencies.

Fourth, the problem of meshing watershed and river basin development, like that of relating water development to comprehensive planning, also calls more for articulation than for integration. This invites the question: What pragmatic factors condition the extent and method of articulating watershed and river basin developments? I suspect that we should go beyond the rough guide of "the extent and manner in which the people of the watershed identify themselves with the river basin's problems." For example, the physical and hydrological constraints so frequently invoked in arguing watershed-river basin integration need probing and differentiating. In addition, our earlier discussion suggests that the relation of the watershed area as a market to the total market region and to the river basin in terms of market as well as water flow invites study for distinctions significant to articulating watersheds and river basins.

Fifth, the concepts of benefit-cost analysis must be extended beyond the calculus of efficiency. The identification of who benefits and who is going to pay in terms of their location relative to the watershed, the river basin, the comprehensive planning region, and established governmental jursidictions are major factors in the political decisions implicit in watershed development — decisions which the planning process should be committed to serve.

As Brinser has pointed out, the problem goes beyond economics and into what he defines as political economy.

Eugene C. Buie is watershed planning specialist with the Engineering and Watershed Planning Unit of the Soil Conservation Service in Spartanburg, South
Carolina. Ernest F. Carmichael, John E. McLean, and John W. Roehl are also on
the staff of this unit in Spartanburg, as hydraulic engineer, agricultrual economist,
and geologist, respectively.

Chapter 7

EUGENE C. BUIE

Assisted by Ernest F. Carmichael, John E. McLean,
John W. Roehl

Interdisciplinary Teamwork

in Watershed Planning

W ATERSHED project planning in the Soil Conservation Service is
a coordinated analysis by a team of technicians representing
various disciplines. The principal disciplines are economics,
hydrology, geology, engineering, general soil science, and plant technology. There is no defined line between the areas of responsibility of each
of these; each is dependent upon and interrelated with the others. Formulating a watershed plan requires that the technicians select an economically feasible system of improvements compatible with the economic
and social conditions of the watershed.

This chapter reviews the planning process, emphasizing requirements
for successful teamwork.

PREPLANNING ACTIVITIES

Field Examination

Activity of the Soil Conservation Service in watershed planning does
not begin until the local sponsoring agencies make application for

87

assistance under the provisions of Public Law 566. The first step thereafter is a field examination of the proposed project area. The field examination attempts to determine the nature of the watershed problems, the physical availability of sites for works of improvement, the presence of damageable values, the interest of the landowners in a watershed project, and the possibilities of local people assuming their part of the costs.

Field examinations usually are made by a team comprised of representatives of all interested agencies. They are of a general reconnaissance nature, and the findings are recorded in a brief report. They provide the state agency, which has supervisory responsibility over watershed programs, with a basis for approving the application for assistance and for establishing the priority of the watershed for planning.

Preliminary Investigation

The preparation of a watershed workplan requires the input of considerable technical effort. It is desirable, therefore, to have some assurance that this effort will result in a plan which is feasible and that the planned works of improvement will actually be established in the watershed. Field examinations usually are of a limited reconnaissance nature and are indicative in only a general way of project feasibility. In order to provide a greater degree of assurance that full planning effort will result in an active watershed project it is necessary that a preliminary investigation be made.

The preliminary investigation is made by the watershed planning party after priority for planning has been established by the state agency. Its objective is to make an adequate determination of project feasibility and to determine the ability and willingness of the sponsors to meet their share of the costs and other responsibilities in carrying out a watershed project.

The preliminary investigation requires a detailed reconnaissance of the watershed, utilizing available maps and aerial photographs as well as field reconnaissance. Damage areas are located and damageable values estimated. Engineering surveys are made to establish critical relationships. Potential structural sites are located, and the key sites are identified. The minimum protection to the flood plain that will meet the people's objectives is determined. The costs and the benefits are estimated. Based on the purposes to be included in the project and the legal cost-sharing requirements, the distribution of costs between federal and non-federal interests is estimated. This information is presented to the local people as a first estimate of the costs.

The people also are informed of the benefits that can be expected, of the types of measures needed, and of the location of key structure sites and of other needed sites and their alternates. They are asked to reconsider the project in the light of the findings of the preliminary investigation and give assurance that they will accept their responsibilities. When they provide the state conservationist with this assurance, he is ready to proceed with the development of a watershed workplan.

Work Outline

The development of a watershed workplan requires careful coordination of the activities of the various technicians. A technician of one discipline frequently is dependent on data developed by technicians of the other disciplines. For example, the hydrologist cannot make an adequate location of the valley cross sections that will be used for valley flood-routing until he and the economist have agreed on the evaluation reaches, which in turn are dependent upon damageable values. Before the hydrologist can use these valley cross sections for flood-routing, the engineer and the survey party must make surveys and plot their field notes. The soil scientist and the geologist must provide the hydrologist with soil-cover-complex information for the various segments of the watershed. The engineer cannot prepare the preliminary design for a floodwater-retarding structure until the survey party makes surveys, the geologist determines the volume for sediment storage that should be provided, and the hydrologist estimates the volume of floodwater to be stored and calculates the runoff curve numbers to be used as a basis for emergency spillway and freeboard design. The economist cannot estimate the reduction in floodwater damages until the hydrologist prepares the stage-area inundation curves for without-project and with-project conditions.

Since watershed planning is a team activity, it is necessary to prepare a guide for the timing of activities of each member. The preliminary investigation provides the party with information as to detailed investigations needed. With this information as a guide a work outline is developed.

DEVELOPING THE WATERSHED WORKPLAN

Investigations

After the Administrator of the Soil Conservation Service authorizes a certain watershed for full planning effort, the state conservationist instructs the planning party when to concentrate effort within the watershed. Data from the preliminary investigation are used in the detailed planning. The following items guide the investigations of the various members of the party:

1. The number and identity of evaluation units.[1]
2. The identity of the evaluation reaches in each evaluation unit.[2]
3. The approximate number of valley cross sections.
4. The basis for developing the principal spillway hydrographs for the floodwater-retarding structures.
5. The method of valley flood-routing for each evaluation reach.
6. The method of collecting data for the soil-cover-complex determination.
7. Base datum for engineering surveys.
8. The intensity of investigations by evaluation reaches.
9. The percent of the flood plain to be covered by damage schedules.
10. The minimum acceptable level of protection by locations or the specific objectives of the local people.
11. The testing procedure to be followed for project formulation.

Economist. The economist is responsible for data on crop production practices, costs of production, flood-free yields, and prices. By personal interviews with farmers in the flood plain he develops damage schedules for representative areas. These interviews cover floodwater damages to crops and pastures and to fixed improvements. Damage schedules for roads and bridges are obtained from highway agencies. The interviews are aimed at obtaining the relationship between depth of flooding and damage.

In addition, the economist collects information on another important project effect, namely, probable changes in use of the flood plain if various levels of protection are provided.

From the interviews, land use in the flood plain is estimated for without- and with-project conditions. Interview answers may be adjusted taking account of land use capabilities in the flood plain, managerial ability, availability of markets, and restrictions imposed by acreage allotments and marketing quotas.

Damageable values are then estimated, and stage-damage relations are prepared by seasons of the year.

Hydrologist. The hydrologist determines the location of high-water marks produced by specific floods, including the largest recent flood. These are located on aerial photographs, and with the use of a stereoscope the flood plain is delineated. The flood-plain area is measured by evaluation reaches. These areas are furnished to the economist and serve as a basis for estimating damageable values.

After an analysis of climatologic data, a rainfall evaluation series is selected which will be used as the basis for project evaluation. In consultation with the economist, the valley flood-routing reaches are

---

[1] An evaluation unit may consist of (1) a group of structural measures which function interdependently with respect to each other but more or less independently of other structural measures, or (2) a single structural measure which functions independently of other structural measures.

[2] An evaluation reach is a section of the flood plain which has similar hydraulic characteristics and like damageable values provides a suitable area on which to bring together hydrologic and economic data for determination of stage-area-damage relationships.

selected. Within these reaches the locations for valley and channel cross sections are selected. These are identified for the engineering survey crew so that necessary surveys can be initiated.

In cooperation with the geologist, soil scientist, work unit conservationist, and a Forest Service technician where applicable, soil-cover-complex conditions are developed for the various segments of the watershed for without- and with-project conditions. Hydrologic soil groups are identified. Runoff rates are calculated for the entire watershed for present and future conditions. In addition, runoff curve numbers are calculated for the drainage areas above potential floodwater-retarding structures.

Using the calculated runoff curve numbers, the hydrologist estimates the runoff to be expected for the storms of the evaluation series. When the valley and channel cross sections have been surveyed and the field notes plotted, stage-discharge curves are developed for each cross section. These may be based on water surface profile calculations or on Manning's formula.[3] Then stage-area inundation relations are developed for each evaluation reach. These are furnished to the economist, who uses them to develop stage-damage relations.

Geologist. An early activity of the geologist is to assist the hydrologist with the delineation of the flood plain. He also works with the hydrologist and economist in the selection of evaluation reaches.

Sediment and flood-plain erosion damage areas are located on a map and tabulated by evaluation reaches to be used by the economist. The nature of the sediment in each of the sediment damage areas is determined. This information, together with the location of the damage area, is related to the sediment source by the use of sediment delivery rates.

In the majority of watersheds, most of the geologist's time is taken up with investigations of the foundation conditions of each site, availability of fill material, geologic conditions at the emergency spillway, and the determination of sediment storage requirements.

The geologic investigations of each site are most often performed with a hand auger. Power auger equipment may be utilized for more intensive investigation of key sites that have questionable foundation conditions.

When site conditions are found to be favorable and the site is selected for evaluation, sediment storage requirements are determined. This involves studying erosion and the resultant sediment yields above each site. These determinations are made for present and future soil-cover-complex conditions. Sediment delivery rates are determined and the total yield of sediment is calculated for the design life of the structure, usually fifty years.

Investigations are also made of geologic conditions of proposed channel locations. These findings identify any geologic limitations

---

[3] An empirical formula developed to use hydraulic characteristics to compute velocity of flow in open channels. See George E. Russell, *Hydraulics* (New York: Henry Holt and Co., 1945), p. 274.

which the engineer must consider in developing the hydraulic design of
the channel. They also provide information used in developing cost estimates.

Engineer. Planning is facilitated by having all engineering surveys
referenced to a common datum. If there are bench marks sufficiently
near the watershed, all surveys are referenced to mean sea level.
Otherwise an assumed common datum is used. The first activity of the
engineer is to have the survey party establish vertical control along the
main-stem flood plain and up the valleys of the major tributaries on
which structures are contemplated. Any surveys made during the preliminary investigation are tied into this system of bench levels.

As soon as the locations of valley and channel cross sections are
selected, these are surveyed and the notes plotted. Since the hydrologist needs these cross sections early in his investigations, priority is
given to completing these surveys.

While the valley and channel cross sections are being surveyed, the
engineer and the geologist select sites for potential floodwater-retarding
structures. These are located on maps and necessary surveys made.
The surveys consist of a profile of the center line of the embankment
and a topographic map of the reservoir basin. During this investigation
the structure failure damage class of each dam is determined.

Analyses

As soon as data begin to accumulate from the investigations, the
hydrologist begins to analyze the physical effects of floods under present
conditions. He develops hydrographs of the streamflow caused by
storms and checks these against known high-water marks of the same
storms. In this manner he adjusts his assumptions so that estimated
peak flows and hydraulic characteristics of the valley conform to actual
conditions.

Selected storms are flood-routed through the valley using the con-
cordant flow method or the storage indication method.[4] From these valley flood-routings, stages at the various valley cross sections are calculated for the storms of the evaluation series. These stages are furnished
to the economist, who carries them through his stage-damage tables to
determine flood damages which would occur in the flood plain during the
period of the evaluation series if present conditions prevail. These
damages are converted to an annual equivalent to provide average annual
floodwater damages under present conditions. A similar analysis is
made using estimated future soil-cover-complex conditions to determine
the effects of the planned land treatment measures.

The hydrologist then estimates the amount of reduction in flooding
which will be necessary to meet the objectives of the local people. He

---

[4] Soil Conservation Service, *National Engineering Handbook*, Sec. 4, Suppl. A, Chap. 3,
p. 17.

projects this into an estimate of the percentage of the runoff from the watershed which must be controlled. With this reduction in mind, the hydrologist, engineer, and geologist select those potential structure sites that appear to be the most efficient. They consult with the economist to determine which are most favorably located with respect to critical damage areas. Since the peak discharge at any selected cross section depends on the size of the drainage area above that point, this peak discharge can be reduced proportionately by controlling a like proportion of the watershed. There is a direct relationship between depth of inundation and floodwater damages. Damage reductions usually are greater proportionately than the reduction in peak discharges.

The hydrologist develops inflow hydrographs for the structures that have been selected for further investigation. These hydrographs consist of a principal spillway hydrograph, which establishes floodwater-detention storage requirements; an emergency spillway safe-velocity hydrograph, which provides the peak discharge for emergency spillway design; and a freeboard hydrograph, which establishes the height of the dam.

The hydrographs are furnished to the engineer, who prepares preliminary designs for each structure. To complete these designs he uses engineering survey data developed by the survey party, sediment storage requirements developed by the geologist, and inflow hydrographs developed by the hydrologist. He determines the required height of the dam, the dimensions of the emergency spillway, and with the hydrologist determines the capacity of the principal spillway. He then estimates the total cost of each structure, getting assistance from the economist on the value of land, easements, and rights-of-way.

It may be desirable to add other floodwater-retarding structures to the system or provide increased channel capacity by means of channel improvement. If the existing channel is shallow and has a low capacity, channel improvement should be included. The initial design capacity is determined for selected cross sections. This can be done by determining from project objectives the maximum permissible frequency of flooding at these selected cross sections. From the rainfall evaluation series the magnitude of the largest storm which will not exceed that frequency is determined. The peak flow at the selected cross sections with the proposed structures in place can be approximated with point hydrographs. The channel then is designed by the engineer to contain the runoff from this magnitude storm as within-bank flow.

The hydrologist flood-routes the same floods as before through the valley, assuming both the structures and channel improvement in place. The stages for the storms in the evaluation series, based on this flood-routing, are furnished the economist.

Using the stages calculated for the evaluation series with the proposed structures in place, the economist estimates the remaining floodwater damages. The difference between these damages and those remaining after land treatment is the floodwater-damage-reduction benefit attributed to the structural measures. He also evaluates reduction in sediment and erosion damages that have been determined by the geologist. These are added to the floodwater-damage-reduction benefits to determine total flood-damage-reduction benefits.

Based on the levels of flood protection which the proposed measures will provide, the economist estimates as benefits the increase in net income associated with change in use of the flood plain as a result of the project. These benefits are classified under three categories: (1) restoration of some areas of the flood plain to levels of former productivity, (2) more intensive use of the flood plain, and (3) changed land use.

The total benefits are related to the sum of the amortized installation costs and the estimated costs for operation and maintenance to determine the economic feasibility of the project.

Project Formulation

Project formulation is a continuing process that begins as soon as investigations are initiated.

Land treatment measures are included if they are effective in reducing serious sedimentation hazards; have measurable physical effects in preventing floodwater, erosion, or sediment damages; or are necessary to assure the realization of benefits used in the justification of proposed structural measures. These measures are considered the initial increment for project formulation. The effects of other improvements are not evaluated until the effects of the land treatment measures have been translated into damage reduction.

Various combinations of structural measures are analyzed by the procedures described in the preceding section. These combinations include the key structure sites and alternative sites for the other structures, together with various sizes of channels.

The first objective is to provide the minimum acceptable level of protection at least total cost. Priority is given to detention of floodwaters to lower peak discharges rather than to reduction of flood stage by means of channels alone. The more rapid removal of floodwater from the watershed in channels alone usually creates adverse flooding conditions downstream. Damages thus incurred may further increase the total cost of the project. After the minimum objectives have been accomplished, additional elements may be added to the project so long as they tend to increase net benefits and are acceptable to the local people.

Alternative systems are evaluated and their physical as well as their economic effects are explained to the local people. The people must then decide whether or not they can and will obtain the necessary easements and rights-of-way for each structure. Sometimes conditions beyond their control make it impossible to obtain one or more sites. On other occasions they are unwilling to obligate themselves for the

cost and legal action necessary to obtain a site. In either case, the removal of a site from a proposed system requires reanalysis and re-
evaluation using alternate sites.

All structural measures included in any evaluation unit are evaluated together, total costs being related to total benefits. In order to ensure that each element produces measurable benefits at least equal to
its cost or is necessary to meet project objectives, various testing
procedures are used. These are difficult to apply when floodwater-
retarding structures and improved channels are interrelated. However,
separate flood-routings or least-total-cost tests usually provide the
needed information.

Re-evaluation and retesting procedures for alternative measures
included in a system that already has been evaluated greatly increase
the time for completion of a watershed workplan. For this reason the
planning party keeps the local people currently informed of all measures and sites being analyzed.

When a proposed system is accepted by the local people, final cost
estimates are prepared, costs are allocated to purposes, and cost-
sharing policies are used to determine the share of the costs to be
borne by the local people and the federal government.

This discussion has been limited to projects where the purposes are
watershed protection and flood prevention. Other purposes may involve
different procedures but the same principles.

Ludwig L. Kelly is in charge of watershed-runoff investigations for the Soil and Water Conservation Research Division of the USDA in Beltsville, Maryland. Formerly with the Soil Conservation Service, he assisted with studies of the Missouri Basin and the inter-agency study of the Arkansas, White, and Red River Basins.

Chapter 8

LUDWIG L. KELLY

State of Hydrologic, Geologic, and Engineering Data

AN ADEQUATE PROGRAM for basic data involves more than recording of the raw facts. They must be evaluated for validity, processed in an orderly manner, made available in meaningful and useful terms, and above all be given objective interpretation.

As the times change and emphasis on various phases of water resource development shifts, there will be a need for new and different data. Too, as understanding of the climate and the physical nature of our resources increases, we may find that we no longer need data of a particular type, but of a new type. The use of radar and other technological developments in meteorology, for example, may well revolutionize some of our ideas on methods for collection of precipitation and other climatic data.

The data discussed here pertain to topography, geology, cadastral surveys of public lands, precipitation, snow, climate, streamflow, ground water, chemical and sanitary water quality, sedimentation, upstream watershed management, and soil moisture.

Various groups have made evaluations of programs for collecting these data. Reports are available from the National Resources Committee,[1] the President's Water Resources Policy Commission,[2] the Presidential Advisory Committee on Water Resources Policy,[3] and the Engineers Joint Council.[4] The recommendations of the first three groups mentioned are in reasonable harmony on what constitutes an adequate federal program. The recommendations of the Engineers Joint Council were more conservative, and stressed the need for more responsibility to be assumed by state and local agencies.

The President's Water Resources Policy Commission of 1950 performed one of the most systematic analyses of existing and needed data. The recommendations of that group, hereinafter called "Commission," are used in this discussion to give an idea of the magnitude of data collection programs generally thought to be needed.

It should be emphasized that the data collection programs discussed here are largely those in which federal agencies take leadership; that practically all of the programs are cooperative in some way or another with other federal agencies, and state and local agencies; and that there is also some data from federal, state, and private sources that time does not permit mentioning.

TOPOGRAPHIC MAPPING

Topographic mapping is the science of measuring and depicting on maps the elevations, drainage, and cultural features of a region. Such maps serve as base maps for planning the location of water control structures, reservoir sites, power lines, roads, and canals, and for determining watershed boundaries, stream lengths, and land and channel slopes. Because topography is related to many other factors, the maps serve as a basis for extrapolating information on precipitation, climate, geology, and ground water.

The principal producer of topographic maps is the Geological Survey. Its maps are tied into a framework of controlling positions of latitude and longitude and elevation as established by the Coast and Geodetic Survey.

In general, the maps considered acceptable for planning purposes are at scales of either 1:24,000; 1:31,680; or 1:62,500; depending on the type of terrain and the possible uses. The contour interval is 5, 10, 20, or 40 feet, depending again on the terrain.

Maps of these scales are available for about 42 percent of the country. Included in this figure are some areas which for various reasons require remapping.

The 1950 report of the Commission recommended that the task of

---

[1] "Deficiencies in Basic Hydrologic Data," Special Advisory Committee on Standards and Specifications for Hydrologic Data (Washington, D.C.: Government Printing Office, 1936).

[2] "A Water Policy for the American People," President's Water Resources Policy Commission (Washington, D.C.: Government Printing Office, 1950).

[3] "Water Resources Policy," Presidential Advisory Committee on Water Resources Policy (Washington, D.C.: Government Printing Office, 1955).

[4] "Principles of a Sound National Water Policy," National Water Policy Panel of Engineers Joint Council (Ann Arbor, Mich.: Edwards Brothers, 1951).

topographic mapping of the United States including Alaska be completed within 20 years, i.e., by 1970. This would require a substantial increase in the rate of mapping. Increased efficiency, largely through photogrammetric methods, has enabled some speed-up of this work.

GEOLOGIC MAPPING

The character, distribution, and inclination of the rocks of the earth's crust, particularly that relatively thin layer near the surface which is accessible to our observation, are shown by geologic maps. The maps and reports that accompany them are interpretations of the structure of the earth's crust and the interrelationships between the varied bedrocks that compose it. These maps and reports are prime requisites for investigations of mineral resources, underground waters, construction materials, and foundations for engineering structures. The planning of water control structures requires knowledge of the strength, durability, water-tightness, and ease of excavation of the geologic materials that underlie them. Agricultural developments, whether by irrigation, drainage, or other means, as well as the classification of lands for these purposes, require knowledge of the permeability of the rocks beneath the soil and of the chemical nature of these materials. Even though a geologic map might not be available, no engineering structure is built today without detailed geologic investigation of the site.

Geologic maps are varied in scale, degree of accuracy, and completeness, depending both on the purpose for which they were prepared and on the date of their preparation. It is commonly held that a general-purpose geologic map of a scale of 1 inch = 1 mile or less is necessary to show adequately our subsurface resources, though this is not the only criterion. Only about 16 percent of the United States is thus mapped. The Commission recommended that the task of mapping the geology of the United States to this minimum scale be completed in 30 years, i.e., in 1980. This goal will not be met at the present (1960) rate of mapping.

CADASTRAL SURVEYS OF PUBLIC LANDS

The cadastral survey of public lands is carried out by the Bureau of Land Management for the purpose of subdividing the areas into units suitable for administration or disposal and to mark the boundaries on the ground. These surveys are necessary to properly determine federal responsibilities in project areas, to identify lands leased under the Oil and Gas Act and the Taylor Grazing Act, and to identify federal forest lands when timber sales are made.

The title to almost 50 percent of the area of 11 western states and much smaller portions of the eastern states is with the federal government.

In the 11 western states there still remain approximately 100 million acres of public lands over which the rectangular system of surveys has not been extended. In addition, approximately 50 million acres of public lands require resurvey. The Commission recommended that this task be completed by 1960.

During recent years, it has been possible to accomplish the survey and resurvey of approximately 1,700,000 acres annually in all of the United States, including Alaska. However, it may be pointed out that a substantial portion of the unsurveyed area in the 11 western states may never require survey under the rectangular system. Substantial areas within national forests or other permanent reservations are not administered by section, township, and range, but rather on the basis of watershed or other natural boundaries.

The granting of statehood to Alaska carried with it a grant of about 104 million acres of public lands to the new state. The act requires that the land selected by the state shall be surveyed and that the selections shall be completed within 25 years. This enactment will necessarily make the survey program in the 11 western states subordinate to that in Alaska.

STREAMFLOW

The regimen of streams is measured by stream-gaging, and from these measurements estimates of expected maximum, mean, and minimum flows are prepared as a basis for the design of works for irrigation, flood control, navigation, water supply, hydroelectric power, and other water use and control improvements. In measuring the flow of a stream the water level or stage of a stream is recorded on a chart. These water-level readings, in conjunction with current meter measurements of discharge to determine the relation of stage to discharge, make possible the computation of the rate of flow or discharge of the stream.

The stream-gaging program as carried out by the Geological Survey involves a network of primary stations to operate on a long-time basis and to serve as base stations to define climatic trends in streamflow, plus secondary stations which need be operated only long enough to characterize the contributing watershed.

Presently (1959), records at about 7,050 stream-gaging stations are maintained by the Geological Survey, usually in cooperation with a state or another federal agency. Of these, 2,550 are in the network of primary stations.

The general recommendations of the Commission were for the stream-gaging program to be increased to about 12,100 stations by 1960. At present rate of expansion it will not be possible to meet this goal. Many technological advances are being made in the recording of water stages and in eliminating the laborious processing of data. But the difficult problem of finding a substitute for the manual current meter measurement has not yet been solved.

GROUND WATER

Ground water is the chief source of rural domestic and stock water for many small communities and industries, and even for some of our larger cities. It is becoming of increasing importance, too, in irrigation. Ground water is the source of dry weather streamflow and is a key element in many drainage projects. Much interest is developing in ground water recharge data.

Information on ground water is developed through geologic studies, exploratory test wells, geophysical probing, and pumping tests. The Geological Survey is the principal federal agency involved in this program, and substantial amounts of work are done by state agencies. As one perhaps somewhat inadequate measure of the size of the ground water program, the Geological Survey in 1953 was making observations of artesian pressure and water level on 8,000 wells.

Figure 1 gives some idea of the extent of coverage for ground water data. The dark areas are those where some degree of ground water information is available. There is little information on the white areas.

The Commission recommended that by 1960 reconnaissance surveys be carried out on all areas where no ground water data exist and that the intensity of coverage be stepped up on areas where projects were being planned or constructed.

PRECIPITATION

Accurate and comprehensive information on precipitation is fundamental to intelligent planning of water use. The source of all important surface and ground waters is rain and snow. Knowledge of their distribution over the country is the basis of all water conservation studies. Precipitation data are used in watershed planning to estimate the frequency and magnitude of floods and dependability of water supplies in watersheds where streamflow measurements are not available or are of short record, to synthesize design storms for the engineering design of structures, for planning of flood-warning systems, and for planning and design of drainage systems. Because of their relatively extensive coverage and long history, precipitation data are especially valuable to the hydrologist as a basis for extrapolating streamflow data.

Precipitation is measured by nonrecording and recording gages. Nonrecording gages are usually read once daily by cooperative observers; recording gages produce a continuous record on a chart, from which intensities may be computed.

Many agencies collect precipitation data for special project uses, but the precipitation network maintained by the Weather Bureau is the

LEGEND

PERCENTAGE ADEQUACY OF GROUND-WATER INFORMATION COVERAGE

— LEGEND —

☐ 0-25%
▨ 26-50%
▩ 51-75%
▨ 76-100%

Compiled by the U.S. Geological Survey April 1950

Figure 1. Percentage adequacy of ground-water information in 1950. Patterns show present status of available ground-water data, in percentage of complete coverage, based chiefly on published U.S.G.S. studies. Complete coverage allows development of large-scale, long-term, ground-water projects without further investigation. Only a minute part of the country is included in this category.

principal source of basic information concerning amount and areal distribution of precipitation throughout the United States. Presently, about 9,000 nonrecording and 3,100 recording gages are in operation, the data from which are compiled in various usable forms by the Weather Bureau. In 1950 the Commission suggested a 1960 goal of about 15,600 gages, with about half of them to be the recording type.

A new meteorological observation tool, radar, has demonstrated its usefulness for measurement of storm rainfall. The Weather Bureau has about 75 weather search radars, which provide for surveillance of about one-third of the United States. Though presently used primarily for hurricane and storm tracking, the meteorologic potential of this new tool is enormous. Its use may greatly influence the future requirements for long-term records.

In recent years, substantial effort has been devoted to the interpretation and analysis of precipitation data by the Weather Bureau and by other federal and state agencies. Much of the data on rainfall has been punched on IBM cards. With the support of other federal agencies, Yarnell's rainfall intensity-frequency studies[5] have been brought up to date. By defining the influence of topographic parameters it has been possible to improve the accuracy of mean annual and seasonal precipitation estimates in mountainous regions, where inaccessibility has prevented extensive data collection.

CLIMATE

Climate is the build-up of weather from day to day. Weather data include precipitation, which has been mentioned above; air temperature, wind, humidity, evaporation, and solar radiation, as well as other factors. We generalize from the weather data to describe the climate of an area. The knowledge of climate is important in the planning of any program involving vegetation or the growing of crops. It is the basis for estimating consumptive use of water by crops, and hence the water supply for irrigation projects, and for estimating evaporation from reservoirs. Too, climate is important in the design and estimation of costs for structural items such as power lines, which are affected by wind and icing; foundation requirements, which are affected by frost; and rip-rap requirements, which are affected by wave action.

The Weather Bureau is the largest producer of weather data. Currently there are about 500 each of evaporation, humidity, and wind stations; 500 air temperature stations which provide hourly values; and 5,500 which provide daily maximum and minimum values.

The Commission recommended in 1950 that the large backlog of climatological data be processed, using modern machine methods, and that maps giving meaningful expressions of climate be prepared. This

---

[5] David S. Yarnell, "Rainfall Intensity-Frequency Data" (Washington, D.C.: Department of Agriculture, Miscellaneous Publication No. 204, Aug., 1935).

is being carried out to the extent possible. All current data are being placed on punch cards at the National Weather Center at Asheville, North Carolina. Some of the backlog of data has been punched through the cooperative effort of various state agricultural experiment stations and the Agricultural Research Service. In general there has been substantial progress made in the analyses of climatological data and the distribution of the results, but there is still much to be done.

CHEMICAL QUALITY OF WATER

The chemical quality of water is directly related to its suitability for a great variety of purposes. The concentration of dissolved mineral matter which all natural water contains in varying amounts determines whether the water is good, poor, or unsatisfactory for industrial, municipal, agricultural, and other uses.

Much of the data on chemical quality of water is collected and analyzed by the Geological Survey, though other federal and state agencies contribute substantial data. In 1955 this agency maintained 486 regular sampling stations for the study of the chemical character of surface waters of the United States. The recommendation of the Commission was for about 1,400 stations by 1960.

SEDIMENTATION

Sedimentation data are needed in watershed planning for estimation of downstream damages due to deposition of sediment in reservoirs, navigation channels and harbors, and on flood plains; for design of reservoirs and water treatment and other structural works; for studies of channel aggradation and degradation; for determining suitability of water for fish, wildlife, and recreation; and for evaluating the effects of control works. Data on sedimentation are collected in two major forms: suspended-load data, which consist of periodic samples of the streamflow, from which sediment content of the water may be computed; and reservoir data, in which the reservoir is surveyed in a manner that permits the computation of the sediment deposited in the reservoir pool.

There were about 300 suspended-load stations in operation in 1950, the Geological Survey operating about half of these stations and various other agencies operating the remainder. The Commission indicated a need for about 1,600 of these stations.

As of 1953, sediment accumulations had been measured in about 700 reservoirs in the United States. Many agencies have contributed to this program. The Commission recommended a reservoir survey program of about 1,400 reservoirs, each to be surveyed once every ten years on the average.

The Subcommittee on Sedimentation of the Inter-Agency Committee

on Water Resources has been active in coordinating the efforts of the
various agencies interested in sediment. Their efforts have resulted
in summarization and assembly of most of the available information on
reservoir surveys and much of the information on suspended load.
They have encouraged support of various projects to develop improved
instrumentation and uniform processing of data.

UPSTREAM WATERSHED DATA

The relation of upstream watershed management to floods, water
yield, ground water, erosion, and sedimentation has been a matter of
much concern in recent years. The philosophy of upstream watershed
research has been to develop an understanding of the relation of climatic and watershed factors to runoff and water yield. Then the findings are extended from experimental watersheds to ungaged upstream
areas, for obviously it is not possible to measure the streamflow and
sediment production of the thousands of small subareas of the United
States.

In this research, data has included mapping or taking measurements
of topography, geology, soils, land use, rainfall, snow, runoff, sediment,
ground water levels, evaporation, wind, and many other factors that influence the hydrologic cycle.

There are a considerable number of watershed research projects,
and several federal agencies are involved. Some research is also being
done by states. Figure 2 shows the location of the federal research
areas. The size of the experimental watersheds ranges from about an
acre to somewhat more than a hundred square miles.

In January, 1959, the Forest Service had about 140 watersheds under
measurement, the Geological Survey about 90, the Tennessee Valley
Authority about 20, and the Agricultural Research Service about 160.
In connection with evaluation of the Watershed Protection and Flood
Prevention Program, the Soil Conservation Service is collecting hydrologic data on upstream watersheds, measuring the runoff from about a
hundred areas. The work of these agencies is cooperative with other
federal or state agencies, and there may be some overlap in the figures
above.

The President's Water Resources Policy Commission and other
committees making recommendations on collection of basic data have
not made their suggestions on upstream engineering data and watershed
management in terms of a numerical size of program. Their recommendations are for the general expansion of the program, and increased
emphasis on analysis, interpretation, and distribution of data, with particular attention to bridging the gap between conclusions drawn with regard to small experimental areas and their application to larger watersheds. I believe it is the general consensus of hydrologists that these
recommendations are not being adequately supported.

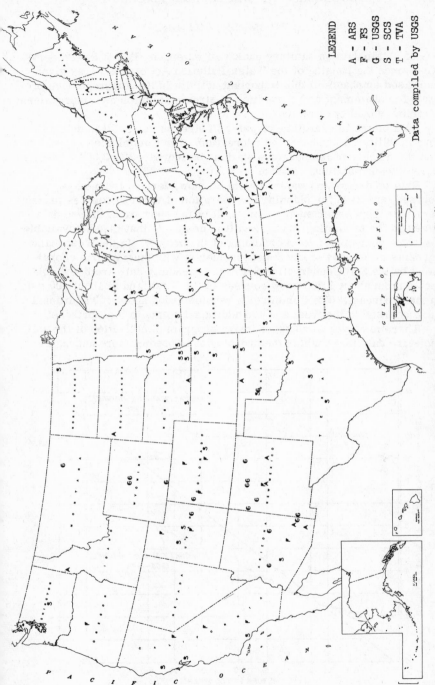

LEGEND

A – ARS
F – FS
G – USGS
S – SCS
T – TVA

Data compiled by USGS

Figure 2. Federal Upstream Watershed Management Studies.

OTHER IMPORTANT DATA

To obtain data on sanitary quality of water, the Public Health Service — since the passing of the Water Pollution Act of 1948 — has given increased emphasis to this important activity in its comprehensive program for abatement and prevention of stream pollution and improvement of sanitary quality of water.

Data on the temperature of water in streams is useful in determining its suitability for industry and recreation. The Commission suggested that the number of temperature stations be increased to 3,000. There were 400 such stations in 1956.

Data on depths and water content of snow, derived from snow courses, are used for planning the operation of water resources projects receiving their water supply from melt of the snow pack. These data are used for predicting runoff, and it is desirable that they be available for some years prior to the planning of the project. In the West many agencies make snow-course measurements, with their efforts coordinated by the Soil Conservation Service. Presently data are being collected from about 1,300 snow courses in the West, and at about 400 points in the Northeast. The Commission recommended about 550 additional snow courses in the West and 100 additional points in the Northeast.

There is as yet no comprehensive program of collection of the soil moisture data that enables the hydrologist to predict more accurately

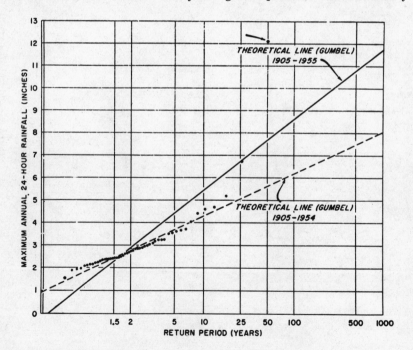

Figure 3. Rainfall frequency data for Hartford, Conn., 1905-55.

the fractions of precipitation that will become streamflow or ground water. A few soil moisture stations have been installed by the Weather Bureau in connection with flood forecasting and by the Soil Conservation Service in connection with snow surveys.

There is no comprehensive program of repeated observations of erosion and aggradation and degradation of stream channels, though construction agencies maintain observations on streams in which they operate projects. Here, too, the Commission recommended additional effort.

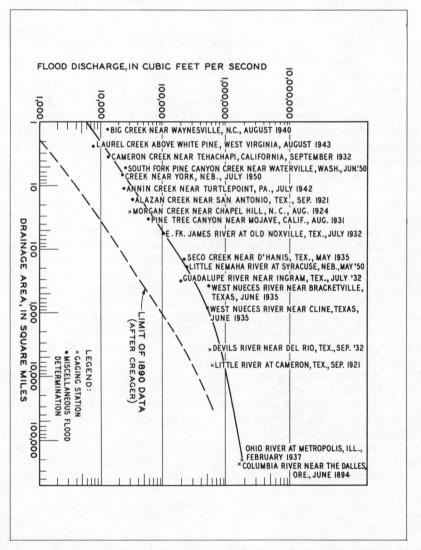

Figure 4. Maximum discharges in relation to drainage area.

IMPROVEMENT OF DATA

Though the various data collection programs are not being expanded as rapidly as hydrologists and engineers would wish, progress is being made. Once topographic mapping is done, for example, the information becomes immediately useful and will remain so for some time. With the types of data that vary with time, however, a need is for the stations to be operated over a long period of time to assure a good sample of the climate.

The need for this long period of record is illustrated in Figure 3. Here the inclusion of one more year of record increased the estimated 100-year, 24-hour rainfall about 40 percent.[6] The analyst is faced with a knotty problem. How much weight should be given this one great event? Various regional analyses can be and are made to evaluate such events, but there is no substitute for time.

Hoyt and Langbein[7] present another illustration of the need for long periods of record. Their lower curve of Figure 4 shows the known maximum floods in the United States as of 1890, and their upper curve, the maximum floods as of 1950. The upper curve is about five times the lower. This is no evidence that floods are changing. The upward shift of the curve is due entirely to the increased number of gaging stations and the period of record; in 1890 there were only about 1,000 station years.

In project evaluation and design the engineer bases his part of the analysis on a sample of weather and streamflow taken from the very recent past. The longer and better this sample is, the better will be his prediction of what will happen in the future. This prediction is no different in many respects from prediction of future economic values of products of agriculture and industry, or numbers and location of our population. In some respects there is less hazard in the hydrologic predictions. Man influences economic values and population, though most of the time he seems to exercise little conscious control.

But so far we seem to have little influence on the weather. Climate follows natural physical laws. The discovery and understanding of these natural laws are the most promising fields for improvement of the hydrologic and engineering aspects of watershed evaluation. This has been recognized by all agencies in the data collection and research business. But it has been difficult to get support for these activities. It seems to be easier to erect a building than it is to pay the salary of a scientist to work in the building.

Though our data collection program is not entirely adequate, it is far more so than the analytical program. Without question, the one item that could improve the hydrologic and engineering data used in

[6] D. M. Hershfield and W. T. Wilson, "Generalizing of Rainfall Intensity-Frequency Data," International Association of Scientific Hydrology, General Assembly of Toronto, Vol. 1, Sept., 1957, pp. 449-506.

[7] W. G. Hoyt and W. B. Langbein, *Floods* (Princeton, N.J.: Princeton University Press, 1955), p. 59.

land and water resource planning and evaluation is to give the data more intensive analysis. This applies not only to such items as bridging the gap between small watersheds and major basins, but also to the whole field of hydrology, hydraulics, and resource engineering.

WILLARD M. SNYDER | *Comment*

HYDROLOGIC, geologic, and other resource engineering data must serve many purposes. What may be an adequate schedule for one purpose may be inadequate for another. For instance, data from stream gage and rain gage records are usually adequate for designing engineering structures. However, for evaluation of land use changes in watershed planning, in many instances the data are inadequate. Evaluation involves comparing the effects of different watershed programs, implying enough precision to reveal hydrologic differences between programs.

Data collection cannot be evaluated without appreciating that improvement is an economic problem. Within allowable budgets how can the greatest amount of useful data be provided for watershed planning? The answer has already been given by Mr. Kelly. There must be increased emphasis on analysis. He has also mentioned progress through technological advance. Automation offers some of the best possibilities. As an example, if meteorological and hydrologic information are recorded directly on punched paper tape for input to an electronic computer, the substantial work of visual translation and transcription is eliminated.

Observation, analysis, and interpretation are the three functional phases of data processing. Let us examine these functions according to whether a watershed program is one of engineering control or one based on agricultural or land use concepts.

Kelly has implied that the data for watershed analysis are not quite adequate but that progress is being made. This seems correct for engineering control, or for estimating the effect of engineering structures in watershed programs. However, the situation with regard to land use concepts is less favorable. In his discussion of upstream watershed data Kelly pointed out the number of watershed research projects carried on by various agencies. Collection of data of this type probably stands in reasonable comparison with other data, but its adequacy in

Willard M. Snyder is head of the Hydrology Section, Hydraulic Data Branch, Division of Water Control Planning of TVA. He was a meteorologist for the U.S. Air Force and a hydrologist for the Pennsylvania Department of Forests and Waters before joining TVA in 1950.

terms of analysis and of program synthesis is open to more serious questioning. I am not advocating agricultural or land use programs at the expense of programs based on engineering control. These two approaches to watershed development are much more complementary than competitive. However, we have hardly begun to reach the interpretive phase for upstream watershed data. We must at some point reach an evaluation of a large number of interacting factors. This evaluation will be necessary before the gap from small watersheds to large basins can be bridged. Stated another way, we must develop methods of analysis and methods of synthesis. Analysis will untangle the maze of information, and synthesis will assemble it in relation to proposed programs.

The most serious deficiency is probably a lack of computational methods which have stood the test of application to many sets of watershed data. The engineer developing a program based on engineering control has the advantage of a well-defined model of structure and site. To bring the agricultural programming to an equivalent objectivity will require the development of computational models. If these models can be developed, they can be applied to proposed watershed programs. Hydrologic response could be synthesized over large drainage areas.

Advances are being made in the development of computational procedures. Statistical methods are increasingly recognized as a tool in watershed data analysis. New methods of statistical and numerical analysis coupled with electronic computers have opened many new approaches. Recognition of the possibilities must lead to recognition of the requirement for personnel competent both in the basic sciences such as hydrology and geology and in modern methods of analytic and computational techniques.

C. V. Lyle is an agricultural economist stationed at Raleigh, North Carolina, where he is responsible for river basin activities and advisory relations of the Land and Water Research Branch of the Farm Economics Research Division of USDA in the southeastern area. He was a work unit conservationist and then agricultural economist for the Soil Conservation Service from 1941 to 1956.

Chapter 9

C. V. LYLE[1]

The State of the Economic Data

T HE TRUISM that the strength of a chain is determined by its weakest link may be well illustrated in watershed planning. The results of planning evolve from a series of interrelated statistical determinations, and the dependability of conclusions rests on the accuracy of each. Physical scientists have certain weak links to mend in their data. There are also shortcomings in the theory, philosophy, and policy of watershed planning. Consequently, the improvement of over-all planning results cannot depend upon the improvement of economic data alone.

Yet, as this chapter will bring out, the needs for better economic data are pressing. For certain deficiencies, needs are so obvious that at times lack of improvement appears ludicrous to the planner forced to use the data available. There are also less obvious needed improvements involving more difficult relationships — those concerned with relatively complex economic principles, frequently based largely upon opinions and assumptions.

[1] The opinions expressed in this paper are those of the author and do not necessarily represent official views. The author is indebted to William A. Green and Elco L. Greenshields for reviewing and making suggestions on an earlier draft.

Under procedures now in use, certain data that serve as building blocks in the development of a small-watershed workplan or of a river-basin study report are usually inadequate in many respects. They may be discussed under the following sub-heads:

1. Prices and costs
2. Agricultural land use and production
3. Production costs and net returns
4. Consumptive and nonconsumptive water uses and needs
5. Interest rates
6. Associated project costs
7. Project costs
8. Flood damage and damage reduction benefit relationships
9. Nonagricultural land use and production
10. Other nonagricultural data

The final two, representing nonagricultural data, are important, but I shall confine the discussion that follows largely to agricultural data.

PRICES AND COSTS

Agricultural benefits are commonly defined as the excess of the economic value of agricultural production with the project over the value without the project, less the economic value of additional farm inputs expended with the project. A minimum of two sets of net return calculations are necessary, one for the "with" project situation and one for the "without." Commodity and input-output price relationships are significant to the calculations in three respects: (1) in combination with given resource supplies available they indicate the combination of enterprises; (2) they influence the amount of any resource to be expended in production and the rate of substitution between resources; and (3) they determine the economic value attached to the resulting agricultural production.

Agricultural economists experienced in farm budgeting are aware of the sensitive nature of the imputational process and of the large change in an estimate of net return that may result from relatively small changes in either commodity prices or production costs. The use of two sets of cost-return calculations does not assure that errors in one offset those in the other.

The most common current usage among the federal agencies for watershed planning purposes usually restricts unit price considerations to "current"[2] and "projected"[3] price data. Several years ago, agricultural economists in general rejected current price data as a basis for

---

[2] Current unit prices (and costs) are usually interpreted as the market prices prevailing during the most recent calendar year for which complete price lists are available in published form (seasonal prices are sometimes used).

[3] Projected prices and costs referred to here are contained in Agricultural Research Service and Agricultural Marketing Service, *Agricultural Price and Cost Projections for*

most watershed planning purposes. As a result, the policy of the Department of Agriculture requires the use of projected prices in watershed planning, except for items — principally project costs — where full value is expected to be realized in five years or less. For example, a nonrecurring cost expected to be incurred within five years from the inception of the project is evaluated at current cost levels.

The only apparent arguments in favor of the use of current prices and costs rather than projections are that they are sometimes more readily available and may have more applicability to local conditions. However, the arguments for some form of projections appear to outweigh by far the few arguments against.

There are several needed improvements of available projections. First, the available lists are incomplete. Second, the presentation of prices paid at the national level and prices received at the state level within the projected prices-and-costs publication leads the planner into error in the development of net return data. This may be improved by presenting each in comparable detail and for comparable economic areas.

Probably the greatest need for improvement involves the entire theory of price projections. One suggestion would be to make basic price and cost studies by market areas rather than by such political units as states. Another would be to check projections within the areas for which they are intended by using farm budget analyses for alternative enterprise combinations. Subsequent comparisons between areas and regions might be used to check reasonableness on a comparative basis, as well as to help in estimating the likely effects of interarea and interregional competition. Linear programming and other modern analytical techniques could be helpful in these studies.

While a rather large assignment has been outlined in the immediately preceding suggestions, it should be recognized that assumed prices and costs greatly influence watershed planning results.

AGRICULTURAL LAND USE AND PRODUCTION

Principal secondary sources of land use and production data are the U. S. Census of Agriculture and data from state statisticians' offices of the Agricultural Marketing Service. It is rare when these data are close to being adequate for use in watershed planning. A universal characteristic of watershed planning is the need for separate evaluations of flood-plain land and nonflood-plain land. Usually, the flooded areas are comprised largely of alluvial (bottom land or river delta) soils, which tend to be relatively level and which in many other respects differ from the areas that are not flooded. Under present conditions,

---

Use in Making Benefit and Cost Analyses of Land and Water Resource Projects (Washington, D.C.: USDA, 1957). To quote in part: "In general, the projections reflect the long-term levels that might reasonably be expected with production and requirements in balance under competitive conditions" (p. 4).

the planner has no choice but to make rather hurried field studies to develop the data needed in planning a specific watershed. The secondary data available are not well suited to use in watershed studies because (1) they pertain to political subdivisions; (2) they represent averages for all land areas within the political unit and, even when they represent averages for a natural unit, there is seldom a satisfactory means for distinguishing the areas that must be evaluated separately for watershed planning purposes; and (3) they are inadequate for establishing the multiple relationships that exist between land use, productivity, soil types, excess water problems (such as flooding and poor drainage), drought, and other management problems.

Examination of reports of river-basin and small-watershed studies prepared in the Southeast from 1936 to 1959 reveals that agricultural benefits account for a range of approximately 60 to nearly 100 percent of total project benefits, with the probable exception of projects that involve power production and navigation as primary purposes. Methods used in determining agricultural benefits rely heavily upon land use and yield data. Inaccuracies in these basic data may obviously be expected to produce erroneous final results. These may be of even greater magnitude than the original error because of pyramiding effects. An example of the possible effects may be cited from a study of a project where preliminary calculations indicated a benefit-cost ratio of 1.05 to 1.00. Agricultural benefits accounted for approximately 65 percent of the total. As corn was a major crop in the benefited area, a reduction of 5 to 10 bushels in the per-acre yield of corn could reduce the benefit-cost ratio below unity. The average yield actually used in the evaluation was 70 bushels per acre. Current yields in the area average less than 30 bushels per acre.

The solution to this problem is in a multiple approach. *First,* the secondary data could be made more usable if the Bureau of the Census and the Agricultural Marketing Service could be persuaded to take action to obtain improvements. This would require that they become familiar with watershed planning needs.

Second, greater emphasis on photo-interpretation studies and methods of obtaining certain data by specific areas from air-photo analysis can be valuable. Preservation of all existing photographic flights and addition of new flights at periodic intervals in the future can be of value not only in watershed planning but for many other uses.

Third, yield studies conducted on a macro-research approach basis by soil types are needed. The "Macro-Analysis" discussion presented by D. B. Ibach at a Conference for Cooperators in the TVA Agricultural Economics Research Activities held at Knoxville, Tennessee, March 24-26, 1959, is an excellent illustration of the general idea.

A relatively small field team might be relied upon to accumulate the necessary local field information. A group to set up such studies would profit from inclusion of one or more of each of these specialists: (1) agronomist, (2) drainage engineer, (3) irrigation engineer, (4) agricultural economist, and (5) soil scientist. This is not intended to exclude other specialists. Measurement of all significant yield variables should be the main objective of these research studies.

AGRICULTURAL PRODUCTION COSTS AND NET RETURNS

Rather than attempt to outline the many reasons why most of the production cost and net return data now available are unsatisfactory for use in watershed planning, I shall list some requirements for usefulness of this type of data.

1. The data should be available for reasonably homogeneous areas, not by states or less homogeneous areas. A soil-problem area map of the United States upon which a type-of-farming area map is super-imposed could be utilized to delineate reasonably homogeneous areas.
2. Within reasonably homogeneous areas, production cost and net return data should be available separately for flood-plain and nonflood-plain lands, or at least studied sufficiently to determine that no appreciable difference in average costs exists. In the eastern mountains of Kentucky the costs of crop production on upland and bottom land differed greatly, whereas in the piedmont of Virginia no great difference was found in average total costs per acre between the flood plain and the average for all land areas. However, there were significant differences by operations. In analyses of floodwater damages, these differences can be important.
3. Production-cost data must be complete and detailed. In addition to the specified costs, which are usually given in some detail in most production-cost publications, overhead and management costs are also needed. All significant details available from the original study should be described. Perhaps more detail than is usually obtained in original studies is needed.
4. More complete separation of cost items by operations, or by time of year, is needed, particularly in analyses of flood damage.
5. Development of curves or tables of significant variables would be most helpful.

The effect of erroneous production-cost data on the watershed project recommendations may be illustrated by the following example. Assume: (1) total annual equivalent costs of a flood prevention structure are $1,000; (2) annual benefits are $1,500 — they result from a reduction in flood hazard and associated poor drainage conditions on a 300-acre area now used only as forest, which it is anticipated will be converted to production of corn as a result of building the structure; (3) erroneous production-cost data indicate the annual net return from corn to be $15 per acre, whereas the correct return is $5; (4) associated project costs (including land clearing and smoothing costs, drainage costs, and loss of net return from forest products) are $10 per acre on an annual equivalent basis. As far as the planner is aware, the correct net annual benefit is $5 per acre, or $1,500. This provides him with a 1.5 to 1.0

benefit-cost ratio. Under the assumption, however, a total annual net loss of $2,500 would result if the structure were installed and the indicated conversions made ($1,000 structure cost plus $1,500 loss of net returns and associated project costs). The actual loss would more likely be between $1,000 (the structure cost) and $2,500, as probably most of the conversions would not be made or would be only temporary.

A partial solution might come through those who are currently doing production-cost research. An understanding of what is needed, and why, plus a minimum of extra effort on the part of those researchers now doing production-cost research for other purposes could be utilized to improve available data. However, it is doubtful that this approach will succeed in obtaining the total improvement needed. A procedure believed most likely to produce the desired result is to obtain personnel specifically for this purpose. They would be expected to tackle the problem systematically by reasonably homogeneous problem areas, make the greatest possible use of other work, and then fill in gaps through original research.

AGRICULTURAL WATER USES AND NEEDS

In general, water has been plentiful in the humid areas of the United States from the earliest settlement. Prolonged periods of drought in recent years have resulted in severe water shortages, particularly in heavily populated urban and industrial centers. This has resulted in greater recognition of water as a limited and exhaustible resource. Fortunately, although localized and usually temporary, these water shortages have stimulated considerable interest in water problems. However, there is still a dearth of data that relate needs to availability and use. Water-resource reports give considerable detail on names of surface streams, variations in flow, oxygen and mineral content, and other similar and necessary statistics. Specific data and information concerning the use, or need, for this surface water; the location, quality, and quantity of alternative sources of water such as ground water; the relative costs of making water available from the various sources for specified purposes; and the trends in both consumptive and non-consumptive uses are lacking.

Thus far in river basin and small-watershed planning it has been assumed that sufficient water will be available to meet all needs planned as well as all competitive needs not taken into account in planning. At best, only superficial information has been available concerning the total available water supply, and there has been only partial information concerning needs. As far as planning for agricultural use of water is concerned, about the only specific estimates attempted are for irrigation purposes.

It might be helpful to encourage groups concerned with water resources to make more comprehensive studies.

INTEREST RATES

Currently (1959) in federal watershed studies certain interest rates are specified by the Bureau of the Budget for purposes involving expenditure of federal funds. The required rate is 2.5 percent for converting federal costs to annual equivalent values. The most commonly used rates for private funds are 4 and 5 percent. Although these rates may be appropriate for certain purposes, there is serious doubt that they give a true indication of the value of resources in alternative uses. A comprehensive study of the entire interest-rate complex, relating interest rate to risk and to anticipated use of the resource involved, is needed. Cooperative efforts of business and agricultural economists is indicated for some watershed interest-rate problems, such as those that involve urban and industrial expansion into formerly agricultural areas and those where vertical integration involves complex manufacturing processes as well as farming activities.

The importance of using appropriate interest rates in watershed evaluations may be illustrated by the following example. The cost of land (agricultural and nonagricultural) used for project purposes is its average current market value. All project costs, including those for land, are converted to annual equivalent values through an amortization procedure using a 2.5-percent interest rate and a 50-year amortization period (established by the Bureau of the Budget as the interest rate chargeable on federal expenditures and the maximum evaluation period for any watershed project cost or benefit purpose). These annual equivalent costs are compared with annual net project benefits from land areas protected by the project, on which interest charges usually range from 5 to 6 percent. Recent study in a localized area of North Carolina indicates that the current average interest rate in the area is approximately 6 percent on farm real estate mortgage loans, with the loan period ranging from 1 to 40 years and averaging less than 30.

To simplify comparisons, the perpetuity concept is used, since differences are not greatly affected thereby. For each million dollar increment of capital cost amortized at 2.5 percent instead of the more appropriate rate of 6 percent, the annual value of costs is reduced by $35,000 ($1 million amortized at 6 percent into perpetuity amounts to $60,000 annually, while at 2.5 percent it amounts to only $25,000). Consider a project having an annual equivalent cost of $1 million as determined at 2.5 percent (approximately a $30 million capital cost project) with a benefit-cost ratio of 1.2 to 1.0. If any amount of the capital cost over about $6 million were to be amortized at 6 percent instead of 2.5 percent, the benefit-cost ratio would be reduced to less than unity.[4]

---

[4] Discounting at 2.5 percent, the annual equivalent benefits are $1.2 million and the annual equivalent costs are $1 million, or an excess of $200,000 of benefits over costs. Amortizing $6 million of the capital costs at 6 percent would raise the annual equivalent costs by 6 times $35,000, or $210,000.

ASSOCIATED PROJECT COSTS

A separation of drainage costs is sometimes made into project costs, which include the costs of main canals only, and associated project costs, which include costs of community-type laterals and of individual farm drainage ditches. An error in these associated costs is just as important as in other production costs.

The development of transportation and other farm and community facilities for new areas brought into production by a project must receive consideration. Furthermore, less expansion of existing facilities may be required in areas producing at a lower level without the proposed project than might be expected with the project fully effective.

These data may be improved, in part, by including sufficient detail in production cost studies. However, additional special studies are needed.

PROJECT COSTS

More reliable data are usually available for costs of dams and other structural measures than for costs of vegetative or water use measures. Analysis of vegetative proposals, e.g., sod waterways, generally involves data that could be made available as part of the previously discussed production-cost data. What was said about production-cost data applies equally to the use of sod waterways and to other land use changes that are project costs.

Greatest deficiencies seem to involve the total costs for reservoirs of intermediate size and land costs for all reservoirs. Individual agency policies and criteria may tend to obscure the central problems. Further study of very small reservoirs (with drainage areas of less than 500 acres) to determine their true feasibility for floodwater detention purposes and multipurpose uses appears to be needed, particularly in certain eastern mountain areas where the topography often precludes the use of larger structures. Design criteria used for structures must vary to take into consideration soils, terrain, rainfall-runoff relations, and the size of the drainage area controlled. Once such factors have been accounted for, another must be considered. This is the "hazard" factor, which determines the hazard class of a given structure, or of a group of structures in series. Although comparatively few structures have failed, the adverse publicity resulting may have led to federal requirements for safety measures in small structures that are not warranted by any realistic appraisal of probable damages from failure. It is possible that the cost of including these safety factors in small structures is responsible for many of them being ruled out as not economically feasible.

Improvement can probably best be accomplished by a study group independent of any agency involved directly in watershed planning.

FLOOD DAMAGE AND DAMAGE REDUCTION

BENEFIT RELATIONSHIPS

The dearth of adequate basic data for study purposes is most apparent in this relatively complex field. Data concerning the relationships existing between floods and the damages resulting therefrom are usually collected anew for each watershed study. Transposition of these data, as currently obtained, from one watershed to another will probably result in inaccuracy, as will transfer of data from one stream reach within a given watershed to another dissimilar reach.

Consideration of some of the factors that contribute to agricultural flood damages may help in visualizing the complexity of the problem.

1. Depth of floodwater. The significance of this varies with the type of vegetation. Such factors as duration, velocity, and turbidity of floodwater tend to vary with depth within a given reach of a stream. As a result, current methods rely largely on depth relations in damage studies.

2. Duration of flooding. Length of time of flooding often becomes paramount, as it would when prolonged to the point of destroying certain forest species.

3. Velocity of water during flooding. This is variable with head and gradient. It can cause considerable damage to many crops without great depth or long duration.

4. Condition of floodwater. Turbidity is usually the prime consideration, but temperature and chemical content may be important. For certain low-growing pasture plants, deposition of silt on the edible portion of the plant is frequently the major consideration. If the floodwater is heavily laden with silt, a few inches of depth may do more damage than several feet of relatively clear floodwater.

5. Time of year or stage of plant growth. Direct damage to a specific crop is not expected from a flood occurring early enough to permit usual preparation of land and planting of crop. Furthermore, susceptibility to damage varies greatly from one stage of growth to another.

6. Soil type. The internal drainage and other characteristics of the soil affect flood damage.

7. Climatic conditions. Rainfall, temperature, and humidity before and after the time of flooding may affect damages.

8. Variety of plant. This deserves greater recognition. For example, there is a tendency by some to group all hay or pasture plants together. Also, a significant difference in damage to corn may result from varietal differences in height of the ear from the ground and in the strength of the stalk.

9. Management. For some crops this may equal variety in importance. The following variables are relevant: row direction, drainage considerations and method of planting on a bed, relatively flat, or in a

furrow. These may be particularly significant when the depth of the floodwater is two feet or less.

Research to isolate, measure, and establish adequate flood damage curves for each separable flood damage factor could save considerable time in the long run because these data could then be used, as needed, in almost any watershed through a determination of the degree of applicability of each factor. More accurate results than those obtained under current procedures might also be expected.

Benefits from more intensive use of flood-plain lands are also inseparably involved in these evaluations. These benefits frequently account for more than 50 percent of all agricultural flood damage reduction benefits. An example of the effect which use of erroneous data in the estimation of these benefits may have upon study results was presented in the preceding section entitled "Agricultural Production Costs and Net Returns." Any errors made in estimating the effect of varying degrees of flood hazard upon land use, yields, the ability of landowners to finance needed improvements, and similar factors should be added to the effect upon study results of errors in production-cost data.

CONCLUSIONS

If planning results are to be improved, it is believed that we must start by improving the basic data upon which the planning studies depend. Concurrent with or following this must come improvement in the basic framework of theory, philosophy, policy, and criteria used in the study and formulation of land and water resource development programs.

Piecemeal improvement of basic data may be accomplished through current procedures and under current organizational arrangements, but past accomplishments do not indicate that sufficient improvements will be made to meet the needs. It is believed that more satisfactory results could be obtained for the purpose from a centrally organized, independent group of a permanent nature having a scope of responsibility and organizational structure somewhat similar to that of recently created study commissions. While this group should not be permitted to replace or duplicate the work of state, federal, and private organizations currently doing research, it should have the responsibility for basic data of all types needed in the study, formulation, and development of land and water resource programs. It should also have the authority and latitude to make new studies which are necessary; coordinate studies being made by others to secure maximum usefulness of the data; accumulate, reorganize, and rework data already available into more usable forms; and make appropriate distribution to individuals and groups needing the information. The mere fact that needed data are in existence in some form and at some unspecified place may be of small value to a study group not having reasonable access to such data.

MOST DEFECTS in watershed reports are traceable to faulty laws and faulty regulation by executive agencies. Mr. Lyle has made a commendable effort to show how the field economist struggling under these handicaps can improve his watershed reports.

The Corps of Engineers, the Bureau of Reclamation, and the Soil Conservation Service do nearly all federal watershed planning. The distinctive responsibilities of these three agencies — large-basin development by the Corps, irrigation by the Bureau of Reclamation, and small watersheds by the Soil Conservation Service — are logical specializations that should be maintained. The agencies employ most of the watershed specialists of the nation, many of whom have other duties to perform along with their watershed work. Any attempt to place the personnel of these three agencies in a single watershed agency is probably not the road to better resources planning.

However, a cause for concern is that each agency tends to follow its own convenience on standards of project evaluation. In its justification of projects, the Soil Conservation Service does not count secondary or "indirect" benefits, that is, benefits from increases in local business due to the processing and distribution of products arising from irrigation. The Bureau of Reclamation often relies heavily on secondary benefits. The Soil Conservation Service classes increased use of flood-plain land as flood control benefits and charges the cost of these to the federal government, whereas the Corps seldom uses such benefits because half of their costs are charged to local beneficiaries.

The Bureau of Reclamation submitted plans for the San Juan-Chama and the Navajo projects of New Mexico at about the same time. Both have the same reservoir on the San Juan River as a source of irrigation water. The Navajo project plan carries 52 percent of all benefits as indirect benefits and only 48 percent as direct benefits, whereas the other project credits irrigation with 77 percent of direct benefits and indirect with 23 percent. No valid evidence is given as to why such a great difference arises from indirect benefits. Furthermore, any project is questionable if it cannot stand or fall on direct benefits.

On the Waxahachie Creek watershed of Texas, the Corps of Engineers submitted a project for Bardwell Dam and claimed a benefit-cost ratio of 1.02 to 1.00. The Soil Conservation Service submitted a project for 22 small dams above Bardwell. The two agencies asserted that no

Jesse T. Sanders retired as Collaborator, Land and Water Research Branch, Farm Economics Research Division of USDA, in 1959. From 1925 to 1936 he was Head of the Department of Agricultural Economics at Oklahoma State University. He has held positions in a number of other governmental and private agencies dealing with agriculture.

benefit claims were duplicated. The Soil Conservation Service claimed 24 percent of its benefits was for increased use value of lands largely below the Bardwell Dam. The Corps claimed no increased use benefits, although the latter's project probably would give more flood protection to the fertile bottom lands than would the project of the Soil Conservation Service. The Corps' ratio would have been raised from 1.02 to 1.27 had it claimed increased productivity benefits comparable to those of the Soil Conservation Service.

All three agencies' reports are usually defective in methods of calculation of agricultural benefits, and Soil Conservation Service reports are especially faulty in this respect. While the Navajo project plan of the Bureau of Reclamation gives reasonably satisfactory data in this respect, no such data are given for the San Juan-Chama project. These differences in arriving at irrigation benefits from two similar projects create grave doubts as to the soundness of the analyses. Out of 31 Soil Conservation Service projects approved for construction in the southeastern states before January 1, 1959, the plans for only 10 projects contain data on the effects on crop acres, crop yields, and net increased livestock production from the projects. The record for the projects of the southwestern states is worse — only 4 out of 34 approved projects gave basic data on which agricultural benefits were estimated. In these 65 projects, 32 gave no data to enable one to check the validity of agricultural benefits and contained no statement explaining how agricultural benefits were calculated. The reviewer of a typical Soil Conservation Service project in this group has no other source for judging its soundness but his faith in the field economists. The responsibility for this shortcoming can be placed on the administrative doorstep of the Soil Conservation Service. It could be corrected readily by a statement that such data are required in all project plans. This administrative policy should also be adopted by the Corps of Engineers and the Bureau of Reclamation.

The generally accepted rule of the limits of costs for a project is the addition of increments to the point where total net benefits are at a maximum. Such a rule is sound only where funds are unlimited. The President's Water Resources Commission of 1950 estimated that the cost of resources work needing to be done in the next generation would probably amount to 100 billion dollars.[1] Whether this is or is not a meaningful guess I do not know. About a sixth of this amount has already been done. At the present rate of development a century could lapse before 100 billion dollars were expended. A vast gap between work to be done and available money will continue for some time. If so, the goal of maximizing net benefits for a project should be changed to the goal of maximum return per available dollar. A step in this direction would be the requirement of a benefit-cost ratio goal of, say, 1.5 to 1.0 for all projects, with practical exceptions where permanent impairment results from postponed development.

[1] Report of the President's Water Resources Policy Commission, "A Water Policy for the American People" (Washington, D.C.: Government Printing Office, 1950).

This is an imperative goal, especially for Public Law 566 projects. The projects needed are multitudinous, relatively small, and scattered in the widest field of political interest and pressure. A 1.5 to 1.0 benefit-cost goal would be an excellent means of resisting local and Congressional pressure.

A predetermined or "agreed on" level of protection is required for a project plan in the *Economics Guide* issued January 1, 1959, by the Soil Conservation Service for field guidance.[2] Structures are to be combined in testing for benefit-cost relationship, and instructions are clearly given and illustrated by a numerical example. Structures yielding an unfavorable benefit-cost ratio may be included in the group if these structures are needed to bring protection up to the agreed-upon level. Obviously, people who are given all construction costs by the federal government are inclined to require "100 percent protection" from floods regardless of how many unprofitable structures are required to be included in the grouped structures. The only restriction on grouping for testing over-all feasibility of the group is that the structures must yield benefits "in a common flood plain" and the over-all benefit-cost ratio of the group must be at least 1 to 1. If one goes downstream far enough from any set of reservoirs, he is likely to find "some common benefited flood plain." Hence this is no bar to any grouping whatever.

This rule for structure grouping could not have determined the results of grouped structures approved for construction prior to January 1, 1959. However, grouping had been practiced before that date. For projects approved prior to January 1, 1959, one can ask, "How do benefit-cost ratios for grouped and ungrouped structures compare?"

Approved projects in the southeastern states provided for 70 reservoirs grouped for benefit-cost analyses, and 83 separately analyzed reservoirs — a total of 153 reservoirs. In the southwestern states, approved projects provided for 108 grouped and 352 separately analyzed reservoirs. In the former states the weighted average benefit-cost ratio was 1.90 to 1 for the grouped reservoirs and 2.29 to 1 for those separately analyzed, or 39 cents on the dollar greater return for the separately analyzed reservoirs. For the southwestern states the respective ratios were 1.94 and 2.10, or 16 cents greater return on the invested dollar for the separately analyzed reservoirs.

A detailed analysis of projects of the Corps and the Bureau of Reclamation might well show equally great violations of sound incremental analysis as that just presented for Soil Conservation Service projects.

Legal provisions passed by Congress allowing all flood control measures to be constructed at federal expense are the source of grave defects, especially in projects of the Corps and the Soil Conservation Service. As a result of these provisions both agencies are at fault in proposing single-purpose flood control projects where multipurpose projects are needed.

---

[2] Soil Conservation Service, *Economics Guide for Watershed Protection and Flood Prevention*, USDA, Dec., 1958, Chap. 2.

A tabulation for all Soil Conservation Service projects approved up to January 1, 1959, for the 12 southeastern and southwestern states and involving 438 reservoirs shows that 99.46 percent of all storage capacity was to be built for flood prevention and only .54 of 1 percent for water storage purposes, excluding sediment storage capacity. Estimated total flood prevention benefits from all measures of these projects will be 94.2 percent of all benefits.

There can be little doubt that there is an economically justified need for increased water storage capacity in many of these reservoirs for recreational, agricultural, and nonagricultural purposes. Great damage is being done to sound future multipurpose use of the sites of these reservoirs.

I believe a simple legal provision could help a great deal to correct the tragedy of single-purpose plans. All laws authorizing and appropriating funds for resources work should provide that no plan should be presented for approval that did not present full facts on all potential feasible uses of the watershed's land and water resources. It would be difficult for the Congress to object to writing such a provision into each authorization and appropriation act. If Congress then wished to omit a better paying part of a project which required local cost-sharing and wished to include a less remunerative part for which the federal government paid all construction costs, the blame would rest *with Congress, where it belongs.* Now everyone is able to evade the blame for incomplete, wasteful, single-purpose plans.

At present both the Corps of Engineers and the Soil Conservation Service can plan certain small watershed works and face no review of them by anyone except their own personnel. Even the present interagency reviews are far from meritorious. In reviewing a plan of another agency, each agency is reluctant to call attention to faults in the other's plans that are found in its own planning or to faults that invite retaliatory attacks on other faults that are peculiar to its own plans. As a result, practically no completely unbiased review ever gets to the approving congressional committees.

Considering flood control projects only, Weinberger estimates potential future expenditures in the United States of 7 billion dollars under Public Law 566.[3] This figure could probably be doubled if a truly multipurpose program were undertaken. Every congressman for decades to come probably can have a sponsored project in his own district, reviewed only by the Soil Conservation Service, or possibly ineffectively reviewed by another agency that treads lightly in its criticisms. This possibility could eclipse any log-rolling the nation has ever experienced. This situation calls attention to the need for an independent, unbiased, competent, national review board. The need for such a review is equally as great for the projects of the other two agencies.

The present review work of the Bureau of the Budget is the nearest approach to the kind of review that is needed. But the Bureau has a

---

[3] See Chap. 4.

hopelessly inadequate staff for this work. A staff of competent economists, engineers, and hydrologists, in an agency completely independent
of any planning and operating federal agency, protected by Civil Service
status, and attached to the President's office as a National Watershed
Review Board, would work marvels.

Such a review staff should be backed up by a clear-cut national
watershed policy statement that, among other things, spells out general
principles of tests of economic feasibility, essentials of coordination of
works within river basin areas, and more equitable bases of cost-sharing
and joint planning than we have had to date.

Such an independent review board, I believe, could be set up by executive order of the President without the necessity of congressional
approval if the President were convinced its importance justified with-
standing the political pressure that would surely follow from the Congress and from pressure of "friends" that each of the three agencies
under the President's own jurisdiction would inspire. This review
function is one of the most valid functions of the executive, as was
clearly the issuance of the A-47 Memorandum[4] by his Budget Bureau,
by which he undertook to standardize evaluation procedures for water
resources development agencies. Congress, of course, could ignore
the board's findings, but in so doing, the blame for vast wastes could be
shifted to the Congress, where it ultimately should rest.

The enormous resources expenditures of the federal government
have not only been made without adequate review in the past, but without
any systematic research. The best one can say for current watershed
research is that each agency makes fragmentary analyses of its own
programs with a view to facilitating its operating functions or presenting
its own program in the most appealing way. I know of no unbiased over-
all research done on the overlapping functions, the effects of conflicting
rules, the comparative claims of benefits, the lack of coordination, and
the extent to which planning has been faulty and incomplete for the different planning agencies.

The nearest approach to this is probably the work of the temporary
national commissions set up to make an appraisal of the field, such as
the Hoover Commission and the President's Water Resources Commission. All these temporary commissions were so limited in time that
detailed research was impossible. The commissions have usually been
staffed with writers, engineers, and administrators rather than technical
researchers. Even national private foundations and planning groups
have almost all devoted their talents and funds to special problems
rather than to research on putting the parts of the national picture
together.

Why this strange absence of any interest in effective research in a
field into which billions of dollars of the general revenue are being
poured? Is this because congressional politics is against it or cares
little, and administrators of projects prefer to spend their funds

---

[4] Budget Circular A-47, Bureau of the Budget, Dec. 31, 1952.

unhampered by sound research guidance more than they desire the most efficient watershed development? There is a strong suspicion that this is the case.

Some of the defects mentioned in this discussion may appear to be insurmountable and inevitable defects of the democratic process. I think this is not the case. Rather, the defects represent misguided democracy, the correction of which through public enlightenment is probably not so formidable as it appears.

George S. Tolley is Professor of Agricultural Economics at North Carolina State
College. He came to that institution from the University of Chicago, where he
was Assistant Professor of Economics. Ralph A. Freund, Jr., a member of the
staff of Niagara Chemical Company of New York, did graduate work at North
Carolina State College after receiving a B.S. degree from Colorado State University.

Chapter 10

GEORGE S. TOLLEY

RALPH A. FREUND, JR.

Does the State of the Data Suggest a Program for Modifying Planning and Evaluation Procedures?

THIS CHAPTER analyzes a reach of a watershed in the piedmont
area of the Southeast in order to throw light on the sensitivity of
agricultural flood protection benefits to economic and hydrologic
assumptions.

Benefits are evaluated under five different types of agriculture that
might prevail in the flood plain. Three sets of assumptions are considered for percentage loss in crop values associated with a given degree of inundation. For the number of floods there are three different
assumptions, and there are also three for average flood stage. In addition to considering sensitivity to the assumptions individually, a
probability distribution of benefits is derived.

The chapter is concluded with a discussion of implications. Comparison of sources of variability in benefits is useful in revealing which
data call for relatively more or relatively less efforts at improvement.
Since refinements warranted in manipulating data depend on their reliability, time-saving simplifications in planning may be indicated. The

[1]Journal Paper No. 1012 of the North Carolina Agricultural Experiment Station. We
received invaluable aid from Lacy Coats and C. V. Lyle.

study is relevant to choosing among projects, inasmuch as the probability distribution of benefits permits comparing the relative risk of
different projects.

HOW FLOOD PROTECTION BENEFITS ARE ESTIMATED

The benefits to be measured comprise the difference in the future
between net income to land if the project is installed and net income if
the project is not installed.

This is approached by first estimating the change in income, ignoring losses from flooding. The change is often substantial, due to the
fact that flood protection may result in farmers growing more valuable
crops in a protected flood plain. This part of the benefit requires estimating acreages of crops in the future with and without the project.
Estimates are also needed for yields, prices, and production inputs, as
well as costs incurred in switching from one land use to another.

A second part of the net income change is the difference between
flood damages without the project and with the project. The first calculation overstated income to land in both situations by ignoring flood
losses. These further calculations remove the overstatement. For
projected future agriculture *without* the project, flood damages are estimated using a series of floods assuming no flood protection. Then,
for future agriculture *with* the project, damages are estimated using
the same series of floods but assuming the reduced levels of inundation
estimated by hydrologists to be accomplished by the project measures.

To summarize: Estimated benefit is increase in net income to land
assuming no floods *plus* flood damages without the project *minus* flood
damages with the project. The reader familiar with the current Soil
Conservation Service method may verify that it aims at giving the same
project benefit as the one used here.[2] Our procedure is simpler due to
the elimination of several intermediate flood damage analyses encountered in attempts to break down benefits as between land enhancement,
flood damage reduction, and the like, as well as in attempts to find
benefits associated with each type of measure. The present study concerns total flood protection benefits and is not aimed primarily at
throwing light on the breakdowns just referred to.

SOURCES OF VARIABILITY

Type of Agriculture

A reservoir of 462 acre-feet capacity is proposed as the sole pro-
tector of a 4-mile distance along the creek. The area of the flood plain

---

[2]Soil Conservation Service, *Economics Guide for Watershed Protection and Flood Prevention,* 1958, Chap. 3, p. 1, and Chap. 4, pp. 1-2. Also see Soil Conservation Service,
Watershed Protection Handbook, 1957, Sec. 6, pp. 5-6.

is 169 acres.[3] There is usually at least one serious flood each year. The dam would reduce this to about two in three years, at the same time cutting down on the level of remaining floods.

A typical farming unit consists of about 10 acres of flood plain and 15 acres of upland. The bottom lands are loams and fine sandy loam soils. In this reach they are well drained and are planted in about equal acreage to corn, hay, and pasture. Per-acre yields run 65 bushels for corn, 2 tons for hay, and 7 animal-unit-months of grazing for pasture. The uplands are sandy surface soils with clay-textured subsoils. Operators plant these same crops on the uplands, but the yields run less than half those of the flood plain. The corn, hay, and pasture are used for feeding livestock maintained for family purposes. Typically, the only farm cash income is from a few acres of tobacco on the upland.

Part-time farming predominates. Within a circle of 30-mile radius there are five towns averaging 50,000 population offering numerous kinds of manufacturing employment. The farming connected with the flood plain is neither high management nor high investment, nor does there seem to be a tendency now to go in these directions, inasmuch as farming is not the chief source of income for many.

Following the method outlined in the preceding section leads to the estimate that the dam would have a benefit on an average annual basis of $8.68 per acre. This is a *medium* or most likely estimate in all assumptions, designed to reflect existing evaluation practices.

In regard to agricultural conditions the estimate assumes that, without the project, acreages and yields would continue as at present. The building of the project is visualized to induce 15 additional acres of corn to be planted in the flood plain, accompanied by reductions in hay, pasture, and idle land. The 15-acre estimate is based on answers from farmers as to what they would do if the dam were built. This is consistent with the idea that land use could profitably be intensified with greater flood protection. It reflects the frequent situation in small watersheds that increased net income results more importantly from a changed pattern of land use than from actual flood damage reduction.

To begin our exploration in variability, consider agricultural conditions conducive to *high* benefits. Suppose the flood plain came to be part of a high-management dairy or livestock operation. While perhaps not as likely as the previous assumption, this is still certainly in the realm of non-negligible probability. It is made unlikely by the fragmentation of holdings and current low land turnover. Nonetheless, sufficiently rapid industrial development of the region could increase the demand for dairy products and at the same time expand job opportunities so as to draw off present farmers. Sufficiently increased national demand for meat would also make for the possibility of a large cattle-fattening operation.

---

[3] The dam is responsible for benefits farther down in conjunction with structures on other tributaries, but these benefits are not examined in this study.

Commercial operators might, even in the absence of the project, find it profitable to plant 60 percent of the flood plain in corn, in contrast to the present 30 percent. Yields would be higher. Pasture and hay would come more largely from upland acreages, all the more so with flood protection. If the project were built, flood-plain corn acreage might be increased to about 75 percent. These changes would be expected from high management going in the direction of maximizing return per acre as dictated by the comparative advantage for corn in the bottom lands.

Benefits would be $14.09 per acre, or over half again greater than was found for the medium assumption. The increase is due both to the more impressive change in land use induced by the project and to a greater initial acreage of corn leading to greater flood damage reduction.

This is not the limit of crop intensification. The type-of-agriculture assumptions involve economic predictions that verge on being anyone's guess. The purpose of this part of the chapter is more to emphasize this fact than to pretend to make an exact representation of all future possibilities. Although still less likely, consider an *extremely high* estimate of benefits. Pushing the reasoning of the preceding estimate further, we might assume the flood plain planted entirely to corn in the absence of the project. If the project were built, 25 percent of the land might be put in the still more valuable crop — sweet potatoes. The estimate visualizes the conjunction of highest management coming into the area and population growth leading to rapidly increasing demand for agricultural products.[4] This extremely high estimate leads to benefits of $18.48 per acre.

A not too unlikely *low* estimate derives from visualizing rapid industrial growth in the region, but without a concomitant growth in demand for agricultural products. More farmers might obtain urban jobs, leaving only the less mobile, lower management, individuals carrying on agriculture. Localized increases in the demand for food could be met from more distant areas where there was better management. The flood plain would veer toward less intensive use — say 10 percent corn, 25 percent pasture, and 45 percent hay, in contrast to about equal amounts for these uses under the medium assumption.[5] Because of low management there might be no change at all in land use accompanying installation of the project. The latter would eliminate the important benefits associated with changed land use. Average annual benefits per acre would drop to $1.09.

For a less likely *extremely low* estimate, assume that virtually all present residents obtain full-time urban employment. The flood

---

[4] More complete flood protection might make it possible to visualize still higher benefits connected with all of the flood plain going into truck crops. This was ruled out altogether for the present project, inasmuch as it would still allow floods two out of three years. Flood damage to truck crops would be so large that, given the investments required, the losses would not seem sustainable.

[5] The remaining 20 percent of the flood plain would be woodland or idle land.

plain might be used for grazing by family milk cows owned by those working in town who happened to live in the flood-plain area, or perhaps the land would be taken over for grazing by a commercial livestock enterprise. In either event the flood plain would be planted entirely to pasture both with and without the project. We get down to benefits per acre of $0.16.

Percentage Loss of Crop Value for Given Inundation

More objective measures of variability are fortunately available as we move away from type-of-agriculture assumptions. In this study variation has been studied in farmers' estimates of losses due to given depths of inundation. High, medium, and low estimates were derived according to a method described in the appendix (page 139). Table 1 shows the assumptions for corn.[6]

In calculating benefits these figures are applied to acreages and values of the flood plain in a damage analysis for each flood in a 20-year series. Use of the medium estimate for percentage losses gives the *medium* estimate noted earlier of $8.68 average annual benefits per acre. Still holding type-of-agriculture and other assumptions at their mediums, but dropping down to the *low* estimate for percentage losses gives benefits of $8.28. In a similar way the *high* estimate is $10.17.

Table 1. Percentage Loss in Corn Values by Depth of Inundation:
High, Medium, and Low Assumptions

Depth	June	July	Aug.	Sept.	Oct.
			Percent		
One foot					
High	78	52	26	18	14
Medium	37	15	10	5	5
Low	27	8	6	3	3
Two feet					
High	100	80	49	36	33
Medium	52	32	22	13	10
Low	38	20	15	7	4
Three feet					
High	100	100	84	72	67
Medium	75	63	32	25	20
Low	59	48	19	13	8
Four feet					
High	100	100	100	93	91
Medium	92	78	45	35	30
Low	80	48	30	20	15

[6] The figures are for percent loss of "damageable value," where the latter term for crops not replantable means sales price less expenses that would be incurred up to sale. If flood occurs early enough for replanting, damageable value is the replanting cost.

Number of Floods

Use of a 20-year flood series introduces variability, since the number of floods will depend on the particular historical sequence chosen. To get an idea of the magnitude of variability, suppose the number of floods per year is a random variable. Then we can apply a probability approach worked out in the appendix. Moving from the benchmark *medium* estimate, we then add four floods of average size to obtain *high* estimate of $9.06 average annual benefits per acre. Subtracting four average-size floods gives the *low* estimate of $8.30.

Average Flood Stage

Estimates of the amount of inundation associated with each flood were varied in light of informed opinion that an accuracy is obtained within one foot 60 percent of the time. The appendix describes how this information about flood stage was incorporated on a basis as similar as possible to the assumptions already discussed. As we move away from the benchmark medium, the *high* estimate is average annual benefits per acre of $9.51, and the *low* estimate is $8.04.

SUGGESTIVE PROBABILITY DISTRIBUTION OF BENEFITS

When it is considered that one assumption might be at its low when another is at its high or medium or low, and so forth, the variations we have considered above make for the possibility of 135 different outcomes for project benefits. By making probability assumptions for each variation, a probability distribution of benefits for the project can be constructed. A set of assumptions is shown in Table 2. All but the type-of-agriculture probabilities are supportable on a largely objective basis; type-of-agriculture probabilities require much judgment.[7]

Table 2. Assumptions Used in Deriving Probability Distribution of Benefits

Type of Assumptions	Probabilities			
	Type of Agriculture	Degree of Damage	Number of Floods	Stage of Floods
Extremely High	1/20			
High	1/5	1/2	1/4	1/4
Medium	1/2	3/8	1/2	1/2
Low	1/5	1/8	1/4	1/4
Extremely Low	1/20			

[7] In support of the judgment approach it may be said that the alternative situations were constructed in consultation with farm management researchers who were asked to think in terms of betting odds for each outcome.

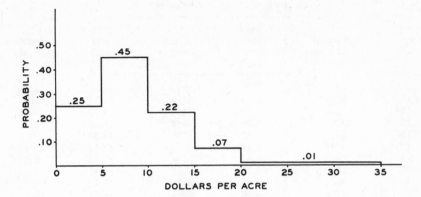

Figure 1. Frequency distribution of benefits per acre by class intervals
of five dollars.

Figure 1 shows the resulting probability distribution of benefits per
acre for class intervals for $5.00. Examination of the outcomes re-
veals that the lower class interval is associated with the low and extremely low type-of-agriculture assumptions. The long upper tail of
the distribution results from the concatenation of the various high
estimates.

Fuller detail can be gleaned from the cumulative distribution of
Table 3. It adds the information that there is a skip in benefits from
$2.57 to $7.53, due to the fact that the low assumption for type-of-
agriculture ends and the medium begins.

The significance of the probability distribution may be considered
in the following way. A realistic cost for this project might be $5.00
per acre. Then, following the usual procedures associated with the
medium assumption of $8.68 benefits, the benefit-cost ratio for this
project would be calculated as 1.74. This is a good estimate as a
measure of central tendency and most likely outcome. However, for
project choice, it may be relevant to know that the chance is one in four
that benefits will fall short of cost. That is, the project has risk connected with it, as revealed by the dispersion of the probability distribution.

The element of arbitrariness, particularly for type-of-agriculture,
has been noted in connection with the elemental probabilities of Table 2,
on which the distribution is based. What is the sensitivity to these elemental assumptions? If we make the extreme assumption tending toward wider dispersions, that all outcomes are equally probable, probability is naturally pumped outward and away from the mean class
interval. However, certain characteristics that would be important to
project choice may not be too much affected. For most ranges of project costs encountered, the chance of benefits falling short of costs is
increased from one-fourth to only two-fifths.

Table 3. Cumulative Probability Distribution of Benefits Per Acre

Benefits Per Acre $	Cumulative Probability	Benefits Per Acre $	Cumulative Probability	Benefits Per Acre $	Cumulative Probability
.09	.0031	7.97	.3555	14.74	.8969
.11	.0094	8.04	.3789	14.78	.9000
.12	.0125	8.28	.4414	14.79	.9094
.13	.0188	8.30	.4648	14.80	.9156
.16	.0312	8.31	.4766	14.82	.9172
.17	.0344	8.44	.4922	15.12	.9188
.19	.0406	8.60	.5234	15.28	.9281
.21	.0469	8.68	.5703	15.76	.9312
.24	.0500	8.85	.6016	15.92	.9375
.51	.0562	8.90	.6055	16.07	.9406
.60	.0609	8.99	.6172	16.17	.9438
.62	.0734	9.06	.6406	16.18	.9500
.72	.0891	9.26	.6562	16.42	.9531
.79	.1016	9.40	.6641	16.66	.9547
.85	.1062	9.51	.6875	16.77	.9578
.91	.1156	9.54	.6953	17.21	.9594
.95	.1406	9.91	.6992	17.50	.9605
1.03	.1422	9.96	.7031	17.74	.9617
1.09	.1672	10.04	.7148	17.89	.9641
1.11	.1797	10.17	.7305	18.01	.9680
1.24	.1828	10.68	.7383	18.15	.9742
1.25	.1875	10.80	.7461	18.31	.9766
1.28	.1969	11.40	.7500	18.48	.9812
1.31	.2094	11.71	.7562	18.53	.9824
1.43	.2125	12.06	.7688	18.87	.9836
1.46	.2141	12.38	.7734	19.08	.9859
1.51	.2234	12.41	.7797	19.54	.9891
1.54	.2297	12.54	.7922	19.65	.9922
1.73	.2359	12.86	.8016	21.29	.9938
1.78	.2406	13.06	.8266	23.31	.9941
1.82	.2422	13.35	.8312	25.01	.9949
2.02	.2453	13.40	.8406	26.25	.9957
2.20	.2484	13.41	.8469	26.72	.9961
2.57	.2500	13.58	.8594	28.92	.9976
7.53	.2656	14.09	.8781	29.22	.9980
7.75	.2969	14.11	.8906	31.29	.9988
7.77	.3086	14.38	.8953	32.14	.9996
				35.05	1.0000

WATERSHED DEVELOPMENT IN LIGHT OF DATA VARIABILITY

Understatement of Variability in the Foregoing, With, However,
Some Justification for Neglect of Prices and Technology

A feature of the foregoing analysis is its conservatism. The estimates were aimed at being realistic, but were shaded toward not over-
stating variability where there was doubt. The effect of several more

factors could have been studied, each of which would introduce additional dispersion into the probability distribution of benefits. The procedural alternatives in the details of benefit-cost calculation are examples. These include alternative interest rates, assumptions about the time path of benefits other than the constancy implied by the "average annual" analysis, and many more.

Economic predictions not included earlier that add dispersion pertain to prices and to secular changes in agricultural efficiency. While these latter economic considerations truly increase variability, perhaps they have limited effect for the reason that prices and efficiency are together in a causal relationship with the return-to-land. Recall that the benefit we are trying to measure is the change in return to the agricultural flood-plain land resulting from the watershed development. When we change projected prices or the projected outputs per unit of input, this will appear in the benefit-cost analysis as a change in net income to land. The question is: Taking account of economic equilibrations, do we really expect a general rise or fall in the price of agricultural commodities or general increases in efficiency to have more than temporary effect on land return? If not, then we could bias project benefits by allowing for them.

The net return-to-land per acre is not free to vary without inducing adjustments that tend to limit the variability. Suppose rapid growth of the demand for agricultural products raised prices and this was reflected back in increasing income to land. Adjustments of two kinds would be (1) substitution for land of variable factors such as fertilizer and hired labor, and (2) bringing in new land at the various margins of cultivation. The latter include draining and leveling of land already in cultivation, which raises the effective amount of land, as well as the clearing of new land. Particularly in the Southeast, there are large acreages of land suitable for cultivation that could be cleared. All these adjustments would tend to bring the return per acre to agricultural land back toward its original value. Our argument is that the tendency should not be ignored for the return to land to be governed by marginal land adjustments. If the return to land rises, new land will tend to be brought in. If the return falls, land will go out. In the longer run the adjustments may put narrow limits on net income per acre to land.[8]

Flood protection of agricultural land may itself be viewed as an increase in the effective supply of land. The benefits from this type of activity depend on equilibrium return to land. We are hypothesizing that assumptions about prices and efficiency causing big changes in the

---

[8]Evidence bearing on these hypotheses is given in G. S. Tolley, "Alternative Land Development Possibilities," in *Modern Land Policy*, ed. H. G. Halcrow, to be published by University of Illinois Press; and G. S. Tolley, "Reclamation's Influence on the Rest of Agriculture," *Land Economics*, Vol. XXV, No. 2, May, 1959, pp. 176-80.

return per acre to agricultural land over the entire country may tend to be verified only for short periods of time, if at all.[9]

Towards Data Improvement

The analysis of this watershed indicates that the type-of-agriculture assumptions appear the weakest used in project evaluation. The preponderant part of the variability summarized in Figure 1 is due to type-of-agriculture.

While variability is associated with farmers' estimates of flood damages, the comparative lack of dispersion in their answers would seem to indicate that this is a less important source of variability. Assumptions as to number of floods and average flood stage have a perceptible effect, but they are even less important.

An implication is that efforts at data improvement should be directed at agricultural conditions for protected flood plains, with and without projects. Analysts on watershed planning teams hardly have time to do the more fundamental projecting needed here. It might be helpful if they were supplied with studies of general economic and managerial trends in areas where projects are contemplated.

With the background of these trend analyses, detailed studies directed more at the farm firm might be supplied. These would have to do with the farm economics of flood-plain use. Taking the total farm situation, what are the economic incentives regarding flood-plain use with the present degree of protection, and how are these changed with reduced flooding? Farmer reflections on what they would do may often be given without much serious thought. Estimating the change may be a way to help circumvent reliance on these. Two cautions in doing these researches in bottom-land economics are: (1) results under a significantly wide range of underlying economic assumptions should be considered, including different sizes and types of farms (say livestock versus cropping) and factor costs; and (2) realistic levels of management should be used aimed at predicting actual conditions and not the ideal performance that is sometimes implied by taking results from farm management researches concerned mostly with optimum farming.

Though less important, percentage losses of value from flooding might also be the subject of more research. Consideration could be given to establishing test plots for farming areas, such as the piedmont or coastal plain areas of North Carolina, to determine flood losses experimentally. Along with this, experimental research surveys on farmer reactions to floods might be needed. Depending on management,

---

[9]We have been speaking about relative returns in an economy of substantially full employment of resources and stable general level of prices. We will not continue the discussion by relaxing these assumptions. To the extent that unemployment or inflation affect benefit calculations, then they are an additional source of variability. Without going further here, we opine that it may be proper for benefit-cost calculations to ignore general unemployment or inflation possibilities.

a crop may be restored after flooding or merely abandoned — acts having effect on benefits from flood damage reduction.

Modifying Evaluation Procedures

The data are never going to be perfect, inasmuch as that would imply predicting the future exactly. Here are observations about evaluation in the light of variability. First, it would appear that more accurate results could be obtained for each planning dollar by care with type-of-agriculture assumptions at the expense, if necessary, of precision in physical effects of projects. Second, efforts using refined techniques, such as extremely complex flood-damage-reduction analyses based on unreliable type-of-agriculture data, could likewise be used to obtain more accurate results by concentrating on the underlying data and using simpler though more approximate flood damage analyses. Third, more rational choices of projects by decision-makers may be possible if cognizance of data variability is maintained.

In connection with the first two observations calling for redirection of effort, it might be helpful to examine the sensitivity of benefits to particular type-of-agriculture assumptions, primarily to determine for which crops this is important. Table 4 reports an analysis of benefits from one flood that appeared modal for our project. It can be seen that only corn, hay, and sweet potatoes account for sizeable benefits. A large flood-damage-reduction benefit can come from a crop having a high damageable value, a high percent damage for a given inundation, or a large number of acres in the flood plain. By multiplying these three figures together, it is possible to obtain an estimate of which crops are important and then concentrate on them for data accuracy. Less time needs to be spent on the others because their effect on total benefit will be small.

The third observation above suggests that rather than one very refined analysis of a situation deemed most likely, several simplified analyses of alternative situations might be preferable. These might be carried in workplans and other materials presented to project choosers. In addition to numerical results for a project, workplans might desirably give greater detail on the total agricultural economy for the farms which involve the flood plains. The procedure was exemplified in the discussion of type-of-agriculture in the present study. Alternative future types of agriculture might be discussed — even if no numerical estimates for them are presented — so that the choosers themselves could judge likelihood of different benefit outcomes.

Risk and Project Choice

The inherent irreducibility of data variability is a manifestation of the fact that decisions on watershed development, like other decisions, involve risk of more than one outcome.

Perhaps the best way of taking account of this has already been

Table 4. Damage With and Without Project, Flood of July 15, 1945

Crop	Percent in Crop	Damageable Value Per Acre	Percent Damage Due to Flood[a]	Flood Damage Per Composite Acre[b]
		With project		
Corn	42.8	$ 80.51	6.390	$2.20
Ladino clover	5.3	6.15	7.195	.02
Meadow hay	29.3	16.19	3.375	.16
Improved pasture	5.3	2.10	6.425	.01
Native pasture	4.2	1.60	7.935	.01
Sweet potatoes	2.1	146.32	11.845	.36
		Without project		
Corn	32.6	$ 76.90	16.059	$4.03
Ladino clover	5.3	6.15	16.634	.05
Meadow hay	31.5	16.19	8.417	.42
Improved pasture	5.3	2.10	13.911	.02
Native pasture	4.2	1.60	17.049	.01
Sweet potatoes	2.1	146.32	30.930	.95

Difference Between Flood Damage With the Project
and Without the Project by Crops, Per Acre[c]

Corn	$1.83
Ladino clover	.03
Meadow hay	.26
Improved pasture	.01
Native pasture	.00
Sweet potatoes	.59

[a] Sum of proportion of land inundated at each depth times percentage loss of crop value for that inundation.
[b] Result of multiplying the preceding three columns together.
[c] Difference between columns showing flood damage per composite acre with and without project.

noted, namely, give those deciding on projects enough background information to get a feel of the likelihoods.

There are more formal possibilities, however. The rate of discount might be increased so that it would equal the rate for investments of comparable risk in the private sector of the economy. Some study would be required to determine this rate. Another possibility is as follows. If the present low riskless interest rate continues to be used in discounting, a "risk indicator" might be included for each project. The indicator would reflect the probability of loss. A suitable indicator may be the number of chances out of one hundred that project benefits will fall short of costs. If a project were sure to pay off, the risk indication would be zero. A risk indication of 50 percent would mean it was as likely not to pay off as to pay off, and an indication of 100 percent would mean sure failure. The reader may refer back to the discussion of the probability distribution of benefits and see that for the dam considered in this study the risk indication is 25 percent.

APPENDIX ON PROBABILITY ANALYSIS

Problem

Flood protection benefit may be represented as follows:[10]

$$\sum^{i} (r_{i1} - r_{i0})\, q_i - \sum^{i} \sum^{j} \sum^{k} (r_{i1} s_{jk1} - r_{i0} s_{jk0})\, t_{ij} u_{ijk}, \text{ where}$$

r_i = proportion of flood plain area planted to i^{th} crop,

q_i = net return to land if the flood plain were planted entirely to the ith crop,

s_{jk} = acres flooded at k^{th} depth in the jth month,

t_{ij} = damageable value per acre for the ith crop in the jth month,

u_{ijk} = proportion of damageable value lost if the ith crop is flooded at the kth depth in the jth month.

This complex multiplicative-additive expression appears to make it unfeasible to work with continuous probability distributions. The alternative is to approximate the probability distributions of the component variables with discrete distributions. Project benefit can then be viewed as a compound event. From the expression above, benefit can be evaluated for each set of component events. The probability of the set can also be calculated since, if the component events are statistically independent, the probability of the compound event is found by multiplying together the probabilities of the components.

In approximating in this fashion two tasks are: (1) to limit the number of components by grouping them into subsets where it is assumed that the correlation of events in a given subset with events of other subsets is zero, and the correlation of the events within the subset is perfect; and (2) for each subset, to choose a few discrete alternatives, assigning probabilities to them that total one. In regard to the first task, it seems reasonable that the four groups of events considered in this paper (type-of-agriculture, percent damage to various crops from a given degree of inundation, number of floods, and average flood stage) are uncorrelated. A long list of reasons could be given why the events *within* each group are not perfectly correlated as they ideally should be. While the effect of this violation is probably to underestimate the dispersion of benefits, it is probably most important for type-of-agriculture, where it may fortunately tend to be swamped by the huge effect that acreage of a few crops can have.

More significant problems arise in relation to the second task. For each compound event a project evaluation must be carried out involving lengthy flood-damage-reduction calculations, as indicated by the expression for benefit given at the outset of this appendix. Then, after we narrow to four component events, the number of combinations gets large quickly as more alternatives for each event are admitted. The additional accuracy is not needed for most purposes.[11] Having a few alternatives for each event gives a large number of outcomes for project benefit, as can be seen by considering that if there were three different outcomes for each of four component events, we would have 3^4, or 81 compound events.

---

[10]The subscript 1 refers to the situation where the project is in existence, and the subscript 0 refers to the situation where it is not in existence.

[11]With few alternatives we may lose long low-probability tails of distributions, but these do not appear important in the present analysis.

Because of the multiplication of probabilities, the likelihood of each compound event is correspondingly small.

A problem, then, is how to approximate a continuous probability distribution with a discrete distribution containing few points.

Derivation of Three-Point Approximation of Symmetrical Distribution

A prime requirement of our approximation is that it have the same mean and variance as the true distribution. Maintenance of variance is particularly important in view of the fact that our main purpose in being concerned with probability distributions is to study variability. After this requirement has been met, remaining freedom is used to ensure that the probability of being within any particular interval according to the approximate distribution is made close to the true probability.

Let $\phi_L = \phi_U = \phi$ be the probability at the upper or lower observation of a three-point symmetrical distribution. If the middle observation is a true mean, the three-point approximation will also have this mean. Let σ^2 be the true variance. Setting this equal to the variance of the approximation

$$\sigma^2 = 2 \phi k^2 \sigma^2, \quad \text{or} \quad \phi = \frac{1}{2k^2}$$

where k is the number of standard deviations out from the mean at which the upper and lower observations are placed.

Figure 2 illustrates the relation of admissible values of ϕ and k, pointing out convenient combinations that might be chosen. Although satisfying the variance requirement, the probability distributions implied by many of the combinations would be quite different from the true distribution because they would overconcentrate probability in the upper and lower observations at the expense of the middle, or vice versa.

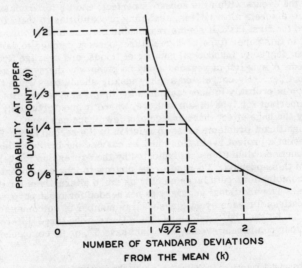

Figure 2. Values of ϕ and k for three-point
symmetrical approximation that maintain
original mean and variance.

Suppose we visualize the approximation as applying to midpoints for a three-class-interval division. This would need to be done if we wished to make probability statements about the variable in question for values other than the three points of the approximation. The center class interval would extend $k\sigma/2$ on either side of the mean. The upper and lower class intervals would extend $k\sigma/2$ to $3k\sigma/2$ out from the mean.

If we know the shape of the true distribution, we now have a criterion for choosing among the combinations of ϕ and k, namely, the combination which comes closest to satisfying the true probability that the variable falls within the class intervals just mentioned. For a normal distribution, $\phi = 1/4$ and $k = \sqrt{2}$ come closest of the convenient combinations. Thus, $\phi = 1/4$ compares with a probability of .242 in a normal distribution of being more than $\sqrt{2}\sigma/2$ out on one side from the mean. The results for the normal distribution are shown in Figure 3.[12]

The Four Approximations of This Study

Type-of-agriculture. Not being scalar, the type-of-agriculture assumptions had to have probabilities assigned subjectively after choosing alternative outcomes as described in the chapter text.

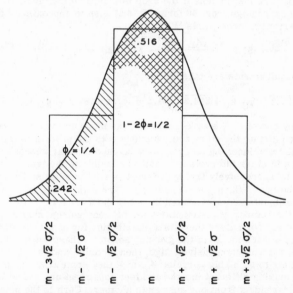

Figure 3. Comparison of true normal distribution and three-class interval approximation for $\phi = 1/4$ and $k = \sqrt{2}$.

---

[12]In a normal distribution the probability of being more than $k\sigma/2$ out of one side is a decreasing function of k, but it does not decrease as rapidly as ϕ satisfying the variance requirement. We want the intersection where ϕ satisfying the variance requirement as shown in Figure 2 equals the probability of being more than $k\sigma/2$ out. To see that at $k = \sqrt{2}$ we are near the intersection, we may note that, for $k = 1$, the true probability is .309, though from Figure 2, ϕ satisfying the variance requirement would then be 1/2, whereas for $k = 2$ the true probability is .159, though ϕ would then be 1/8.

Percent loss of damageable value due to given inundation. Based on farmer answers, the frequency distributions for percentage losses appeared asymmetric, with a pronounced bulge below the mean. A three-point approximation was made along the lines described in the preceding section, but the assumption of symmetry was dropped. The requirement that the mean of the approximate distribution equal the true mean becomes:

$$m = \phi_L (m - k_L \sigma_L) + \phi_M m + \phi_U (m + k_U \sigma_U) ,$$

where $\sigma_L{}^2 = E[X_L - m]^2$ and $\sigma_U{}^2 = E[X_U - m]$, X_L being values below the mean and X_U those above. It can be seen that the requirement pertaining to the mean reduces to:

$$\phi_L k_L \sigma_L = \phi_U k_U \sigma_U .$$

The requirement that the variance of the approximate distribution equal the true variance is:

$$\sigma^2 = \phi_L k_L{}^2 \sigma_L{}^2 + \phi_U k_U{}^2 \sigma_U{}^2 .$$

Let us illustrate the use of these requirements as applied to percent of damageable value of corn lost in June if the crop is inundated four feet. We have guesses at this percentage from 48 farmers, and wish to approximate the distribution of answers with three points.[13]

As $\dfrac{\sum (x - m)^2}{N - 1} = 261.5$, $\dfrac{\sum (X_L - m)^2}{N_L - 1} = 87.2$ and $\dfrac{\sum (X_U - m)}{N_U - 1} = 514.2$ the mean

and variance requirements are taken to be

$$\phi_L k_L \sqrt{87.2} = \phi_U k_U \sqrt{514.2}, \quad 261.5 = \phi_L k_L{}^2 87.2 + \phi_U k_U{}^2 514.2 .$$

If we choose any two of ϕ_L, ϕ_U, k_L, and k_U, the mean and variance requirements just given dictate the other two. Analogous to the procedure followed for symmetrical distributions, the freedom may be used to make approximated probability of falling in class intervals as close as possible to the true probability. This was done by successively trying different ϕ's. The most satisfactory values were found to be $\phi_L = 1/2$, $\phi_m = 3/8$, and $\phi_U = 1/8$ with which, from the mean and variance requirements, are associated $k_L = 1.0$ and $k_U = 1.7$.

An idea of the number of distributions for percent damage may be had by remembering that for corn alone there is a distribution for one, two, three, and four feet inundation for each month of the growing season. These were varied together, i.e., all put simultaneously at high, then medium, and then low. The estimates seem likely to be highly correlated, since they come from respondents who were aware of making different months and feet consistent and whose biases would not be independent from one answer to another. Corn is the most important crop to project benefits, and it is the only one for which percent damages were varied. While varying together the assumptions for feet and month may tend to overestimate variability, neglect of other crops tends to underestimate it.

---

[13] It might be thought that to use answers from farmers overstates variability attaching to flood damage estimates. However, answers were obtained only from intelligent, experienced farmers who, in the absence of experiments, apparently represent the most expert available opinion. Partly, the variability reflects ignorance about ascertainable facts on damage from a given degree of inundation, and partly it reflects the situation that a given degree of inundation has varying effects depending on water turbidity, velocity, and the like.

<u>Number of floods</u>. Flood protection benefits were calculated running through a 20-year historical series of floods.[14] A source of uncertainty about benefits is that frequencies based on history cannot be expected to repeat themselves exactly during the life of a project.

There were four years having no floods, nine years having one flood, and seven years having two floods — or 23 floods in all. Suppose we take these relative frequencies as estimates of parameters of a trinomial distribution, as shown in Figure 4. The number of years having zero, one, or two floods will tend toward being normally distributed as the sample of years increases.[15]

Let P_0 = 4/20 be the probability of no floods, P_1 = 9/20 the probability of one flood, and P_2 = 7/20 the probability of two floods. We are interested in the total number z of floods that will occur in a sample of N years: $z = n_1 + 2n_2$, where n_1 and n_2 are the number of years having one and two floods respectively.

From the rules for variance of a sum:

$$\text{var } z = \text{var } n_1 + 4 \text{ var } n_2 + 4 \text{ cov } n_1 n_2 \ .$$

The characteristics of the trinomial give

$$\text{var } z = NP_1 (1 - P_1) + 4NP_2 (1 - P_2) - 4NP_1 P_2 \ ,$$

so that for N = 20, var z is 10.55 or $\sigma_z = \sqrt{10.55}$. The expected value of z is, of course, 23.

We may now apply the three-point symmetrical approximation derived earlier. For $\phi_L = \phi_U = 1/4$, the upper and lower points would be put $\sqrt{2}\sigma_z$ (= 4.60) on either side of the mean. In other words, our lower estimate is 18 to 19 floods and our upper estimate is 27 to 28.

To obtain high and low estimates of benefits, annual benefits for the original analysis of 23 floods were divided by 23 and multiplied by the assumed number of

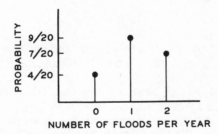

Figure 4. Probability distribution of floods.

---

[14] The sum is divided by 20 to obtain average annual benefits. It can be shown that, if each year is a random event, this method gives the same result as calculating the present value of benefits. If there were no bias, average annual benefit would be the payment on a 20-year annuity whose value equals the present value of benefits. The type of bias introduced if each year is not random has been pointed out by Otto Eckstein, *Water Resource Development* (Cambridge: Harvard University Press, 1958), pp. 108-9. In small watersheds there may be bias, not allowed for here, due to the fact that benefits take time to build up. In particular, lags can be expected in changing over to new land use induced by flood protection.

[15] This characteristic of the trinomial distribution is demonstrated by H. Cramer, *Mathematical Methods of Statistics* (Princeton: Princeton University Press, 1949), p. 318.

floods for the upper and lower estimates. Implicit, then, is the idea that floods added or subtracted are characterized by average benefit.

Flood stage. In view of measurement variability, for a reach flood stage σ typically may be about 1 foot. However, these errors are largely independent between reaches. For a watershed there will therefore be some tendency for them to cancel. To get a σ typical of a watershed we should divide by the square root of the number of reaches that analysts have subdivided it into. Assuming nine reaches, we arrive at 1/3 foot as flood stage σ for the watershed.

On a judgment basis the foregoing estimate was raised to 1/2 foot to allow for broader changes not included in the benefit-cost analysis, such as (1) effects of changed land and water use upstream, (2) changes in the "coefficient of roughness" in the watershed stream bed that might affect flood stage, and (3) possibly even a cyclic change in weather conditions.

Following the three-point symmetrical approximation as before, with $\phi = 1/4$ and $k = \sqrt{2}$, we arrive at upper and lower flood stages .7 feet on either side of the original or mean estimates.

If it is assumed that, given the flood stage, the effect of dams on level of inundation can be forecast accurately, the stages should be lowered and raised simultaneously for analysis with and without the project. Moreover, the variation probably tends to be common to all floods, being based on initial observational errors. Hence, for the lower estimates, the analysis was run with all flood stages down .7 feet, and conversely all up by .7 feet for the high estimates.

MELVILLE H. COHEE | *Comment*

BY HYPOTHESIZING future intensity of land use and other factors in an example flood-plain area, and then appraising a given change in level of flood protection through differences in average annual benefits, Tolley and Freund provide bases for certain criteria to be followed in watershed program formulation and evaluation.

Five different "types of agriculture" are considered which might prevail in the future. They range from permanent pasture to field corn and sweet potatoes. Truck-crop farming or any other more intensive type of farming was omitted because of the low level of flood protection with the project. It would have made an interesting appraisal, however, had the authors attempted to determine at what level of flood protection the benefits from truck-crop farming exceeded costs for flood protection by an amount greater than that for the highest of the five types which they did consider. This point is made to call attention to the

---

Melville H. Cohee is an agricultural economist with the Soil Conservation Service in Milwaukee, Wisconsin. Previously he headed the Project Plans Division of SCS in Washington and was a Resident Consultant at the Graduate School of Public Administration at Harvard University.

proposition that with different levels of flood protection there are not only different accompanying costs per unit of land protected, but practical inducements for considerably different intensities of farming. The authors assume that, with one level of flood protection, contrasting intensities in type of farming may take place. Broadly speaking, the variable permitting such an assumption is management, and is dictated by further assumptions regarding demands for crop production predicated on possibilities for illustrating increased benefits from a given input of project costs. This approach cannot rightly be criticized so long as the reader does not lose sight of the stated purpose, namely, that "The type-of-agriculture assumptions involve economic predictions that verge on being anyone's guess. The purpose of this part of the chapter is more to emphasize this than to pretend to make an exact representation of all future possibilities."

The authors appear to lean in the direction of minimizing the influence of hydrologic data. A 20-year flood series including 23 floods and their resulting damages was appraised. The influence on average annual benefits of variability in the number of floods was determined by the authors through a probability approach wherein four floods of average size were subtracted from the medium to obtain a low estimate and four were added to obtain a high estimate. The difference in average annual benefits per acre between low and high was only $0.76. The authors very correctly do not imply that this procedure gives any added reliance to selection of the particular historical sequence chosen by the hydrologist.

Because hydrologic engineering is commonly thought of as exact science, it often follows that these data are not debated or questioned so much as are the benefits or economic evaluations. Only insofar as the particular historical sequence of floods is representative of expected floods in the future, can resulting economic evaluations be supported. Projections of extremely limited hydrologic data are very often necessary. The chance of error in these projections may far overshadow limitations placed upon certain economic data such as future cropping patterns, yields, prices, crop production practices, and costs.

Conclusions presented in the sections on "Towards Data Improvement" and "Modifying Evaluation Procedures" are indicative of a genuine attempt to interpret results of this empirical evaluation into the field of practical application in everyday watershed planning activities. I am in full agreement with the proposal that watershed planning teams be "supplied with studies of general economic and managerial trends in areas where projects are contemplated." Certainly the caution is well taken that "Realistic levels of management should be assumed aimed at being predictions of actual conditions and not necessarily the ideal performance that is sometimes implied by taking results from farm management researches concerned mostly with optimum farming." If the studies proposed are objective and interpretation of their results is equally constructive, they could lead to a substantial improvement of the information now available to the watershed-planning agricultural economist. Furthermore, such studies should help materially in "depressurizing" the over-enthusiastic watershed project supporter who presses for uneconomic projects.

I question the conclusion that number of floods and floodstage-damage evaluations may not be as important for future data improvements as intensities of farming of the flood-plain area. Although this conclusion may be justified for this particular example area, it does not appear to be consistent with results of a large number of watershed evaluations with which I am familiar. More study should be given to improvement of evaluation procedures regarding physical effects of projects before concluding that retraction in this area might properly afford more consideration of type-of-agriculture assumptions.

The close interrelationships of the technological or physical problem and the economic evaluation should never be overlooked or de-emphasized. Appraisal of damage reductions and other types of benefits should be directed toward establishing the relationship between floodwater damages and flood sizes for significant variations in flood-plain and hydrologic conditions. For example, very often it is tempting to assume a composite acre land use and cropping pattern for a flood-plain area in order to reduce benefit-evaluation time requirements, when, as a matter of fact, both hydrologic and economic data can be obtained for the physical stratifications as they truly exist. Absence of such breakdowns may cloud the magnitude of effects due to physical differences in flood-plain characteristics.

Every reasonable effort should be made by watershed planners to concentrate on important variables, and not to evaluate unessentials. Interestingly enough, this already finds wide application in those projects where preliminary investigations point toward very favorable benefit-cost ratios to support project justifications.

It is not clear whom the authors refer to as "project choosers." If we presume that they are the local people who sponsor the watershed project and who will be the primary beneficiaries, they certainly should be aware of those land use opportunities which are claimed in project justification. Unless reliable appraisals are made as to when expected results with project are to take place, then refinements in project evaluation are of little consequence. Furthermore, if project choosers only consider alternatives with a view to underwriting the one or ones which give favorable project justification and accompanying nonprivate subsidy, with no view to the likelihood of benefits materializing, then watershed planners may have inadvertently caused discredit to all concerned.

This third observation is disturbing in that it implies that watershed planners do not have close working relations with project choosers. This should not be true, although it must be admitted that it has happened in some instances. Furthermore, the professional watershed planner must resist pressures that may tend to cause him to invent what Wantrup refers to as "the creation *ad hoc* of some sort of 'cost

free' land economics in order to make proposed actions appear economically desirable when they are not; although these actions may be
of great social value from other aspects and may deserve consideration
for that reason."[1]

My last comment concerns the method of estimating benefits: "Increase in net income to land assuming no floods *plus* flood damages
without project *minus* flood damages with the project." The authors
have correctly indicated that this procedure gives the same project
benefit as the method used by the Soil Conservation Service. The Soil
Conservation Service method, however, evaluates floodwater-damage
reduction benefits separately from changed land use benefits; summation of the two benefits would give the same product as the three-step
method proposed in the paper.

This method would be appropriate if one is interested only in aggregate benefits and not the source of these benefits. In some watersheds reduction of floods makes drainage enhancements possible. The
proposed three-step method of benefit determination would obscure
these particular benefits. In addition, if project choosers are to be entirely familiar with alternate possibilities for obtaining project benefits, they must go through several evaluation steps not spelled out by
the authors. Once these underlying evaluations have been made there
is little, if any, difference in the time requirements of the two methods.
My purpose in making this point is to remove any implications that the
Soil Conservation Service method goes through unnecessary steps without a reasonable purpose, rather than to question the method used by
the authors or the purpose it served.

JACK L. KNETSCH | *Comment*

THE CENTRAL IDEA presented by Messrs. Tolley and Freund represents a very worthwhile addition to the formulation of information to be
used by decision-makers. Characterizing the benefits and actually,
therefore, the benefit-cost ratios as a probability distribution is, I
think, a plea to make available more information on which to base
watershed development decisions. This would appear to be more useful

[1]S. V. Ciriacy-Wantrup, "Economic Aspects of Land Conservation," *Jour. Farm Econ.*,
Vol. XX, No. 2, May, 1938, p. 472.

Jack L. Knetsch is an agricultural economist with the Agricultural Economics
Branch, Division of Agricultural Relations, of TVA.

in making rational decisions than the use of a single number representing the ratio of project benefits to project costs, which has no recognized probability of any deviation — although it may implicitly be known
to have a variance in the minds of the decision-makers.

There are some other advantages in using this concept, but probably the most useful is in setting out the returns to a project in terms of
both their magnitude and their variability. If, for example, one project
or project alternative has a greater average benefit and less variability
attached to this return than some other alternative, then no question
arises as to preference — at least economically. However, if one project has a greater average benefit but also a greater variability of the
possible benefits than the alternative, then it is not immediately obvious which is to be preferred. The question of preference would seem
to involve some measure of compromise.

The degree to which the variability of returns is a disadvantage or
hindrance would seem to depend somewhat upon the amount of benefit
going to smaller groups of individuals and those going to society as a
whole. Society would gain the greatest benefit from selecting those
projects with the greatest payoff — regardless of their individual distributions of outcomes — because of its ability to absorb the consequences of project benefits falling both above and below the expected
return in order to achieve this greater average benefit. Thus, if we
know enough about probabilities to compute certainty equivalents, society would want to select those projects which promised the greatest
expectation, regardless of their individual distribution. These may or
not be the same projects as those having the greater benefit-cost ratios. However, smaller groups of individuals such as might be affected
by the benefits in individual small watersheds would be more inclined
to sacrifice some higher average expected benefit for a greater assurance of some lower level of return. This would likewise appear to be
of importance in choosing among various alternative solutions to a
given problem or set of problems.

As Tolley and Freund point out, watershed data seem to be inher-
ently variable, and we are left with a risk as to the ultimate outcomes
of project initiation. I agree that the best way to handle such variability may be to make more information about such risks available to the
project choosers. However, if this doesn't seem to be an acceptable
practice, as the present concentration on a single benefit-cost figure
as a summation of project economics would seem to suggest, then the
use of their "risk indicator" giving the probability of loss may be a
good "shorthand," at least for giving some indication of a distribution
of benefits to the decision-makers. We should realize, however, that
this figure, like the benefit-cost ratio, is an abbreviation and leaves
relevant information behind.

Another attribute of looking at returns in a probability framework is
the clearer distinction of the relative importance of precision in the
different sets or types of data that go into benefit determination. This
should, as is implied in the paper, make it easier to equate marginal

returns to investigative funds in all of the various individual analyses. As more projects are looked at, we may be able to get a good idea as to when and where the different types of data going into benefit calculation become more or less important.

In regard to this, we should also note the very probable existence of diminishing returns in the usefulness of further increments of information and the increasing costs of securing these increments. As we begin to look at the data problem more in terms of the ideas presented in this paper, it would seem that the approximate range in data precision where the value of added precision is worth less than the cost of its acquisition would become more definable. With limited funds we may be able to specify the magnitudes of project benefits with a very wide variance, and with increased investment we may narrow this range and "sharpen up" the analysis. Thus, we may be concerned with the joint problem of allocating investments in the various portions of the analysis and also of determining the total investment to be made in the complete analysis.

As to the other factors that cause variation, I would suspect that Tolley and Freund's conclusion about prices and technological change being of little importance is approximately correct. I do think they may give a little too much credit to the economic system's ability to make the proper adjustments, but it should go a long way in this direction. In the more extreme cases, say when a very profitable crop becomes impossible to grow and there is no good substitute, one would expect some change in the returns from what had been anticipated. However, I believe that such events would fall into the same group of factors with, for example, possible changes in the institutional environment that bring about returns different than anticipated. This type of consequence would seem to go beyond the variation that can, or should, be looked at in the present type of analysis, as the analyst is probably in no better position to anticipate this type of outcome than the decision-makers.

The analysis of the watershed presented suggests that the type-of-agriculture assumption is an important cause of the variability of anticipated total project benefits. This implies that data improvements aimed at this portion of the analysis would improve the resulting benefit estimates. One means suggested for accomplishing this is to study the economics of the individual farms on the flood plain and thereby achieve a better indication of the anticipated type-of-farming adjustments. Two cautions in doing this are presented: (1) that a wide range of underlying economic assumptions be considered, including sizes and types of farms, and (2) that realistic and not optimal levels of management be assumed, so as to arrive more nearly at actual conditions. A third caution might well be included. This added consideration involves the large changes in flood probabilities and/or income changes that seem to be needed to induce significant land use changes. Little change in land use patterns would probably come about with only small changes in the chances of flooding or in income levels. Some notion of the magnitude of flood reduction that may be needed to bring about any adjustment may come out of studies such as the Interstate Managerial Survey.[1]

The calculations of project benefits in such a way as to credit all land use improvements as benefits to a project raises a question. This procedure seems to assume that the flood-plain farms are in some sort of good, if not optimal, adjustment at the beginning of the analysis period. But is there really any reason to expect these farms to be any better adjusted than other farms? It may well be that incomes could be raised on these farms without a flood control project. Even though this change may involve some costs — for example, for added educational activities — would not this higher level of income be a more appropriate level from which to calculate added benefits than the initial land use pattern?

Although the paper is only concerned with agricultural flood protection, the amount of variation associated with these benefits suggests to me that as we begin to look at other factors that are included as benefits in watershed projects — such as irrigation and recreation — in the same way, that is, magnitudes together with their variations, we may become more conscious of the inherent variability of benefit estimates and more concerned with its implications.

---

[1] A series of papers describing this study was presented at the 1955 meetings of the American Farm Economics Association and appears in the *Jour. Farm Econ.*, Vol. XXXVII, No. 5, Dec., 1955, pp. 1097-1125.

George A. Pavelis was a field technician with the Water Resources Development
Corporation in Denver in 1951-52 and a research associate at Iowa State University from 1954-56, before joining the staff of the USDA, where he is an agricultural economist in the Land and Water Research Branch, Farm Economics
Research Division.

Chapter 11

GEORGE A. PAVELIS[1]

Applying Economic Principles in Watershed Planning

THIS REPORT on watershed planning emphasizes operational aspects of the planning process, although it has been influenced by
the philosophic and institutional aspects of watershed development.
This is because planners of programs such as those being undertaken
under the Watershed Protection and Flood Prevention Act[2] are prac-
ticing social scientists as well as economic researchers. They understand the role of small watershed development in the nation's total program of resources development, and they key their activities to institutional factors that may limit their economic conclusions. This is
particularly true in regard to local organization and financing.

Basic to good planning are definitions of the terms "watershed" and
"watershed development." A watershed can be said to represent a center of economic activity and a composite decision-making unit or "watershed firm" integrating interests of one or more private and/or public
decision-making units.[3] The concept can be broadened to include

---

[1] The views expressed are those of the author and do not necessarily reflect official
views.

[2] Public Law 566, 83rd Congress, amended by Public Law 1018, 84th Congress.

[3] This concept of a watershed as a classic economic firm, but a firm in which numerous
decision-making units might be involved, is attributed to John F. Timmons, "Economic
Framework for Watershed Development," *Jour. Farm Econ.*, Vol. XXXVI, Dec., 1954, pp.
1170-83.

interests outside the watershed proper, if such off-site interests are measurably affected by on-site decisions.

Watershed development can be viewed as a welfare-oriented economic reorganization in which welfare may be increased by two means: (1) a more efficient allocation of resources currently available to the reorganizing participants, and (2) an efficient allocation of additional resources made available for development purposes.[4] According to modern welfare theory, welfare in the aggregate can be increased only to the extent the welfare of any individual participant would not be decreased by reason of watershed programs being carried out. The crux of watershed planning may be viewed as finding the adjustments in resource use required to increase welfare as much as possible.

The resource adjustments are reflected by changed systems of land use or by the installation of water control structures. These are referred to, respectively, as land treatment measures and structural measures.

APPROACHES TO PROGRAM FORMULATION

The simplest method of formulating a program of development for a watershed is to select a set of measures by judgment. For the group of measures as a whole, an estimate is then made to determine whether total benefits exceed total costs. If so, the program is considered worthy of installation. Two disadvantages of the method are: (1) resource requirements for the measures may exceed resource availabilities, and (2) the economic benefits of some of the measures may be less than their cost.

A slightly better approach is to repeat the above procedure for several alternative sets of measures. These are compared to determine which set has the greatest excess of total benefits over total costs. The disadvantages just noted may be lessened, but they are not eliminated by this improvement.

In evaluating the alternatives, it would be still better to require that any set of measures selected be consistent with resource availability. That is, the discarded alternatives would either promise less in net benefits or require more than the available supply of any required resource, or both. It would also be desirable to require that each independent measure yield benefits in excess of costs.

Even with these requirements, the program selected can only be said to be more approximate to the optimum than those discarded. To aim at the truly optimal set of measures, the approach needs to be broadened to aim at considering all possible measures. The raw material is then provided for maximizing net benefits subject to any set of specified planning restrictions.

---

[4]Such an interpretation accords with the thinking of many writers on economic adjustments. For a technical elaboration of the welfare aspects of coincident gains and losses see M. W. Reder, *Studies in the Theory of Welfare Economics* (New York: Columbia University Press, 1947), pp. 13-17.

INFORMATION NEEDED

In following the approach mentioned last, several types of information are needed:

1. Effect on farm incomes of such phenomena as sheet erosion on watershed uplands, gully damage along drainageways, and bottom land flood damage.
2. Effect of the foregoing phenomena on expense incurred by county governments or other public bodies in providing roads and other services.
3. Identification of program beneficiaries and possible losers. This requires noting property boundaries and damage sites, as well as determining hydrologic relations between land use in various watershed sectors.[5]
4. Inventory of watershed resources, including those presently used, those available but not used, and additional resources, such as investment capital that could be made available for development purposes.
5. An array of feasible land treatment and structural measures. To be feasible, a measure must: (a) be reasonable from an agronomic or engineering viewpoint, (b) show promise of having benefits greater than costs when any needs for compensation to parties damaged are considered, and (c) be institutionally permissible, which includes being both legal and possible of adoption within attainable tenure arrangements.
6. Input-output data for each land treatment and structural measure.

FRAMEWORK OF THE NEPPER WATERSHED STUDY

Given the foregoing information, the economist should be able to specify the unique combination of land treatment and structural measures required to achieve maximum net benefits. The rest of this paper will review a study along these lines for the Nepper watershed of western Iowa, a 480-acre drainage area including parts of seven farms and draining into the Maple, Little Sioux, and Missouri Rivers.[6]

The planning objective chosen was that of maximizing net benefits for a given amount of available expenditure, discounting expenditures and benefits over a 50-year planning horizon. Moreover, programs were required not to decrease the discounted net income accruing to any participant.

---

[5] An example is the upland-bottom land relationship of runoff and flooding.

[6] Research in the Nepper watershed was conducted under Project No. 1266 of the Iowa Agricultural and Home Economics Experiment Station in cooperation with the Agricultural Research Service, U.S. Department of Agriculture. Subsequent material herein largely represents efforts of an interdisciplinary watershed research group. Included were agronomists W. D. Shrader and Orvis Engelstad, agricultural engineers R. K. Frevert and H. P. Johnson, and economists J. F. Timmons and the author. Also acknowledged is the earlier investigation by Gertel in the Nepper watershed (Karl Gertel, "Benefits and Costs of Land Improvements," unpublished M.S. thesis, Iowa State University, Ames, Iowa, 1949).

Due to differences in discount rates of participants and other time-related factors, the nature of optimal programs could be influenced by the way costs were shared. Consequently, cost-sharing was integrated with program formulation.

Two techniques of economic appraisal were used. The first was conventional benefit-cost analysis. It was used to eliminate from consideration land treatment or structural measures that failed to promise any discounted net benefits, or possibly involved greater outlays than competing measures providing the same total benefits. Benefit-cost analysis thus served mainly as a screening device, although it was also used later for summarizing project effects and assigning costs.

The second technique was linear programming. Programming offers a systematic method for optimally combining land treatment and structural measures found to provide positive net discounted revenues, and, as such, is a promising tool for formulating resource development projects.

PREDEVELOPMENT RESOURCE USE AND DAMAGE

The Nepper watershed predevelopment situation, from which benefits and costs of measures were computed, was selected as that existing in 1947. A number of improvements, primarily structures, were installed in the watershed in 1948. Selecting 1947 as the benchmark had the advantage of utilizing the data contributed by previous planners on the effects of these structures.

In 1947 roughly 53 percent of the watershed was annually in continuous corn or its erosion-runoff equivalent, 19 percent was in oats, and the remaining 28 percent was in meadow. Very little land was either contoured, terraced, or fertilized.

Under the predevelopment land use pattern, a 1-inch rain occurring within 24 hours was sufficient to produce some runoff. The possible importance of runoff is indicated by the fact that storms in the watershed have ranged to 5.6 inches.

Runoff from about 90 acres above a county bridge increased its annual maintenance cost by $385. Runoff from 215 acres contributed to the advancement of two gullies at a combined rate of 0.18 acres per year, a rate converted to average annual gully damage of $137. Runoff from 293 acres reached the watershed flood plain in the form of 32 acre feet of overflow, which might damage flood plain crops by as much as $2,803 annually.[7] About 43 acre feet of flood runoff left the watershed and caused sedimentation damage along the Maple River amounting annually to $140.

Data in Table 1 show annual costs and returns for the seven

---

[7] This estimate assumed that the flood plain could be cropped to heavily fertilized continuous corn. Actually, a series of flood damage estimates were derived, one for each feasible flood plain management system and over a range of average annual overflow volumes.

watershed farms, for the Monona County government, and for down-stream farmers along the Maple River flooded by Nepper watershed runoff. Annual estimates were discounted over a 50-year economic horizon, with privately incurred values discounted at 5 percent and public values at 2-1/2 percent.

Table 1. Distribution of Predevelopment Returns and Costs, and Optimal Development Benefits and Costs Among Farmers and Public Interests in the Nepper Watershed[a]

Items of Returns and Costs	On-Site Farmers	Monona County	Off-Site Public	Watershed Total
	Dollars	Dollars	Dollars	Dollars
Predevelopment (1947) resource-use situation				
1. Gross crop values	19,750	0	0	19,750
2. Total normal farm expense	8,717	0	0	8,717
3. Flood damage to bridge	0	385	0	385
4. Gully damages	137	0	0	137
5. Flood damage to crops	2,803	0	0	2,803
6. Off-site flood damage	0	0	140	140
7. Total costs (add items 2-6)	11,657	385	140	12,182
8. Net returns (item 1 less item 7)	8,093	-385	-140	7,568
Optimal development, Program C				
9. Gross crop values (I)	+12,171	0	0	+12,171
10. Normal variable farm expense (C)	+4,833	+93	+26	+4,952
11. Flood damage to bridge (C)	0	-273	0	-273
12. Gully damages (C)	-60	0	0	-60
13. Flood damage to crops (C)	-2,803	0	0	-2,803
14. Off-site flood damage (C)	+125[b]	0	0	+125
15. Off-site flood damage (C)	0	0	-77[c]	-77
16. Investment and maintenance (C)	+627	+9	+3	+639
17. Total benefits (add +I and -C items)	15,034	273	77	15,384
18. Total costs (add -I and +C items)	5,585	102	29	5,716
19. Net benefits (item 17 less 18)	9,449	171	48	9,668
20. Net per unit cost (item 19/item 18)	1.69	1.69	1.69	1.69

[a]Program installation costs are in 1947 prices; remaining items are in projected long-term prices.

[b]Increase caused by diversion of on-site overflow with a levee decreasing on-site crop damage by $1,141.

[c]Decrease attributed to upland treatment measures.

DEVELOPMENT POSSIBILITIES[8]

In terms of net returns from agricultural production, the bench-mark data in Table 1 indicate how the various watershed farmers and

---

[8] Livestock enterprises were not evaluated, a deficiency which, while not preventing illustration of planning principles, would seriously limit the relevance of empirical results to actual farm operations.

public groups might view a watershed development program. The interests of all farmers were to obtain benefits of increased crop values, in addition to complementary reductions in damages on their own or neighboring units. Five of the seven farms were being or would be potentially damaged by gullies. Flood damage to on-site crops was limited to one farm, since it controlled all the bottom land. Six farms, therefore, could receive benefits of a damage-reducing nature. Only one farm was unaffected by land use on others.

As shown in the second column of Table 1, the Monona County government would be interested in reducing the expense of keeping its bridge intact. The third column shows the extent of flood damage outside the watershed.

BENEFIT-COST CLASSIFICATIONS

Consistent with the scheme used in Table 1 to summarize the predevelopment situation, program benefits were taken to be (1) increases in gross crop values (item 1), (2) decreases in normal farm expense (item 2), and (3) decreases in damage from runoff (items 3 to 6). Costs included changes in the opposite direction for the foregoing items, plus investment and maintenance outlays for damage control.

Costs were allocated proportionally among beneficiaries, regardless of where changes in land use might be made or where structures might be installed. The proportional assignment of costs was carried through on several assumptions: (1) Watershed development was neither intended to maintain the predevelopment income distribution nor to achieve another given distribution. (2) Beneficiaries would be concerned only with the dollar value of multiple benefits. That is, a dollar of flood-control benefit would be considered equivalent in all economic respects to a dollar of gully-control benefit. (3) At the maximum, beneficiaries would willingly contribute resources equivalent in value to total benefits expected. (4) Beneficiaries would insist that any benefit be obtained at minimal cost.[9]

BENEFITS AND COSTS OF LAND TREATMENT

Cropping sequences, conservation practices, and fertilizer treatments specified by agronomists as feasible for 11 different soil-slope conditions found in the watershed were included as possible land use

---

[9] It will be noted that proportional allocations of costs apply only to specified project purposes and items within these purposes in watershed programs being installed under Public Law 566. Cost-sharing standards applying in each case should be made known to planners, because the character of optimal programs can vary with proportions in which participants with different planning horizons and discount rates will share costs. Planners can then consider these proportions as institutional "givens," and aside from equity aspects involving policy rather than planning as such.

alternatives. Seven cropping methods were specified as reasonable on all cropland, ranging from continuous corn to continuous meadow: CCCC, CCCO, CO_c, CCOM, COMM, COMMMM, and MMM.[10]

Possible conservation practices included contouring and level terraces designed to retain 2 inches of runoff. Contouring was considered feasible on all slopes exceeding 2 percent and terraces on all slopes exceeding 3 percent. Levels of fertilization included zero, a moderate application of nitrogen and phosphorus, and a heavy application of these elements. Long-term estimated yields of corn, oats, and hay were supplied by agronomists, along with corresponding fertilizer recommendations.

The information provided by agronomists made it possible to estimate costs and returns for an average of 50 land use systems for each field, or 1,360 for the watershed.[11] Not all were evaluated, however. A set of further criteria involving maximum permissible erosion, minimum erosion, corn frequency, maximum farm returns per acre, and maximum farm returns per unit of cost were successively applied to reduce the number of systems given detailed benefit-cost analysis from 1,360 to 75, or to about three for each of the 27 fields.

An example of how each of the 75 land use systems was appraised is shown in Table 2. The data apply to a 6-acre field in continuous corn production, and neither contoured, terraced, nor fertilized. Shifting to either of the two alternative systems involved different rotations but the same practices of terracing and fertilizing. The benefits and costs of shifting are presented in the two final columns. Damage reductions shown in the upper part of Table 2 were estimated from the reductions in runoff volumes (for flood damages) or peak runoff rates (for gully damages) resulting from the changed cover conditions and added practices on the field. Six of the 75 systems subjected to benefit-cost analysis as illustrated in Table 2 would result in net losses, or would yield less in discounted net returns than the corresponding benchmark systems for which they might be substituted.

The remaining 69 land treatment measures were then examined to see whether they promised either maximum net benefits per acre treated or maximum net benefits per unit costs. These final conditions left 47 land treatment measures (from 1 to 5 for each of the 27 watershed fields) as possible components of development programs for the Nepper watershed. The 47 measures were allowed to compete with each other and with several structures for available development resources.

---

[10] C = corn, O = oats, O_c = oats with clover catch crop, and M = alfalfa-brome meadow.

[11] Future prices were assumed to be $1.41 per bushel of corn, $0.74 per bushel of oats, and $15.70 per ton of baled alfalfa-brome hay — from a projected prices-received U.S. index of 235 (1910-1914 = 100). Future costs were based on a projected prices-paid index of 265 (1910-1914 = 100). Source of indexes: Agricultural Marketing Service and Agricultural Research Service, *Agricultural Price and Cost Projections for Use in Making Benefit-Cost Analyses of Water Resources Projects* (Washington, D.C.: Sept., 1957).

Table 2. Computational Example of Land Treatment Benefits and Costs

Land-Use Systems and Treatments	Benchmark System	Alternative Systems		Alternative Treatments[a]	
	B	1	2	1 Less B	2 Less B
Cover conditions	CCCC	CCCC	CO_c	CCCC	CO_c
Conservation practices	none	terraces	terraces	terraces	terraces
Fertilizer application	none	heavy	heavy	heavy	heavy
		Total field basis (6 acres)			
Watershed returns and costs	Dollars	Dollars	Dollars	Dollars	Dollars
1. Gross crop values (I)	154	510	348	+356	+194
2. Normal variable crop expense (C)	116	239	171	+123	+55
3. Flood damage to bridge (C)	41	6	4	-35	-37
4. Gully damages (C)	5	2	2	-3	-3
5. Flood damage to crops (C)	148	1	0	-147	-148
6. Off-site flood damage (C)	1	1	1	0	0
7. Total costs (add items 2-6)	311	249	178	x	x
8. Net returns (item 1 less item 7)	-157	261	170	x	x
Treatment benefits and costs		Total field basis (6 acres)			
9. Amortized investment (C)	x	x	x	+7[b]	+7[b]
10. Treatment benefits (add +I and -C items)	x	x	x	541	382
11. Treatment costs (add +C items)	x	x	x	130	62
12. Treatment net benefits (item 10 less 11)	x	x	x	411	320
13. Net per unit cost (item 12/ item 11)	x	x	x	3.16	5.16
14. Reference to table 3 and figure 1				P_1	P_2

[a] For simplicity, treatments are evaluated on the assumption that changes, particularly in gross crop values, result immediately and are constant over the planning period. In this case there is no need for calculating present values as such because the constant values are already in annual equivalents of present values.

[b] Represents equivalent annual investment in 2,890 feet of terraces, installed at a cost of $115.60, with $104.47 spread over 50 years at 5 percent (private share) and $11.15 spread over 50 years at 2-1/2 percent (public share).

BENEFITS AND COSTS OF STRUCTURAL MEASURES

Six structural improvements were analyzed for controlling runoff. Some were designed to function as interdependent units of a system. Consequently, they were appraised as grouped measures. There were thus four independent measures for which to estimate benefits and costs of runoff control. For three of the measures, the procedure was to estimate benefits and corresponding costs per unit of 1,000 cubic yards of earthfill volume, which in turn was considered proportional to detention capacity. A levee system was appraised on a unit basis of bank height. The analysis indicated that one facility, a combination chute-spillway designed to replace the county bridge susceptible to flood damage and also to provide some measure of gully control, would promise less in discounted benefits than its costs per unit of fill. It was discarded. This left three structural measures to compete with the 47 land treatment measures.

RESOURCE AND TECHNOLOGICAL RESTRICTIONS

Principal restrictions on development programs for the Nepper watershed related to land, maximum structure capacities imposed by engineering considerations, and capital. Surveys indicated that additional labor needed for some of the land treatment measures on particular fields would not exceed available labor being unused.

Each of the 27 farm field areas represented 27 land-resource subclasses for which unique inputs and outputs characterizing various treatment measures had been determined. Therefore, each field area was considered as a land restriction.

Limits on structure size specified that one grouped facility could not exceed 40,850 cubic yards of earthfill. Fill in another could not exceed 14,400 cubic yards. The heights of levee banks could not exceed 6 feet. These limits approximated capacities resulting in complete elimination of gully and flood damage, independently of any land treatment measures.

A final restriction on development measures and programs was represented by the present value in 1947 of all investment and recurring outlays necessary to initiate and continue land use changes, or to install and maintain structures over the planning horizon 1947-1997. These amounts were computed (see Table 2) as annual equivalents of capitalized cost. To illustrate program planning both under conditions of limited and unlimited capital, a series of alternative programs were devised that would maximize discounted net benefits for any amount of expenditure that might be specified. Each alternative, therefore, could be termed an optimum corresponding to that expenditure specified.

PROJECT FORMULATION THROUGH LINEAR PROGRAMMING

Given the foregoing steps, the planning problem to be solved by linear programming reduced to the following question: In view of the 31 planning restrictions, how should the 47 land treatment and 3 structural measures have been combined in 1947 and continued over the period 1947-1997 to maximize discounted net benefits for the watershed as a whole? [12]

[12] Restrictions included 27 fields scattered among 7 farms, the 3 limits on structure size, and capitalized cost. The variant of programming utilized to treat the latter as an increasing variable was that developed by Wilfred V. Candler, "A Modified Simplex Solution for Linear Programming with Variable Capital Restrictions," *Jour. Farm Econ.*, Vol. XXXVIII, Nov., 1956, pp. 940-55. Also see Earl O. Heady and Wilfred V. Candler, *Linear Programming Methods* (Ames: The Iowa State University Press, 1958), pp. 233-64.

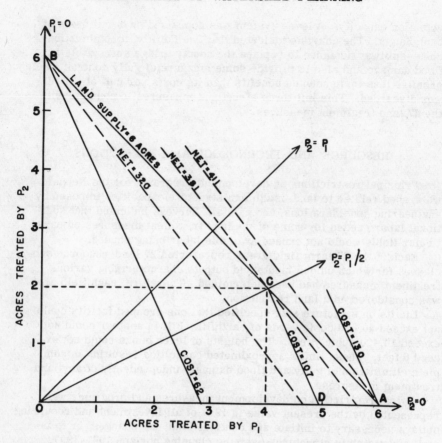

Figure 1. Programming optimal combinations of land treatment.

Figure 1 illustrates how programming principles would operate in determining optimal land treatment for a single watershed field. Relationships apply to the two alternative treatments of Table 2. With capital nonlimiting, any combination of the two treatments bounded under the land-supply line AB would be feasible. Clockwise, the arrows designate proportional combinations of no P_1, equal P_1 and P_2, P_1 twice P_2, and no P_2. Lines labeled with specified costs represent iso-outlay contours and those with specified net benefits denote iso-benefit contours.

In the case of nonlimiting capital, $130 would be allocated to treatment of the entire 6-acre field by P_1 and net benefits would be maximized at $411 at point A. Any capital remaining could be spent for less profitable treatment of other fields or for structural measures, or it could be unused.

If capital were limited to $62, the entire area would be treated by P_2, and net benefits would be maximized at $320 or point B. A lesser outlay would permit proportional partial treatment by P_2, with the rest of the field farmed by the predevelopment system.

Table 3. Partial Programming Tableau of the Nepper Watershed Planning Problem

Resource or Height Restrictions	Resource or Activity Levels	Disposal Activities					Real Activities[a]		
		Land: Field 1 Farm 1	Land: Field 3 Farm 7	Land: Field 4 Farm 4	Levee Height	Capitalized Cost	CCCC Terraces Fertilized	CO_c Terraces Fertilized	Structure I (Levees)
		Programming coded designations							
Code	P_0	P_{51}	P_{76}	P_{77}	P_{79}	P_{81}	P_1	P_2	P_{50}
P_{51}	6.0 ac.	1	0	0	0	0	6.0	6.0	0
P_{76}	22.5 ac.	0	1	0	0	0	0	0	.175
P_{77}	41.6 ac.	0	0	1	0	0	0	0	.175
P_{79}	6.0 ft.	0	0	0	1	0	0	0	1
P_{81}	0.0 dol.	0	0	0	0	1	130	62	107
c_j	0	0	0	0	0	0	411[b]	320[b]	375[b]
z_j	0	0	0	0	0	0	0	0	0
$z_j - c_j$	0	0	0	0	0	0	-411	-320	-375
d_j	0	0	0	0	0	0	-3.16	-5.16	-3.50

[a]Data for P_1 and P_2 are transferred from Table 2.
[b]Discounted net benefits.

If available capital ranged between \$62 and \$130, some combination of P_1 and P_2 would maximize net benefits. For example, if a capital restriction of \$107 were specified, the line segments BC and CD would then represent the relevant transformation function. Maximum net benefits would then be \$381, shown by point C.

While Figure 1 dealt with an optimal allocation of resources between competing treatments for a single field, solution of the general planning problem required application of the same principles to allocate resources optimally among competing treatments within and among fields, and hence, within and among farms or throughout the watershed.

Table 3 is an abbreviation of the initial simplex tableau of the general Nepper watershed programming problem. Complete data are inserted for the two land treatment measures of Table 2 and Figure 1, with the levee system added as a sample structural measure. If planning had been confined to the three measures shown, the second (P_2) would have been partially financed with the first dollar available for development. This was because (as the d_j values indicate) not assigning the measure first priority would have sacrificed more in discounted net benefits (\$5.16) than not including the other two measures. By focusing on capital productivity, alternative programs representing optima for successively greater expenditures were obtained, with the maximum justifiable expenditure indicated by no additional net benefits being sacrificed, or by no remaining negative d_j values.

PROGRAMMING RESULTS

Major results of the Nepper research and the consistence of programming with marginal economic principles are shown in Figure 2.[13] The horizontal axis of the figure measures total program expenditure in annual equivalent terms. The upper vertical axis measures discounted total and net benefits, again in annual equivalents, plotted against costs. Derived average and marginal net benefit-cost ratios can be read on the lower vertical scale.

The program (program A) practically coinciding with the vertical axis of Figure 2 represented the first measure considered in the complete planning problem. The measure involved only the conversion from continuous corn to permanent pasture of a steep field representing a major source-area of gully and flood damages. On an annual equivalent basis, costs were \$9.60, net benefits were \$281, and the average and marginal net return on capital consequently \$29.26, a rate higher than for any other measure.[14]

---

[13] The benefit functions of Figure 2 were generated by carrying the simplex solution of Table 3 (expanded to 81 columns and 31 rows) forward until cumulative net benefits ($z_j - c_j$) could no longer be increased. Values of P_{81} (costs) and net benefits at selected iterations were then plotted, with total benefits obtained as sums of P_{81} and $z_j - c_j$.

[14] Measures optimal for a particular area at lower capital levels were not necessarily optimal at higher levels. This important consideration in watershed planning is illustrated in Figure 1.

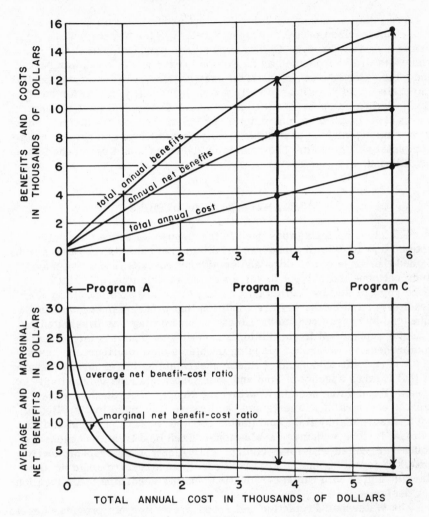

Figure 2. Alternative optimal development programs for the Nepper watershed.

As expenditures exceeding $9.60 were being allocated, it was finan-
cially feasible to consider measures with benefit-cost ratios lower than
the $29.26 ratio for the single measure of program A. For program B
in Figure 2, for example, an expenditure of $3,700 allocated most eco-
nomically would produce total benefits of $11,937 and maximum net
benefits of $8,237. The corresponding over-all or average net benefit-
cost ratio amounted to $2.22, and the marginal ratio to $1.46.

The special case of planning with no expenditure restrictions is
shown by program C in Figure 2. Annual gross benefits would be
$15,384, net benefits a maximum of $9,668, and the maximum justified
expenditure $5,716. The average net benefit-cost ratio for program C
approximated $1.69, and the marginal ratio was zero.

The relation of complete development under program C to the initially summarized predevelopment situation in the Nepper watershed can be noted in Table 1. Optimal changes in predevelopment returns and costs are represented by details on program C in the lower part of the table. Because of proportional cost-sharing, all farmer and public interests would benefit absolutely and proportionally; the latter condition is indicated by equal rates of return of $1.69. The final column shows that, to obtain a maximum of $9,668 in net benefits distributed as shown among various participants, only on-site flood damages would be completely eliminated. The remaining damages would be reduced but not eliminated.

SUMMARY AND CONCLUSIONS

The planning framework used in the Nepper watershed not only showed how to delimit measures promising net benefits, but also how to extend the range of selection and combine measures to achieve maximum net benefits, subject to any specified restrictions. The latter were represented by limited land areas, structure size, capitalized expenditures, and by the welfare condition that programs not leave anyone damaged and uncompensated. Linear programming was illustrated as a useful supplement to conventional benefit-cost analysis for solving comprehensive watershed planning problems on a multipurpose basis.

A particular advantage of linear programming in resources planning is that it takes account of land and water interrelations unique to given areas. By defining each field within the Nepper watershed as a treatment area, input coefficients and benefits were derived that applied to any measure on any field, and thus accounted for both physical and locational factors in damage evaluations. Each land treatment measure could be credited with flood-control, gully-control, or crop-productivity benefits, depending on the area treated. Each structure could be similarly credited with damage-reduction benefits according to its location and design.

The Watershed Protection and Flood Prevention Act provides impetus for refinement of benefit-cost appraisals in planning watershed development programs, both as the appraisals are related to program formulation and to cost-sharing. The Nepper watershed research attempted to demonstrate how such refinements might be applied.

JOE A. MARTIN | *Comment*

SINCE THE PASSAGE of Public Law 566 agricultural economists concerned with watersheds have faced the difficult job of adapting their research tools to small watershed planning. It seems that Dr. Pavelis has provided a breakthrough. His suggested technique calls for the use of two familiar tools: (1) the conventional benefit-cost analysis as a screening device to identify the alternative land treatment and structural measures that appear to be economically feasible under given planning restrictions; and (2) linear programming as a tool for a more refined analysis of the land treatment and structural alternatives which are identified as possibilities by the benefit-cost analysis.

The application of linear programming in watershed planning is essentially the same as in farm management research, except that interfarm and off-site aspects of the problem are included in the program. By taking the most likely alternatives given by the benefit-cost analysis, linear programming offers a sharp instrument of analysis for combining land treatment programs (field by field and farm by farm) and structural measures into a plan that will yield the maximum net revenue over time.

Pavelis suggests that the watershed be recognized not only as a physical and social entity, but also as an economic entity for purposes of planning. His approach recognizes that the watershed entity is made up of many component entities, namely, farms and off-site groups. These smaller entities have their own physical characteristics, economic goals, and social values. Watershed planning and administrative problems grow out of the fact that the farmers in different parts of the watershed and off-site groups may fail to recognize their true interests, and often they may believe (rightly or wrongly) that they have conflicts of interests. These problems call for more than skill in the art of compromise, more than human engineering, and more than education directed toward broadening the social interests and values of farmers up in the hills. All of these will certainly be needed in most watersheds that are organized, but they are no substitute for dollars-and-cents estimates about who pays what and who benefits how. Therefore, the planning techniques suggested by Pavelis, which yield more precise information on the incidence of costs and benefits, have a definite contribution to make to organizing and administering watershed programs.

The concept of the watershed as an integrated physical and economic unit for planning suggested by Pavelis gets around the unrealistic separation of watershed problems into (1) hydrologic relationships which stress the need for more efficient use of water and the need for reducing

---

Joe A. Martin has been on the staff of the University of Tennessee since 1947, and is now Professor of Agricultural Economics. He does teaching and research in land economics and economic development.

erosion, siltation, and flooding, and (2) farm management aspects of the problem which must contend with the hard fact that farmers are engaged in the serious business of making a living. These two problems, of course, cannot be divorced. To ignore the complementarity or conflict associated with the solution of these two sets of problems would seriously jeopardize the chances for success of the small watershed program.

A methodology which integrates the farm management aspect of the problem into the over-all program planning is particularly significant in areas of small farms and low incomes such as are found in the Southeast. We may expect to find in some areas of small crop farms that the interests of downstream and off-site groups can be furthered only at a sacrifice by those in other parts of the watershed.

A study of problems in organizing watershed districts in Tennessee[1] under Public Law 566 indicated that each watershed presents unique problems, but at the heart of these problems was the question of welfare. Although it is generally understood by local people that the law provides for payments for damages suffered as a result of the program, the attitudes of those who did not stand to benefit, as well as those who thought they would be damaged by the program, was with few exceptions negative.

A basic cause of the negative attitude toward organizing a watershed district was a lack of security of expectation on the part of local people concerning their own welfare. They viewed their chance of loss as being too great a risk to take. They therefore set about persuading their neighbors and friends to vote against the organization.

This suggests that local leaders in the watershed programs have a problem of working out their tactics. But, more important, it points to the need for economists to sharpen up analytical tools in the area of welfare economics. Here again, it seems to me that Pavelis has pushed out on the frontier. He has demonstrated in the Nepper watershed plan how to impose the welfare restrictions in planning which are thought to be necessary to achieve economic and social justice for all individuals and groups in a watershed.

---

[1] Joseph E. Winsett, *Problems in Small Watershed Districts in Tennessee Organized Under Public Law 566* (Master's thesis, University of Tennessee, 1958).

Emery N. Castle is Professor of Agricultural Economics at Oregon State College. He joined the staff there in 1954, prior to which time he was an agricultural economist with the Federal Reserve Bank of Kansas City, and Assistant Agricultural Economist at Kansas State University.

Chapter 12

EMERY N. CASTLE

Programming Structures
in Watershed Development

WATERSHED PLANNING often involves the simultaneous determination of a number of variables. Consider the situation where there are multiple dam sites with varying capacities and with a number of alternative uses for water, each use having different seasonal requirements. It may be tempting to think of finding a best set of dams by consecutively holding all variables constant but one, each time calculating incremental costs and returns. If there were no positive interaction an optimum solution would eventually be found. However, most planning agencies have insufficient resources for this laborious procedure. It is usually necessary to make a subjective selection of alternatives. Arbitrary assumptions may be made in order to reduce the work in testing for economic feasibility. Furthermore, there may be an unfortunate division of labor between engineers and economists. Engineers may select the alternatives, with economists testing them for economic feasibility, when in fact, the best alternative has not been included.

Activity analysis or linear programming appears promising as an aid in watershed planning, in view of the large number of interdependent variables that may be involved. This paper is a progress report on research, undertaken in cooperation with engineers, that uses activity

167

analysis to help solve watershed planning problems. In the problems presented, the number of variables has been limited to permit a better comprehension of the approach. The capacity of computers is such that the number of variables may not be a major obstacle, once problems are formulated adequately.

STRUCTURE CAPACITY AND WATER USAGE — A PROTOTYPE SYSTEM[1]

The first prototype system to be considered deals with a watershed where three sites are available. Storage capacity for each site must be chosen. The water can be used in four areas, for either supplemental or full irrigation. Figure 1 shows the watershed situation. The upper

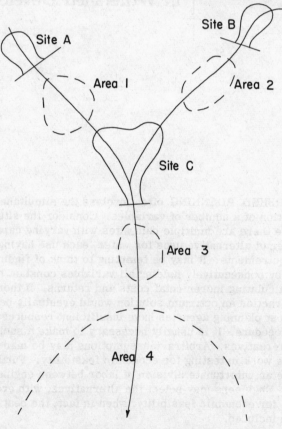

Figure 1. Prototype System I.

[1]J. G. Polifka, Watershed Planning Specialist, Soil Conservation Service, developed this first prototype system. Although Polifka established the technical relationships upon which the analysis is based, he, of course, is not responsible for the analysis.

Table 1. Average Annual Cost Per Acre Foot of Capacity

Increment of Storage Capacity	Average Annual Cost Per Acre Foot		
	Site A	Site B	Site C
	(dollars)	(dollars)	(dollars)
0 - 500	8.08	11.05	16.74
500 - 2,000	6.20	7.62	8.06
2,000 - 2,730	5.73		
2,000 - 3,000		6.78	
2,000 - 4,000			5.83
4,000 - 4,680			5.76

limits of reservoir capacities at Site A (2,730 acre feet) and Site B (3,000 acre feet) are dictated by the upper limits of watershed yields in these two subwatersheds. The upper limit of reservoir capacity at Site C (4,680 acre feet) is dictated by the topography at that site. The total watershed yield is limited to 7,000 acre feet.

In converting capital costs of construction to an average annual basis (that is, finding the value of an annuity whose present value equals construction cost), project life was assumed to be 50 years, and 5 percent interest rate was used. Operation and maintenance costs were estimated at 1/2 percent of construction costs. Costs are presented in Table 1.

The reservoirs are characterized by decreasing average costs. For Sites A and B, both average and marginal costs decrease as capacity increases. In going from 4,000 acre feet of storage to 4,680 acre feet for Site C, marginal costs increase, although marginal costs are less than average costs. This is a troublesome complication as far as linear programming is concerned. If the linear segments of the cost functions are entered as processes, the low-cost process will automatically be selected even though the degree of use is less than the capacity to which these costs would apply. Activity analysis can be adapted nicely to increasing average or marginal costs, and constant costs pose no particular problem. Decreasing cost functions are especially interesting, since economic theory generally treats increasing cost situations as being necessary for an equilibrium. Yet it appears that decreasing costs may describe certain relationships in the resources field where nature sets a limit on the yield forthcoming from certain resources regardless of the inputs of capital and labor. That is, maximum total production is reached in the stage where average product is still increasing.

A number of alternative methods can be devised to meet the problem raised by decreasing costs. Perhaps the most practical method is to run the program using the lowest cost for each reservoir as a process. Increasing cost segments can also be entered as processes. If the solution indicates that the storage called for in a reservoir is less

Table 2. Available Acreage and Storage Requirements Per Acre for Irrigation

	Acres		Acre Feet of Storage Required Per Acre Irrigated	
	Supplemental	Full	Supplemental	Full
Area 1	200	100	2	5
Area 2	100	100	1	5
Area 3	250	150	1	5
Area 4	1,500	135	2	5

than would be applicable, considering the costs which were used, it is necessary to rerun the program using appropriately higher costs. If the problem is being worked by a desk calculator, it is possible to enter the appropriate cost for the capacity which a process calls for when it enters the program. Although this does not give the neat theoretical solution one might like, it does provide a practical method of dealing with the problem.[2]

Let us turn to the profitability of sending water to each area. As indicated by Figure 1, Site A can provide water to Areas 1, 3, and 4. Site B can provide water to Areas 2, 3, and 4. Site C can provide water to Areas 3 and 4. We need to consider profitability for each of these possibilities.

Some of the lands in each of the four irrigable areas have an early season irrigation water supply from uncontrolled stream diversion. In addition, there are some lands not now irrigated which, if irrigated, would require a full irrigation water supply. Irrigation water requirements are expressed in terms of reservoir storage capacity per acre after allowing for evaporation and seepage losses and delivery losses to the farmer's headgates. It is assumed that these losses would be proportionate for all reservoir sites. When this is not the case, the difference could be reflected in the water requirements as expressed in storage capacity. The water requirements by areas are given in Table 2.

Returns data given in Table 3 are net of all costs except water storage costs. By subtracting the water storage costs for each site

Table 3. Increased Net Returns Per Acre, Exclusive of Water Storage Costs

Lands Requiring	Increased Net Return Per Acre
(storage)	(dollars)
1 acre foot supplemental	10
2 acre feet supplemental	16
5 acre feet full	30

---

[2] After this chapter had been written, Allan S. Manne pointed out to me the possibility of using integer programming.

Table 4. Unit Profitability Data in Dollars Per Acre
for Different Areas by Sites

	Supplemental Areas				Full Areas				Processes
	1	2	3	4	1	2	3	4	
Site A	4.54	--	4.27	4.54	1.35	--	1.35	1.35	6
Site B	--	3.22	3.22	2.44	--	x	x	x	3
Site C	--	--	4.24	4.48	--	--	1.20	1.20	4
Total									13

from the returns of Table 3, it was possible to develop unit profitability data. These are given in Table 4. There are 13 profitable processes as possibilities. It will be noted that it would not be profitable to use Site B for full irrigation. Had these uses been profitable, there would have been 16 processes.

From the data that have been presented it is possible to formulate a linear programming problem. The restrictions are available acreages, storage capacity, and total watershed yields. This gives a possible total of 12 restrictions. Full irrigation for Area 2 is not a profitable process from any site. Therefore, it can be eliminated from the restrictions. Since the remaining land is inadequate to exhaust the total water, the total watershed yield can also be eliminated as a restriction. This leaves 13 processes and 10 restrictions.

The profit equation can be developed from Table 4. The objective of maximizing net benefits, which has been accepted by various operating agencies, was adopted. Other objective criteria could be used if desired, although the problem might then need to be formulated differently.

The solution indicates that Sites A and C would be built. Site A would be built to capacity at 2,730 acre feet. Site C would be built for 2,845 acre feet of storage. Areas 1, 3, and 4, both supplemental and full, would be irrigated. Annual net benefits would be maximized at $9,020.61.

Other situations were analyzed where the total yield of the watershed and the total storage capacity were limiting. These results are not reported here, as the type of analysis was the same. It is believed the above results illustrate some of the possibilities of activity analysis in simultaneously determining the height of dams and the use to which water may be allocated.

INTERDEPENDENT STRUCTURES

Thus far it has been assumed that storage capacity adequately measures the services rendered by a structure. Benefits, however, may also depend on time of use and streamflow characteristics. In

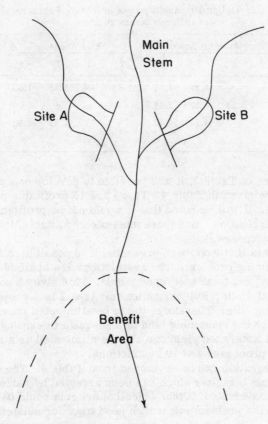

Figure 2. Prototype System II.

trying to take account of these variables, consider Figure 2. Assume Sites A and B each have 1,000 acre feet of storage capacity. However, the hydrology of the tributaries is such that Site A will fill once during the year and 1,000 acre feet can be supplied at any time during the season. Site B will fill three times, and the last time it is filled it can be discharged in either July or August. However, 1,000 acre feet must be discharged in May and 1,000 acre feet in June. Some "free" water will be available from the main stem whether the dams are built or not. Here is a summary of water availabilities, expressed in acre feet:

	"Free" Water	Site A	Site B
May	3,000	1,000 or	1,000
June	2,000	1,000 or	1,000
July	500	1,000 or	1,000 or
August	500	1,000	1,000

Annual operating costs are $8,000 for Site A and $9,000 for Site B. Assume 20,000 acres of land are available that can be devoted to either Use I or II.

There are two beneficial uses that have the following seasonal requirements for water per 100 acres of land.

	Use I	Use II
May	0	20
June	10	30
July	20	100
August	70	50
Acre feet	100	200
Unit profitability	$1,000	$1,200

Although the number of variables is not large, the solution is not self-evident. It is known that water, rather than land, is limiting. Use I may be selected as a starting point, since for the year it gives a greater return per acre foot than Use II. However, since the seasonal water requirements for Use II are somewhat different, we cannot be sure which is really more profitable. In order to evaluate each site, the discharge policy of the other would need to be considered. It becomes obvious a systematic procedure is needed. Table 5 presents a programming model that will meet the main requirements of this problem.

Table 5. Linear Programming Model for Site Evaluation and Discharge Procedure

		1,000	1,200	-8,000	-8,000	-9,000	-9,000
1.	C_j						
2.	P_0	P_1	P_2	P_3	P_4	P_5	P_6
3.	3,000	0	20			-1,000	-1,000
4.	2,000	10	30			-1,000	-1,000
5.	500	20	100	-1,000		-1,000	
6.	500	70	50		-1,000		-1,000
7.	1			1	1		
8.	1					1	1
9.	20,000	100	100				

Line 1 states the net benefit equation. The P_0 column gives "free" water, and site and land availability. P_1 and P_2 give land and water requirements for the two uses. P_3, P_4, P_5, and P_6 give the discharge possibilities from the different sites. The return from P_1 and P_2 less the cost of P_3, P_4, P_5, and P_6 will give the net benefit from the system. Lines 3, 4, 5, and 6 give the water availability and water use by months

(May through August). The May and June discharge possibilities from Site A can be eliminated on the basis of inspection. Lines 7 and 8 are necessary algebraically to limit Sites A and B to one structure each. Line 9 limits the land to 20,000 acres.

It may be helpful to consider line 3 as an illustration. This line states that the amount of "free" water, 3,000 acre feet, must be equal to or greater than the amount of water used in Use I and Use II less the amount supplied from Site 1 and Site 2.

The results obtained are as follows:

Use I: carried to the limit of available water

Net benefits: $16,334.34

Acreage irrigated: 10,833

Site A discharge policy: August, 1,000 acre feet

Site B discharge policy: May, 1,000 acre feet

June, 1,000 acre feet

July, 167 acre feet

August, 833 acre feet

The value of an additional acre foot of July or August water would be $11.11.

The use of this model permits one to proceed directly to the solution which maximizes net benefits. It is not necessary to justify each structure individually, since the structure will not be included in the solution unless the incremental benefits exceed the incremental costs. The procedure of justifying each structure independently may make necessary certain arbitrary assumptions as to the allocation of benefits among structures.[3] The value of the limiting resources, July and August water, may be suggestive in the event all alternative sources of water were not entered in the model.

The type of model used here may have application in evaluating flood control systems where amount of protection received from one structure depends on the operating policy of other structures. It may be that a combination of graphic techniques now used, plus linear programming, will provide the best procedure. In practice, storage capacity may be variable. Then a combination of the models exemplified in prototype systems I and II could be used.

ALTERNATIVE USE RELATIONSHIPS

One of the challenging economic problems connected with water resources development is allocation of water among uses and users. For

---

[3] See the example in Soil Conservation Service, *Economics Guide for Watershed Protection and Flood Prevention*, Chap. 2, p. 12. It appears that arbitrary assumptions as to benefits are necessary to make such a system of analysis feasible.

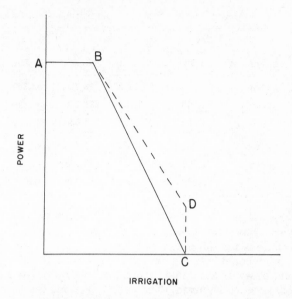

Figure 3. Power and irrigation use relationships.

appropriated water, the problem is complicated by water laws with
varying degrees of flexibility in terms of reallocation. When unappro-
priated water is being considered, conflicts among special interest
groups may make politics rather than economics the controlling force.
Yet the area of controversy may be narrowed, and better choices may
result if clear statements about economic magnitudes are available. As
a case in point, well-informed citizens have expressed their bewilder-
ment at the complexities of the Hell's Canyon controversy. Despite
years of controversy and investigation, all the alternatives have not
been analyzed systematically. There is an uneasy feeling that a choice
will be made from among inferior possibilities.

When new storage capacity is created and water becomes available
for allocation, the selection of uses becomes important. This is because substantial public and private investments depend on how the
water is initially allocated. Moreover, institutional rigidities impede
the reallocation of appropriated waters, making initial misallocations
difficult to correct. If physical relationships among the uses are
known, they can be incorporated into a linear programming analysis.

Consider now a synthesized problem involving power and irrigation.
A seasonal requirement schedule for power was obtained. This was
based on power sales in a rural community which has a fairly uniform
requirement throughout the year. Irrigation requirements are, of
course, much more seasonal. Transformation function ABC is given in
Figure 3. Power and irrigation are supplementary within the AB range.
Points B and C are alternatives and could be used as processes in activity analysis. In the event that some power by-product would result if

Table 6. Benefits and Costs by Purposes and Increments of Capacity

Purpose of Capacity	Increment	Capacity (Acre Feet)	Average Annual Benefit	Annual Cost	Net Benefit	Benefit-Cost Ratio
Irrigation	First	1,000	156,600	63,750	92,850	favorable
Flood control	Second	2,000	140,400	191,250	-50,850	unfavorable
Total		3,000	297,000	255,000	42,000	favorable
Flood control	First	2,000	140,400	95,625	44,775	favorable
Irrigation	Second	1,000	156,600	159,375	-2,775	unfavorable
Total		3,000	297,000	255,000	42,000	favorable

irrigation were the primary use, ABDC would be the relevant function and B and D would be alternatives.

The restrictions for the programming problem were determined by the acreage which could be irrigated, the capacity of the storage sites, and the amount of water available by months. Thirty-three restrictions and 14 processes were involved. The results yielded the storage for each site, the acreage of irrigated land, and the amount of power to be generated. For problems of this size or larger, digital computers probably would be more efficient than desk calculators.

Another of the more interesting relationships is that of flood control and irrigation. Complementarity may exist in many areas, while in others competition may prevail, and the relationship may not be constant from one year to the next. The criterion for the appropriate level of protection from floods may be ambiguous. Protection beyond the point where net benefits are at a maximum may be desired in some cases. If the level of protection is decided upon, the least-cost method of providing that protection can be solved for by activity analysis unless the problem is complicated by competitive or complementary uses. Consider the example of Table 6.

If we assume 2,000 acre-feet storage capacity is required for flood control and that flood control is competitive with irrigation, we have two alternative ways of providing it. One method is to build a reservoir with a capacity of 3,000 acre-feet. This would provide for irrigation and flood control and would return net benefits of $42,000. The irrigation feature would not meet the requirement of a benefit-cost ratio greater than one. The other alternative would provide 2,000 acre-feet of storage capacity which could be devoted to flood control — this would return $44,774 in net benefits. If irrigation alone were developed, it would return $92,850 in net benefits. However, if opportunity costs are considered, building the structure for flood control precludes the possibility of maximizing net benefits which would amount to $92,850 if only irrigation were provided. If this opportunity cost were considered, flood control would not prove economically feasible. The criterion for the determination of the level of protection against floods is somewhat clouded. The Economics Guide for Watershed Protection and Flood Prevention published by the Soil Conservation Service states (Chapter 2, page 12):

The objectives in formulating an economically feasible system of structures are: (1) development of the least costly system to achieve the minimum agreed-upon levels of protection in those steam reaches which it is planned to protect, and (2) strengthening the system to provide a higher level of protection if the net benefits are maximized at a higher level. If, however, the system as a whole does not produce a favorable ratio of benefits to costs at the agreed-upon minimum level of protection, the system is not economically feasible and shall not be included in the project.

The "agreed upon level of protection" is apparently determined by the Service and the local organization. Eckstein[4] states that "until the fundamental objectives of the federal flood control program are defined more clearly, the benefit-cost technique cannot be applied rigorously to the design of projects." Benefit-cost analysis should not only consider the money but also the opportunity cost. These opportunity costs depend upon the transformation relationships between uses.

CONCLUSIONS

The above models are intended to be suggestive rather than definitive, in view of the many complexities of watershed planning. Also, there is a question of fact regarding the relevancy of greater refinement in quantitative procedures. George Tolley[5] has said:

Perhaps the most important thing that needs to be said... is that improved analytical techniques can make a contribution to watershed development, but that they are not necessarily the most pressing needs. The most pressing need in terms of making reliable evaluations may be to obtain better estimates of physical and economic conditions that will prevail in a watershed — particularly in the flood plains — after the development of expenditures has been made. In many instances, reliance in making the prediction of future conditions is put on answers from farmers in surveys. Some scope for supplementing this information with wider use of programming and budgeting techniques seems possible.

Yet, if the engineers consulted in this study are correct, no theoretically complete system exists by which all of the many variables involved in project evaluation can be related. This suggests that efforts attempting to remedy the deficiency would not be wasted. Even if activity analysis does not lead to better projects directly, there may be a substantial indirect benefit. The method provides a framework through which economics and engineering can be integrated. The kind of data required is no different from that used in traditional evaluation procedures, although a programming formulation may make clear that a

---

[4] Otto Eckstein, *Water Resources Development, the Economics of Project Evaluation* (Cambridge: Harvard University Press, 1958), p. 141.

[5] George S. Tolley, "Analytical Techniques in Relation to Watershed Development," *Jour. Farm Econ.*, Vol. XL, Aug., 1958, p. 655.

complete analysis will require more information than would otherwise be used. Engineers have expressed interest in the approach.

This type of analysis will have to come to grips with several important problems. (1) Variability of water yields between years introduces the familiar problems of risk and uncertainty. Work has been done on these in other connections and might be applicable. (2) Related to the foregoing is the need for criteria in choosing the optimum combination of "insurance" and net benefits. (3) The complications introduced by varying degrees of complementarity, supplementarity, and competition among uses deserve further exploration.

MAX M. THARP | *Comment*

THE CONTRIBUTION made by Dr. Castle is the offering of workable models, the use of which would refine the procedures commonly followed by the action agencies. Undoubtedly, maximization of benefits would be approached more closely through activity analysis, because it permits evaluation of a large number of alternatives. In practice, watershed evaluation work parties and program planners are limited as to both time and resources. Often judgment is substituted for rigorous application of economic principles in the solution of the problem. Various pressures and the desires of vocal elements of the local population may determine the plans, purposes, and scope that are to be considered. As a practical procedure, not all alternatives can be considered. The planning agency inevitably selects the alternatives "most likely to succeed" from an incomplete list of possible proposals.

It is important that the best data available be used in the activity analysis. Use of reservoir storage capacity as a measure of irrigation water requirements is subject to several practical limitations. For example, land leveling, water management on the farm, and irrigation practices have significant effects on water requirements after the water is delivered to the farmers' headgates. Adjustments in total requirements could be made in the basic data used in the model, and the analyst should be careful to include these types of refinements.

Castle observed that decreasing costs arise from natural physical limits to water yields regardless of the magnitude of capital and labor inputs. His suggestion for handling the phenomenon by taking specific

Max M. Tharp is head of the Southeastern Agriculture Section, Farm Economics Research Division of USDA. He was executive director of the Southeast Land Tenure Research Committee and Assistant in Farm Management at the University of Kentucky.

segments as separate activities appears appropriate. However, the solution may become complicated when a more complex situation is encountered.

Castle implies that usual project evaluation procedure necessitates allocation of benefits among structures of a watershed protection system. But this is not necessarily the case. Benefits attributable to a structure may be estimated by adding successive increments on a nucleus as long as net benefits for the system are increased. To be included, each structure must pay for itself and must increase system benefits, but it is not necessary to allocate benefits to specific structures.

Castle's illustration of competitive uses of water represents an unusual or special case in project formulation. A more general situation is one in which the first increment of a reservoir (or other structure) has an unfavorable benefit-cost ratio. The example in Castle's paper indicates a favorable benefit-cost ratio for the first increment, but an unfavorable ratio for the second increment. This situation appears to arise because of the admittedly arbitrary assumption that 2,000 acre feet of storage capacity is required for flood control. As the flood control increment is not justified in tangible economic terms, its inclusion must rest on an administrative or legislative determination. If this is the case, it would be more informative to treat the benefits derived from the flood control increment as tangible and to recognize the cost of its inclusion in the economic analysis. However, its inclusion in the analysis provides a measure of the costs of providing the flood control protection and the minimum value of the intangibles involved.

The extent and nature of opportunity costs that may be forgone in selecting a specific project usually are not pertinent as the most advantageous alternatives and combinations are selected. The problem of opportunity costs, as cited by Castle, arises only when the scale of a project is expanded beyond the optimum economic size. This happens in his example, and I agree that under these circumstances opportunity costs are important and should be recognized. However, standard project evaluation procedures do take these costs into account. Thus, in Castle's example, no project would be justified that did not provide at least the $92,850 of net benefits indicated for 1,000 acre feet of irrigation storage capacity.

Castle has assumed simple situations to illustrate his models. This is good for explaining the method, but it may be misleading to the uninitiated linear programmer. A vast amount of work goes into "behind the scenes" efforts to obtain the basic data needed to complete the linear programming matrices. This is particularly true for the model used to evaluate alternative use relationships. I would have liked to see the schematic solution to this problem illustrated in the paper, as was done for the model used for the site evaluation and discharge procedure. It was difficult to follow the procedure suggested in the discussion of the transfer function. The steps followed were not specifically indicated, and it was hard to envision construction of the matrix so as to include the many variables to be evaluated.

If the procedure for models such as Dr. Castle suggests could be standardized, it should be possible for evaluation field parties to supply the information to a central office for machine tabulation. This might save substantial planning funds. Despite the promising possibilities, use of linear programming cannot make up for the deficiencies in basic data. Input-output data of the kind needed for widespread application of linear programming procedures to watershed evaluations often do not exist. Accurate engineering costs and hydrologic data may be more readily and easily obtained than much of the information needed to evaluate benefits. For example, how efficiently is irrigation water used after delivery to the farmer's headgates? Should we use average management and average technology in figuring the value of irrigation water? What is the optimum time of application and amount of water for obtaining maximum yields for selected crops? How do we obtain specific data on future benefits from land enhancement in protected flood plains? How do we compute an accurate figure for flood-free yields? Answers to these questions may require research and assembly of data over an extended time period. We should start immediately on the complex problem of obtaining adequate basic data.

Arthur J. Coutu is Research Associate Professor, Department of Agricultural Economics, North Carolina State College. Since 1954 he has done research in connection with the Parker Branch Pilot Tributary Watershed Research Project located in western North Carolina, and since 1957 he has taught and done re- search in production economics.

Chapter 13

ARTHUR J. COUTU

Estimation of Income and Hydrologic Effects of Alternative Watershed Programs[1]

T HE DESIGN of watershed systems often requires recognizing both income and hydrologic variables.[2] In small tributary watersheds of predominantly low-income producers, the individual producer is more concerned with income effects, while society is concerned in ad- dition with off-site hydrologic consequences. In watersheds where in- dividual operators control more resources, there is likely to be less conflict between income and hydrologic objectives. The research re- ported on here deals with a low-level resource area and, as a conse- quence, with the problems of low net incomes and poor hydrologic conditions.

The conventional starting point in the development of such a water- shed would be a land use system that held erosion losses to some phys- ically acceptable level. Historically, this acceptable level has implied a land use system that will yield optimum hydrologic conditions.[3] The

---

[1] Journal Paper No. 1057, North Carolina Agricultural Experiment Station. Credit is especially due to E. F. Goldston of the Soils Department at North Carolina State College and to W. M. Snyder of the Hydraulic Data Branch of TVA.
[2] The need for alternative development plans is discussed by H. A. Steele, "Economics of Small Watershed Protection," *Agr. Econ. Res.*, Vol. XL, No. 3, Aug., 1958.
[3] See Soil Conservation Service, *Watershed Protection Handbook* (1957), Section 6; and M. L. Weinberger and R. C. Otte, "Economic Evaluation of the Small Watershed Program," *Jour. Farm Econ.*, Vol. XXXIX, No. 5, Dec., 1957, pp. 1256-68.

land capability system employed by the Soil Conservation Service in conservation farm plans is an example of a system designed for this acceptable level. Land use systems can be designed for any specific hydrologic purpose. For example, a land use system designed to give maximum water yields might suggest a minimum forest acreage. Another system with the primary objective of reductions in peak flows might demand a maximum of forest acreage.

When income as well as hydrologic objectives are explicitly recognized, the number of acceptable land use systems increases. With these additional considerations, choosing the most desirable land use system requires knowledge of income and hydrologic interrelationships.

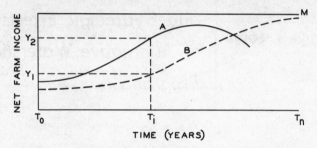

Figure 1. Relationship between net farm income and time under alternative land use systems.

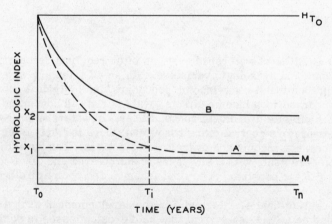

Figure 2. Relationship between hydrologic index and time under alternative land use systems.

These interrelationships can be expressed in a more explicit form by referring to Figures 1 and 2. Figure 1 depicts expected net income relationships over time (T_n). With given resource conditions and states of technology, there is an upper limit to expected incomes — level M. For a given planning period, an unrestricted land use system may provide the opportunity to reach a maximum in a shorter time period, or the rate of increase may be greater. However, with the given time period and exclusion of technological change, net income may decline slowly, due to reductions in land productivity. Line A depicts such income flows over time.

Under a more restrictive land use system, the rate of change in income may be less per time period and may, given a sufficiently long period, exceed levels realized under a less restrictive system. Such income flows are depicted by line B.

Hydrologically, the situation can be diagrammed as indicated in Figure 2. Assume that the hydrologic level, M, is the physical maximum for minimum peaks and quantities of runoff, and minimum sediment loads or other hydrologic variables. Prior to changes in the land use system the hydrologic index for the given drainage area was H_{t_0}. Under a restrictive land use system, the hydrologic index would approach the level M as the system became fully effective (line B). A less restrictive land use system may approach the level of M but at a slower rate and at a different absolute level relative to M (line A).

At some time period, T_i, or span of time, T_0 to T_i, does the value of the increase in hydrologic benefit, X_2-X_1 in Figure 2, exceed the annual income loss, Y_2-Y_1 in Figure 1? If hydrologic condition B is a stated policy, then at a point in time, T_i, a necessary cost of this policy is the value of Y_2-Y_1 as foregone income.

The following section will describe the land use systems and the investigative procedure, and it will present preliminary findings of the effect on farm organization and income of alternative land use systems.[4]

DESCRIPTION OF LAND USE MODELS

The first alternative land use system or model has actually been applied in the Parker Branch watershed.[5] The second model is a synthetic land use model that has not been applied.

---

[4]Hydrologic conditions under alternative land use systems will be estimated as part of the Parker Branch project. Available hydrologic data include rainfall, water flows, and sediment loads. Land cover surveys have been conducted semiannually. Data on infiltration rates, transpiration, and evaporation are available from supporting research. Four hydrologic models will be developed to predict intensities of runoff, total runoff, deposited sediment, and suspended sediment for three specified time periods representing varying land cover conditions. The general form of these prediction equations is linear or quadratic. The independent variables are rainfall, infiltration rates, and three land cover conditions weighted by infiltration data. The three cover conditions for each time period include maximal, intermediate, and poor levels of crop, pasture, and forest cover. The reliability of these estimates can be measured statistically and compared with actual observations for specific storm conditions. The basic equations, with changes in land cover variables, will be used to evaluate the hydrologic consequences of the synthetic land use models.

[5]The research reported here was carried out under cooperative TVA-N.C. State College Project No. 700, the Parker Branch Pilot Tributary Watershed Research Project.

The Actual Model

The farming systems in operation in Parker Branch watershed were developed with the objective of maximizing net farm incomes. Land restrictions were but one of the resource situations used in appraising alternative farming systems. The resource situations, other than land, included: operator and family labor, institutional restrictions, operating capital, investment capital, adjustments in tenure conditions, recognition of variations in management abilities, changes in size of farms, and — for each set of resource restrictions — alternative factor and product price levels.

Parker Branch watershed is located about 9 miles northwest of Asheville, North Carolina. It is an upper tributary of the French Broad River, which flows north into the Tennessee River and eventually empties into the Mississippi River.

In 1953 this watershed contained 47 low-income farm operators who owned 2,431 acres of land. The calibrated drainage area included 1,060 acres. The average farm size was 52 acres. Seven full-time farm operators had an average of 165 acres per farm, and the remaining 40 part-time units had an average of 33 acres per farm. An average sized farm had the equivalent of 0.7 man-years of labor available for farm work, assets valued at $4,684, and low levels of managerial ability associated with a subsistence orientation. These resources and attitudes resulted in a total net farm income of $12,310 in 1953, or approximately $262 per farm.

The area had severe hydrologic as well as economic problems. For the water year 1953 to 1954, sediment loads were estimated at more than three tons per acre per year. Four major storms produced peak discharge rates of more than 70 cfs (cubic feet per second). Instantaneous flows ranged from 0.19 to 570.00 cfs, with an average streamflow of 1.00 cfs. Estimated average monthly runoff was 25.1 percent of total rainfall, and ranged from 13.8 to 52.7 percent of monthly rainfall.

Land use classification. The key to the actual land use model was to classify the land by productivity groups, allow a maximum of continuous cropping, and restrict land to pasture use depending on productivity and slope. All fields with slopes of more than 25 percent and all fields of Wilkes soil (a very shallow and unproductive soil) were restricted to pasture use. All bottom-land soils with slopes of up to 15 percent were classified as land that could be row-cropped continuously. These bottom-land soils were expected to yield 15 to 20 percent more than upland soils.[6]

The remaining land was classed as upland cropland and divided into two groups based on expected productivity. No rotation or other land use restriction was placed on these soils.

---

[6] From annual cropping records there is some evidence that the crops grown on the bottom-land soils have exceeded planning expectations in three of the four years of record. Yields on upland soils have not exceeded expectations.

Alternative farm organizations — given labor, capital, and risk conditions in addition to these minimum land use restrictions — were developed by linear programming procedures. The actual land use system put into effect by the individual producer included a rotation system designed subsequent to the economic analysis.

The actual land use model is presented with stable yields over time, and with yields decreased 15 percent on continuously cropped land to allow for possible reductions in productivity.

The Synthetic Model

Two synthetic land use models are to be used. They are more restrictive than the actual model and are designed to yield maximum hydrologic conditions when land use restrictions are the only conservation inputs considered. The models utilize land capability classes which are based on the degree of limitation for row crop use. Land capability subclasses are based on such limitations as soil permeability, slope, and soil texture.

The land resources in the watershed were classified into five capability classes[7] with one subclass per capability class. These classes and a brief description follow:

Class	Description of the Most Intensive Cropping System
IIe and IIw	Row crop 1 year out of 2
IIIe and IIIe$_1$	Row crop 1 year out of 3 with contour strips and sod waterways
IVe and IVe$_1$	Row crop 1 year out of 4 with contour strips and sod waterways
VI and VIe$_1$	Perennial grasses and legumes or a row crop 1 year out of 6 with contour strips and sod waterways
VII and VIIe$_1$	Permanent pasture

The two synthetic models are based on the above land capability classes and the rotation restrictions accompanying them. The "least restrictive" synthetic model allows land classed as VI or VIe$_1$, which requires a cropping system of one row crop in six years, to be combined with land classed as IVe or IVe$_1$, which permits a row crop one year in four. The "most restrictive" synthetic model classifies class VI land as permanent pasture.

The most restrictive land use model would more closely approximate conditions that would provide for maximum hydrologic control.

---

[7] This classification is used by the Soil Conservation Service and described in *Soil Survey — Buncombe County, North Carolina*, Series 1942, No. 6, USDA, North Carolina State College and TVA cooperating, Aug., 1954. A basic reference is *Soil Survey Manual*, by Soil Survey Staff, USDA, Handbook No. 18, Aug., 1951.

With this class VI land as pasture, the possibility in this pilot watershed of 171 acres of relatively steep upland being planted to row crops in any one year would be eliminated.

COMPARISON OF LAND USE MODELS

Land Use

The results from alternative land use models will be discussed for the total drainage area and then appraised in more detail on two case farms. For the total drainage area of 1,060 acres, the three land use models yield some interesting differences (see Table 1). With the actual model, a total of 824 acres, or 78 percent of the calibrated watershed, is in cropland or pasture. This compares with 760 acres, or 72 percent, under both synthetic models.

Table 1. Comparisons of Alternative Land Use Systems and Calibration Period Land Use Conditions for the Drainage Area

Situation	Acres in Drainage Area			
	Actual Model	Least Restrictive Synthetic Model	Most Restrictive Synthetic Model	Calibration Period[a]
Continuous bottom-land cropland	65.0	0	0	45.0
Unrestricted upland cropland	332.2	0	0	249.9
Rotatable cropland[b]				
1 out of 2 yrs.	0	11.2	11.2	0
1 out of 3 yrs.	0	110.9	110.9	0
1 out of 4 yrs.	0	284.8[c]	113.4	0
Permanent pasture	426.3	353.6	525.0[c]	225.3
Subtotal: upland crop-land and pasture	823.5	760.5	760.5	520.2
Woodland	179.3	242.3[d]	242.3[d]	296.6
Miscellaneous[e]	57.2	57.2	57.2	243.2
Total	1,060.0	1,060.0	1,060.0	1,060.0

[a]The calibration period of the study was devoted to developing benchmark hydrologic and economic conditions.

[b] The rotations refer to one year of an intensive row crop alternated with 2,3,4, or 6 years of a sod or close-growing crop.

[c]In the least restrictive case, this group includes land classed in capability classes IV and VI. In the most restrictive case, all class VI land is allocated to pasture.

[d]The woodland classification includes land in all capability classes and woodland with reasonably complete stands.

[e]This includes idle land, water surfaces, roads, homesites, and related uses.

Main differences in the actual versus the synthetic models are in the use of cropland. In the actual model 397 acres are in crops, with 16 percent in continuous bottom-land cropland. The least restrictive synthetic model has 407 acres in rotatable cropland, but only 30 percent is classed as type II or III, indicating that such land can be row cropped only one year out of three. The most restrictive synthetic model has but 236 acres in rotatable cropland, and 48 percent of this is classed as land that should be row cropped one year in four. The comparison of cropland use is given in Table 2.

Table 2. Comparison of Available Cropland for the Total Drainage Area
Under Indicated Models

Situation	Actual Model		Least Restrictive		Most Restrictive	
	Acres	Percent	Acres	Percent	Acres	Percent
Continuous bottom-land cropland	65.0	16.4	0	0	0	0
Unrestricted upland cropland	332.2	83.6	0	0	0	0
Rotatable cropland						
1 yr. out of 2	0	0	11.2	2.8	11.2	4.8
1 yr. out of 3	0	0	110.9	27.3	110.9	47.1
1 yr. out of 4	0	0	113.4	27.9	113.4	48.1
1 yr. out of 6	0	0	171.4	42.0	0	0
Total cropland	397.2	100	406.9	100	235.5	100

When compared with land use conditions in the calibration period (1953 to 1955), all land use models indicate large potentials in land use adjustments. The more important adjustment possibilities include a large reduction in idle or miscellaneous land use, large increases in land used for pasture and, with the exception of the most restrictive synthetic model, an increase in acreage of cropland or rotatable cropland. Woodland acreage would decline in all the models, but most notably in the actual model.

Case Farm I. In case farm I an important difference between the actual and synthetic models is in the use of land for continuous and unrestrictive cropping, as compared with use of rotatable land (see Table 3). In the actual model the yield expectations for bottom land and continuous cropping sites exceed those for unrestricted upland cropping sites. The upland crop alternatives include grain corn, silage corn, small grain, alfalfa, pastures, and supplemental feed crops. Rotations are designed after the selection of cropping systems. This flexibility permits the selection of a most profitable cropping system and, where possible, the development of conservation inputs consistent with these conditions.

Case farm I has a full-time farm operator, 38 years of age, who is willing to make changes that will increase his income expectations.

Table 3. Land Use Restrictions on Case Farm I

Situation	Total Farm Acreage		
	Actual Model	Least Restrictive Synthetic Model	Most Restrictive Synthetic Model
Continuous bottom-land cropland	14.9	0	0
Unrestricted upland cropland	37.7	0	0
Rotatable cropland			
1 out of 2 yrs.	0	4.6	4.6
1 out of 3 yrs.	0	10.6	10.6
1 out of 4 yrs.	0	50.8[a]	27.1
Permanent pasture	82.1	69.2	92.9
Woodland	12.2	12.2	12.2
Miscellaneous	3.7	3.2	3.2
Total	150.6	150.6	150.6

[a]This figure includes 23.7 acres of cropland that would fall in capability class VIe or VIe$_1$, that specifies a row crop one year in six.

Capital is the most restrictive resource. Consequently, investments with relatively short pay-off periods, given equal returns, are preferred.

   Case Farm II. Case farm II does not contain any bottom-land cropland, but approximately 60 percent of the farm in the actual model has been classified as unrestricted upland cropland (see Table 4). The suitability of this upland cropland for more intensive crops (corn, small

Table 4. Land Use Restrictions on Case Farm II

Situation	Total Farm Acreage		
	Actual Model	Least Restrictive Model	Most Restrictive Model
Continuous bottom-land cropland	0	0	0
Unrestricted upland cropland	25.6	0	0
Rotatable cropland			
1 out of 2 yrs.	0	0	0
1 out of 3 yrs.	0	1.1	0
1 our of 4 yrs.	0	16.7	2.2[a]
Permanent pasture	13.8	21.6	37.2
Woodland	0	0	0
Miscellaneous	2.2	2.2	2.2
Total	41.6	41.6	41.6

[a] This entry contains the 1.1 acres of a 1-out-of-3 row crop restriction and 1.1 acres of a 1-out-of-4 row crop restriction.

grain, and alfalfa), as compared with less intensive pasture crops, is closely associated with the availability of custom harvesting services. These services are in adequate supply in the watershed area.

The most restrictive synthetic model for case farm II has 37.2 acres of pasture out of a total for pasture and cropland of 39.4 acres. Thus, the question might arise: Will an intensive beef operation be profitable on a small farm that purchases all feed except pasture? This is a question faced by many low-income farm operators who operate on a part-time farming basis with limited land and restricted capital.

Note that on both case farms the woodland acreage does not change. This is in contrast with the watershed data in Table 1. Some preliminary tabulations on this point indicate that most forest land in the synthetic models falls in capability classes VI and VII, indicating possible increases in pasture land. More than 85 percent of the forest land is classed as types VI and VII.

Income

Income comparisons can be developed in a number of ways. The most adaptable techniques are budgeting or programming. In this study the latter technique has been used because of the numerous resource restrictions and enterprise possibilities present.

As indicated, the income analysis is for two farms that are functioning organizations. The analysis of land use systems is restricted by the lack of input-output data on conservation inputs associated with appropriate rotations. The analysis is limited to only one year, and only one alternative product price level was considered.[8]

Case Farm I. On the larger case study farm the following conditions were established:

1. Farm organizations were completed for three land use models, two levels of operating capital, and fixed labor and institutional restrictions.
2. Capital levels were programmed at $6,000 and $9,000 per year (only the least restrictive level is discussed below).
3. Crop yields under the actual model were programmed at two levels. The first level assumed no change in annual crop yields as a result of continuous cropping. The second level assumed a reduction of 15 percent per unit, to occur within a five-year planning period.
4. As in the subsequent case, the analysis did not recognize factor or product price reductions.

In 1953 total net family income was estimated at $5,425, with 23 percent from farm resources. At this time the operator was regularly employed in nonfarm work. By the end of 1958 the operator had gone

[8]A dynamic programming model would resolve this time limitation. See L. D. Loftsgard and E. O. Heady, "Application of Dynamic Programming Models for Optimum Farm and Home Plans," *Jour. Farm Econ.*, Vol. XLI, No. 1, Feb., 1959, pp. 51-62.

through an intensive farm reorganization, was fully employed in farm work, and was realizing $8,700 in net farm income.

The farm organizations for three land use models under the least restrictive capital condition are presented in Table 5. These data suggest large organizational changes from calibration period conditions and basic differences in organization for the land use models.

Table 5. Farm Organization Under Alternative Land Use Models, Case Farm I, Least Restrictive Operating Capital

Item	Calibration Period (1953)	Action Period (1958)	Actual Model		Synthetic Model	
			Stable Yields	Declining Yields	Least Restrictive	Most Restrictive
Land use:						
Burley tobacco	2.7	1.4	2.0	0.3	2.0	2.0
Grain corn	6.1	4.0	9.3 (5.7) [3.6]	9.2 [9.2]	3.7 [3.7]	15.0 (15.0)
Silage corn	0	10.6 (6.5)	20.0 [20.0]	20.4 [20.4]	10.2 [10.2]	8.7 [8.7]
Small grain	13.9	12.0 (12.0)	0	7.5 (7.5)	14.2 (10.2)	18.0 (14.0)
Alfalfa	6.8	38.9	33.4 (20.7) [12.7]	43.0 (25.1)	50.7 (25.0) [25.7]	26.7 (25.0) [1.7]
Meadow	0	0	-	0	6.3 [6.3]	18.4
Unused cropland	-	0	14.3	4.8	14.6	7.8
Pasture	51.4 [a]	85.7	68.4	68.4	42.4	53.8
Unused pasture	-	-	13.7	13.7	26.9	38.3
Woods	58.4	12.2	12.2	12.2	12.2	12.2
Idle	12.1	3.7	3.7	3.7	3.7	3.7
Total	150.6	150.6	150.6	150.6	150.6	150.6
Livestock (no. of head):						
Dairy cows	-	30.0	33.0	33.0	17.0	15.0
Dairy heifers	4	-	-	-	14.0	13.0
Beef	8	-	-	-	-	-
Swine	2	1.0	-	-	-	-

[ ]Refers to the use of land owned by the operator and used in connection with the dairy feeding program.
( )Refers to land rented in or share cropped.
[a] Approximately one-third of the pasture acreage was in an improved condition.

The synthetic models, with required rotations, provide for (1) more land to be farmed on a rented basis, (2) increased acreages of unused pasture, and (3) a decrease of about 50 percent in cow numbers. The unique characteristic of the synthetic models has been the specific rotations built into the activities that require land. Some of the rotations require row crop and grass or meadow. In both of the synthetic models land is required for meadows (annual lespedeza and oats, double cropped).

Differences in net farm income among the land use models are presented in Table 6. The actual land use model suggests a farm organization quite comparable with conditions at the end of 1958. It provides an annual income of $2,400 more than the least restrictive synthetic model. Net income under the most restrictive land use model (all class VI land is restricted to pasture use) exceeds that of the least restrictive model

Table 6. Estimated Annual Net Revenue, Differences in Net Revenues
by Land Use Model, Case Farm I, Least Restrictive
Capital Levels and Two Yield Conditions

Condition	Actual Model	Synthetic Models	
		Least Restrictive	Most Restrictive
No changes in crop yields			
Estimated annual net revenue	$12,302.8	$9,901.6	$9,954.0 [a]
Difference in net revenue between actual and synthetic models	-	-2,401.2	-2,348.8
15 percent reduction in crop yields			
Estimated annual net revenue	$11,385.0	$9,901.6	$9,954.0
Difference in net revenue between actual and synthetic models	-	-1,483.4	-1,431.0

[a] Income estimates from this model are expected to be less than for the least restrictive model; future work will attempt to minimize rounding errors resulting from the procedure.

by $53 per year. The actual model provides an annual income of about $2,350 more than in the most restrictive synthetic model.[9]

The use of constant versus declining crop yields under the actual land use model gives different results. In Table 5, crop yields for the actual model are assumed to decrease by 15 percent per acre under continuous cropping. The organization under the actual model with decreasing yields as compared with the same model under constant yields provides an increase in alfalfa and small grain acreage, small shifts in the quantity of rented land, a large reduction in burley tobacco acreage, but no change in the size of the dairy herd. Annual net income estimates are $917.80 less for the model with declining yields.

In Table 5, farm organization under the actual land use model with reduced crop yields can be compared with that for the synthetic models. The differences in annual net income are $1,483 and $1,431 respectively, for the least and most restrictive models (see Table 6).

Case Farm II. On the small farm operated by a part-time farm operator, the following conditions were established:

1. Farm organizations were completed for the three land use models with fixed levels of available labor, operating capital, institutional restrictions, and factor and product prices.
2. Two levels of operating capital were assumed; a restrictive level of $2,000, and a less restrictive level of $3,000.
3. Assumed crop yields under the actual model were not decreased as a consequence of continuous cropping programs.
4. No provisions were made for renting out land or selling land.

[9] A limitation of this preliminary analysis concerns the degree of stability of these farm organizations with respect to changes in product prices. Subsequent analysis, using price mapping procedures or variable price programming, may give quite different results.

Table 7. Land Use Under Alternative Land Use Models as Compared
with Calibration Period Conditions for Case Farm II,
Most Restrictive Operating Capital

Land Use	Calibration Period	Actual Model	Synthetic Models	
			Least Restrictive	Most Restrictive
		(acres)		
Burley tobacco	.8	.6	.6	.6
Grain corn	5.0	8.8	3.8	1.2
Small grain	5.5	7.0	6.9	0
Alfalfa	0	9.1	6.3	0
Truck crops	0	0.1	.2	.4
Subtotal	11.3	25.6	17.8	2.2
Pasture	9.8[a]	7.3	9.8	16.7
Woodland	7.5	0	0	0
Idle	13.0	8.7[b]	14.3[c]	22.7[d]
Total	41.6	41.6	41.6	41.6

[a] All pasture was unimproved.

[b] About 6.5 acres of this idle land is improved pasture which was not utilized; such land could be rented out at $12 to $18 per acre.

[c] About 12.1 acres of this idle land is improved pasture which was not utilized; such land could be rented out at $12 to $18 per acre.

[d] About 20.5 acres of this idle land is improved pasture which was not utilized; such land could be rented out at $12 to $18 per acre.

The land use system proposed in the actual model, with reduced operating capital, is in operation on this farm (see Table 7). Currently, the pasture land totals 13.5 acres, but is not fully stocked. This is also consistent with the actual model.

Land use for the least restrictive capital level is presented in Table 8. Cropland use is virtually the same under both capital levels, as can be seen by comparing Tables 8 and 9. The two synthetic models have less land in crops than the actual model. The most restrictive synthetic model provides 2.2 acres of corn, tobacco, and truck crops (17.8 acres for the least restrictive), as compared with 25.6 acres of these crops plus small grain and alfalfa for the actual model.

In the six organizations described, a bred heifer activity is the only form of livestock. For the most restrictive capital level, the size of this activity varies from 5 to 6 to 11 heifers per year for the actual, least restrictive, and most restrictive models. At the less restrictive capital level, livestock numbers increase to 8, 12, and 17 heifers per year, and more pasture is utilized. This is the only significant effect of more capital on land use. In all cases these levels do not utilize all available pasture; the excess could be rented out at a small net profit or used to hedge against weather risks.

Table 8. Land Use Under Alternative Land Use Models as Compared
with Calibration Period Conditions for Case Farm II,
Least Restrictive Operating Capital

Land Use	Calibration Period	Actual Model	Synthetic Models	
			Least Restrictive	Most Restrictive
			(acres)	
Burley tobacco	.8	.6	.6	.6
Grain corn	5.0	5.7	3.5	1.3
Small grain	5.5	7.0	7.0	0
Alfalfa	0	12.3	6.6	0
Truck crops	0	0	.1	.3
Subtotal	11.3	25.6	17.8	2.2
Pasture	9.8	13.8	18.9	26.2
Woodland	7.5	0	0	0
Idle	13.0	2.2	4.9[a]	13.2[b]
Total	41.6	41.6	41.6	41.6

[a] Pasture acreage not utilized on this unit and available for rent is 2.7 acres.
[b] Pasture acreage not utilized on this unit and available for rent is 11.0 acres.

Table 9. Differences in Annual Net Revenues by Land Use Models,
by Capital Levels, Case Farm II[a]

Condition	Actual Model	Synthetic Models	
		Least Restrictive	Most Restrictive
	Restricted operating capital		
Estimated annual net revenues	$2,220.8	$1,901.1	$1,467.6
Differences in net revenues between actual and synthetic models	-	-319.7	-753.2
	Less restricted operating capital		
Estimated annual net revenues	$2,368.1	$2,230.4	$1,817.9
Differences in net revenue between actual and synthetic models	-	-137.7	-550.2

[a] The net revenues are estimates of returns above variable costs or returns to labor, capital, and management.

During 1953-1955, the farm operator received $4,024 per year from regular nonfarm employment, and $398 per year from the farm. In 1958 his return from nonfarm work had decreased because of a five-month layoff, and net farm income had increased to approximately $1,890.[10]

The net farm income estimates presented in Table 9 indicate differences in favor of the actual model ranging from $138 to $753 per year.[11] Approximately 77 percent of the watershed is controlled by part-time producers like the one described above. If all such producers had reductions in net farm income that ranged from $138 to $753 per year as a result of restrictive land use conditions, the aggregative effects would be substantial. Useful inferences cannot be drawn for the entire drainage area until a larger number of farms are analyzed. However, data on these two case farms suggest that both farm organization and net farm revenues are sensitive to land use restrictions. The income estimates presented are for specific sets of resource assumptions and are normative rather than actual. However, in a more complete analysis, where resource restrictions are altered and price risks are studied, the optimal organization and actual farm adjustments may be comparable.[12]

SUMMARY

This type of analysis can provide data for an evaluation of alternative watershed systems. Some of the limitations include (1) the incomplete input-output schedules for conservation inputs, (2) necessity for evaluating net farm revenues over more than a single year, and (3) need for incorporating changes in resource restrictions and product prices into the programming model.

An important limitation beyond the methodological ones concerns the possible inferences to other upper tributary watersheds. Specific inferences may be limited. However, it seems valid to infer that land use restrictions will also be critical to development of other watersheds, particularly as land use restrictions are related to changes in the type of agriculture that may develop in a watershed.

---

[10] During this extended layoff this operator earned a net of $840 from farming activities carried on with adjoining operators. This would be considered a temporary condition.

[11] These income differences would be less if crop yields under the actual model fell below expectations as a result of continuous cropping. However, evidence to date in the watershed area does not reveal a reduction in crop yields.

[12] In the work to date on the Parker Branch project, many farm organizations have been adopted that effectively recognized actual resource limitations and risk positions.

JOSEPH H. YAEGER | *Comment*

MOST PROBLEMS involving the economics of soil conservation concern both society and the individual on the land. Often there are conflicts or apparent conflicts in the objectives of conservation measures. Some consider soil conservation as a goal within itself, whereas in fact fertility depletion (in contrast to soil deterioration) may be economically sound when the fertility resource can be replaced at a lesser cost than that of maintaining it. Soil conservation is, according to Bunce, a part of a larger problem — "that of allocating resources so that the social net returns are maximized. We cannot plan just in terms of eliminating erosion but must think in terms of farm income, the relationship of crop and feed production to livestock production, the ability of the farm to adjust to price changes, and the institutional framework if the conservation system is to be permanent."[1] It is within this framework that the Parker Branch study is being carried out.

Much of past watershed research has been concerned primarily with measuring and understanding streamflow, water yield, sedimentation rates, and losses of soil and nutrients. The interrelationships of these factors and their separate and combined effects on the economics of agriculture must be explored. Very little information on the hydrologic variables as they relate to the land use models was given by the author. It will be interesting to see the effects of various land use programs on watershed hydrology and, in turn, how the hydrologic variables relate to net farm income. To be complete the study should include consideration of the hydrologic effects on lower tributaries and their economic consequences.

The heavy emphasis on forage in the optimum farm organizations presented for all three land use models, the necessity for roughage-consuming livestock to utilize the land resources as planned, the extensive nature of roughage-consuming livestock enterprises, and the small size of farms suggest that more should be known about the physical and economic effects of strip cropping, terracing, diversions, mulch cultivation, and other conservation measures so that a larger portion of the land might be devoted to cash crops or feed crops and at the same time achieve the conservation objective.

For case farm II, which included a total of 41.6 acres, a bred heifer activity, together with 0.6 acres of burley tobacco and certain feed and pasture crops, was programmed. This resulted in $1,890 net farm income in 1958. The operator continued with off-farm employment but

---

[1] Arthur C. Bunce, "Public Policy and Action for Conservation," *Jour. Farm Econ.*, Vol. XXIV, No. 1, Feb., 1942, p. 97.

Joseph H. Yeager is Professor of Agricultural Economics at Auburn University, where he does research and teaching in farm management and land economics.

was unemployed for five months during the year. It would be interesting to see the results of programming a broiler or layer enterprise of such a size to fully utilize the labor resources available on this farm. As a result of a purchased feed program with broilers or layers it would be logical to assume that crop and pasture yields could be increased from applications of poultry manure.

On case farm I, consisting of 150.6 acres, crop yields under the actual model were programmed at two levels. The first level assumed no change in crop yields as a result of continuous cropping. A 15 percent reduction in yields was assumed in the second case. It is recognized that input-output data for the various rotations used are limited. Academically and possibly realistically, one might assume decreased yields over a period of time with a given state of science and technology. Historically, however, even with continuous cropping practices, yields have increased.

From a practical farm operation standpoint, size of a given enterprise is an important consideration in the organization and operation of a farm. The actual model for case farm I included 33 dairy cows, while the least restrictive and most restrictive synthetic models included 17 and 15 dairy cows, respectively. With today's requirements of bulk milk tanks, pipelines, and milking parlors for fluid milk production, it is doubtful that herds of such size would be very advantageous from an economy of scale standpoint.

When the effects of various land use programs are considered, including those that will yield optimum hydrologic benefits, and resulting net farm incomes are estimated for the Parker Branch watershed, a more complete picture of watershed planning and a better understanding of its methods and problems will be available.

Earl O. Heady is Director of the Center for Agricultural and Economic Adjustment at Iowa State University, as well as Professor of Agricultural Economics
and C. F. Curtiss Distinguished Professor of Agriculture. He has served as
Visiting Professor at the University of Illinois, North Carolina State College,
and Harvard University, and as a fellow of the Center for Advanced Studies in
the Behavorial Sciences.

Chapter 14 — A

EARL O. HEADY

Mathematical Analysis: Models for Quantitative Application in Watershed Planning

THIS CHAPTER presents a model for specifying the optimum scale
of investment and the optimum allocation of a given investment
between alternatives within a watershed. Suggestions are included
on how data might be incorporated in the model and computations made
to provide solutions.

A complete mathematical formulation of an appropriate welfare
economics model would entail specification of utility functions for individuals; demand, production, and cost functions for products both within
and outside the watershed; and the calculus under which social welfare
is maximized. But this model has no current prospect for empirical
application. Some of the quantities, particularly those relating to
utility functions, have no promise of measurement. We must turn to
some programming models of "small watersheds in isolation" as representative of mathematical approaches which are operational in view
of data availability. Even these can become extremely complex if they
recognize the relevant interyear relationships connecting activities of
the system over time, the resulting "intermediate products" (both

[1] Journal Paper No. J-3820 of the Iowa Agricultural and Home Economics Experiment
Station, Project 1135. The comments of John Nordin have improved this paper.

197

within years and between years), the necessary maximum and minimum restraints, the process of capital growth, changes in soil fertility, the appropriate planning horizon or period, forest growth over time, scale relationships, demand functions other than those representative of pure competition, and so forth.

INDIVIDUAL WATERSHEDS AND CONTINUOUS MODELS

If we could make certain assumptions about the degree of perfection in product and factor markets, the conditions specified by less complex models would approximate those of a more complete welfare economics model of a continuous nature. But even some of these have little opportunity of empirical application in view of data availability. This is particularly true for models which might retain the identity of individual firms (and households) in the watershed and those which take into account off-site benefits and other products or services which do not have well-developed markets.

Unlimited Project Funds

First consider the unusual case in which funds might be obtained in sufficient quantity for optimum development of the watershed. We wish to determine both (1) the magnitude of investment, and (2) the allocation of the investment between alternatives within the watershed. We will discuss only a very simple model, in which the watershed is treated as an economic unit. We will assume that markets for factors and products are sufficiently competitive so that maximization of net revenue for the watershed unit serves as an appropriate criterion for investment choice (i.e., approximates the conditions of development and investment which maximize welfare). In cases where a market is not clearly defined for a product or service generated in the watershed, we suppose that appropriate per-unit values can be placed on these, as a substitute for market prices. We suppose that the criterion of maximum net revenue (maximum benefits) provides an appropriate objective of watershed development.

A large number of production functions exist within a watershed. Functions exist for conventional farm and forest products; for irrigation water as a product from labor, land, concrete, and other resources which go into a dam; for stream control as a product from or function of such inputs as labor, stream depth and length; recreation as a product of land and water area, and so forth. Numerous different farm production functions exist, not only for such things as different enterprises, but also for the same crop grown on different soil types. Some inputs for all products are not fixed relative to the watershed area. However, other inputs are predetermined in upper magnitude by size of watershed, amount and distribution of rainfall, amount of a particular soil type, and so forth. In these cases we suppose a short-run production function for which some resources are variable but others are fixed. Within this framework, we can postulate the following production functions for m watershed products or services produced with n resources.

$$
\begin{aligned}
y_1 &= f(x_{11}, x_{12}, \ldots x_{1j} \ldots x_{1n}) \\
y_2 &= f(x_{21}, x_{22}, \ldots x_{2j} \ldots x_{2n}) \\
&\phantom{= f(x_{21},} \vdots \\
y_i &= f(x_{i1}, x_{i2}, \ldots x_{ij} \ldots x_{in}) \\
&\phantom{= f(x_{21},} \vdots \\
y_m &= f(x_{m1}, x_{m2}, \ldots x_{mj} \ldots x_{mn})
\end{aligned}
\tag{1}
$$

Not all products will use each resource, and hence some zero coefficients exist in the production functions. If the watershed is small, revenue functions will be linear and market prices will be constant for most products. In other cases it is possible that values per unit of product will have to be specified by means other than the market, or that price per unit is a decreasing function of output of the product or service.

A price function will exist for each product y_i and might take the following general form:

$$
\begin{aligned}
p_1 &= \phi_1 (x_{11}, x_{12}, \ldots x_{1j} \ldots x_{1n}) \\
p_2 &= \phi_2 (x_{21}, x_{22}, \ldots x_{2j} \ldots x_{2n}) \\
&\phantom{= \phi_2 (x_{21},} \vdots \\
p_i &= \phi_i (x_{i1}, x_{i2}, \ldots x_{ij} \ldots x_{in}) \\
&\phantom{= \phi_2 (x_{21},} \vdots \\
p_m &= \phi_m (x_{m1}, x_{m2}, \ldots x_{mj} \ldots x_{mn})
\end{aligned}
\tag{2}
$$

where p_i is the price per unit of the ith product. Its magnitude is, therefore, directly a function of the magnitude of the y_i, but indirectly of the quantity of resources used for the ith product. We suppose that the coefficient relating p_i directly to y_i, and indirectly to x_{ij}, may be zero for some products (e.g., as in the algebraic example of $p_i = k_i - 0y_i$ for one product). We suppose also that the watershed is small enough relative to the total market that the products are not competitive, and hence price for a particular product is a function only of the quantity of this product.

We can express the profit or net benefit function for the watershed as:

$$
\pi = \sum_{i=1}^{m} p_i y_i - \sum_{i=1}^{m} \sum_{j=1}^{n} c_j x_{ij},
\tag{3}
$$

where π is net benefit, c_j is the cost or price per unit of the jth resource, and p_i is the price per unit of the ith product. (In cases where p_i and c_j are not constants but are functions of magnitudes of y_i and x_j, we would substitute, here, appropriate functions for the per-unit prices and costs.) Profit or net benefit for the watershed is maximized, for the relevant period to which the production functions apply, under the condition that the partial derivatives of profit with respect to the x_{ij} used for each product are zero. Hence, for the resources used for the ith product, we have the n partial derivatives equated to zero.

$$\frac{\partial \pi}{\partial x_{i_1}} = 0$$

$$\frac{\partial \pi}{\partial x_{i_2}} = 0$$

$$\vdots$$

$$\frac{\partial \pi}{\partial x_{in}} = 0 \qquad (4)$$

There will be m sets of these partial derivatives, equating marginal products to zero for resources used on each product.

By substituting the production functions in (1) for the corresponding y_i in (3), the partial derivatives in (4) will be expressed only in terms of resource inputs. With these partial derivatives equated to zero, we could solve for the magnitudes of the x_{ij} for each product which causes marginal benefits from the factor to be zero and which causes total benefit to be a maximum. Hence, we could compute the optimum magnitude of investment in each resource for each watershed product or activity.

Limited Project Funds

However, in case total capital for expenditure in the watershed is limited, we would need to modify the profit or benefit equation:

$$\pi = \sum_{i=i}^{m} p_i y_i - \sum_{i=1}^{m} \sum_{j=1}^{n} c_j x_{ij} + \lambda \left(\sum_{i=1}^{m} \sum_{j=1}^{n} c_j x_{ij} - C \right) \qquad (5)$$

where λ is a Lagrange multiplier and C is the total amount of capital available. In this case, we attempt to equalize the marginal benefit or return per dollar expenditure or investment on each resource used for each product or purpose. The term $\sum_{i=1}^{m} \sum_{j=1}^{n} c_j x_{ij} - C$ indicates the restraint that the total amount spent or invested in resources for various purposes can be no greater than the total quantity of capital available.

The term becomes zero when $\sum_{i=1}^{m} \sum_{j=1}^{n} c_j x_{ij}$ attains the level of C. In this case, we would again substitute the production functions in (1) for the corresponding y_i in (5).[2] To determine the amount of each resource for each purpose that would maximize profits or benefits from the total capital available, we would take the partial derivative of (5) with respect to each resource used on each product and for λ, and set the partial derivatives equal to zero. There will be mn such equations in which the partial derivatives are equal to zero. The mn equations can be solved for the variables x_{ij} and the mn + 1 equations for λ. From these we could simultaneously solve the quantities of each resource used for each product.

We have presented a simple model which supposes a distinct production period where production, price, and cost functions might be known in the form of continuous algebraic equations. We have done so simply to illustrate the complexity in application of such models. They would entail knowledge of production functions for crops produced on particular soil types, for "water producing" and "flood prevention" dams at particular locations. But even if the knowledge were available for a relevant production period for each product or service, the analysis would still be extremely demanding. We actually would need to know production functions for each product or service in each year of the planning horizon for the watershed. The p_i in (2), (3), and (5) would be discounted prices for each relevant production period. Accordingly, the system in (1) would need to reflect the production functions for each of these periods. If there were k such periods, m products in each, and n resources, the system in (4) and the parallel system for (5) could include kmn equations. We would need to use discounted prices for products and factors in order to determine the present value of all future benefits or revenues as a step in determining maximum present or discounted values of these. We would need to know the continuous production functions of corn or cotton grown under irrigation or on dry land. We would need to relate the input of a resource in one year to a product in another year. These considerations could be fitted into the model or approach outlined in equations (1) through (5) by designating outputs and inputs of different years as if they were different products and resources and by using their appropriate discounted prices. However, since data are not likely to be available in these forms for complete watershed analysis, and because the empirical or computational task in determining optimum inputs for different watershed investments would be very great, we turn to models which are less complex.

---

[2] Consistent with (2), we could simply substitute the relationships in (2) into (3) and (5), and have profit expressed simply as a function of the x_{ij}.

PROGRAMMING MODELS

Programming provides models which are simplified versions of the models outlined above and which appear to have feasibility of application with types of data that might be available. Even these are not easy to outline in a small space so that the "plugging in of data" and operation of the models are clearly apparent. Models can be built which: (1) retain the identity of all individual farms and households and their separate objective functions; (2) include the objective function of the watershed as an over-all public planning entity (with the restraints it may place on or provide to the individual farm-household units, the nonfarm industries, and employment opportunities both within and outside the watershed); and (3) specify the interdependence between years for farm and watershed activities, the intermediate products and capital flows between years, and other conditions. Application of some of the models which might be built in this framework would require data in forms not currently available. However, the skeletons of the models might themselves indicate the kinds of data which should be provided if relevant types of analyses were to be made for watersheds. The overall framework of programming models for this or other purposes is not difficult. More complex, however, is a statement of the relevant restraints and the relevant activities in respect to space, time, and individual farm, and watershed. The over-all framework for simple computations can be stated simply as follows: We have the objective function

$$\text{maximize } f(X) = C'X \tag{6}$$

where $f(X)$ is net discounted revenue over the relevant planning period for the watershed, C is a vector of discounted net revenues made up of subvectors as

$$C' = [C_1 \; C_2 \ldots C_t \ldots C_k] \tag{7}$$

where each subvector has elements $c_{j(t)}$ ($j = 1, 2, \ldots n; t = 1, 2, \ldots k$), representing the discounted net price of the jth activity in the tth year. Some $c_{i(t)}$ are positive, as in the case of farm products marketed, while some are negative, as in the case of resources purchased, irrigation water stored, and so forth. The vector X has the form:

$$X' = [X_1 \; X_2 \ldots X_t \ldots X_k] \tag{8}$$

where each subvector X_t contains elements $x_{j(t)}$ expressing the level of output of the jth activity in the tth year. With n nondisposal activities in X_t, there are $nk = \bar{n}$ variables in X, representing this number of real activities. Similarly, C will contain $\bar{n}$ discounted net price coefficients.

The X_t may contain elements representing only the watershed as an aggregate, or it may contain elements identifying activities of individual farms and nonfarm activities both outside and inside the watershed. To include nonfarm activities, or even to specify activities for individual farms, will certainly increase complexity of data collection and computations. This writer would be inclined to exclude nonfarm industries and activities under the argument that they should relate to an economic development model, rather than a watershed model. Still, in the context of watershed development which is consistent with social welfare and the need for a "more general equilibrium model," some analysts may want to include them. Conceptually at least, certain $x_{j(t)}$ will represent activities such as streamflow in particular months of the year, water in dams for irrigation and recreation, and so forth. Prevention of flood damage might be handled by specifying such an activity directly, with a minimum restraint defined for it. However, a more practical procedure might be to specify a streamflow activity for each possible month of flooding, with a maximum restraint defined for it as a mechanism to specify flood prevention. Or there could be several such streamflow activities, competing to meet the maximum restraint, some having requirements for dam volume, some with requirements for land treatment, and others with a combination of requirements for these alternatives. Within each X_t would be elements representing competitive, complementary, and supplementary activities in the use of water or runoff. These interrelationships would be specified by the signs or magnitudes of elements in the requirements of the input-output matrix. Other $x_{j(t)}$ would represent water available in specific months of the tth year fed into the ith restraint of alternative dam capacity (or even runoff volume). If soil conservation is one of the ends to be attained, then an $x_{j(t)}$ will be defined for each relevant soil area. We might "turn these activities loose in the system" to see if they are economic. Or we might specify some minimum level (e.g., soil loss per acre per year) at which they are to be attained.

Equation (6) is to be maximized subject to:

$$PX \lessgtr S \tag{9}$$

where S is a vector of restraints made up of subvectors as

$$S' = [S_1 \ S_2 \ \ldots \ S_t \ \ldots \ S_k] \tag{10}$$

where the S_t contains elements representing the physical resource, legal and institutional restraints of each year over the relevant planning period to year k. Each subvector S_t thus contains m elements, and S contains mk = $\bar{m}$ elements. An $s_{i(t)}$, the magnitude of the ith restraint in the tth year, can be the same physical resource used in different production periods or years. Hence, it will be of the same magnitude each period, but will be restated in different years. The number of acres of each soil type in the watershed would represent such $s_{i(t)}$ for different years. Other $s_{i(t)}$ will be represented initially in all S_t at zero level, with their magnitudes in individual years generated by the subsequent plan. Also, some of these restrictions may vary in magnitude between years.

The subvectors may be "further partitioned" as

$$S'_t = \bar{S}_t \; \overset{0}{S}_t \tag{11}$$

where $\bar{S}_t$ represents restraints of maximum magnitude such as acres of different types of soil and streamflow (if the model is one for which some minimum level of flood prevention is to be specified), while $\overset{0}{S}_t$ represents minimum restraints such as level of conservation (perhaps specified as the "inverse" of soil loss or runoff), water level in dams for recreation (or minimum water level in some months of individual years to allow irrigation in other months), and so forth. Whether the $\overset{0}{S}_t$ restraints should be included would depend on the institutional and legal circumstances surrounding watershed planning. If funds had already been provided for watershed development with specified objectives legislated accordingly, they would be included. However, if the economic desirability of these objectives is to be determined, they would not be included in the equations of production possibilities. The subvector S_t might include one set of restraints representing those for the watershed as a whole, with another set representing those for individual farms. The size of the watershed and the availability of computing facilities would largely determine whether identification of individual farm restraints is feasible. If funds have been legislated for watershed development, their magnitude will be represented by relevant $s_{i(t)}$, and the optimum watershed program will be specified within this particular set of budgeted restraints. If funds have not yet been appropriated and the problem involves determination of the optimum total amount of public investment in watershed development, the "public capital" restraint might be handled this way: First, an activity, $x_{g(t)}$, would be defined within each X_t to allow specification of funds required in the tth year for watershed development. A corresponding restraint or "public capital" supply, $s_{g(t)}$, would be provided in S_t, but would be entered at zero level. Particular watershed investments or activities, $x_{f(t)}$, (such as stream straightening and dam construction) in year t would, in turn, have a positive requirement on the "public capital" supply, $s_{g(t)}$. The "capital supplying" activity, $x_{g(t)}$, in X_t would then increase the "public capital" supply, $s_{g(t)}$, in S_t above zero, if watershed investment were profitable in year t (i.e., if $x_{f(t)}$ should be increased above zero). Hence, the sum of the $x_{g(t)}$, representing the "capital supplying" activities in the various years, would indicate the magnitude and distribution of public investment which is optimum over the k years. The $x_{f(t)}$ would indicate the magnitude of each physical watershed treatment in the tth year, and their sum would represent total physical watershed treatment over k years.

P in (9) is the unit requirements or input-output matrix. Its construction conforms to the vectors of activities and restraints. It is made up of the submatrices:

$$
P = \begin{bmatrix}
\overline{P}_{11} & P_{12} & \cdots & P_{1j} & \cdots & P_{1k} \\
P_{21} & P_{22} & \cdots & P_{2j} & \cdots & P_{2k} \\
\vdots & \vdots & & \vdots & & \vdots \\
P_{i1} & P_{i2} & \cdots & P_{ij} & \cdots & P_{ik} \\
\vdots & \vdots & & \vdots & & \vdots \\
P_{k1} & P_{k2} & \cdots & P_{kj} & \cdots & P_{kk}
\end{bmatrix} \tag{12}
$$

There is a submatrix P_{ij} relating the requirements of activities in a particular year to the restraints in a particular year. Hence, where $i = j$, the input-output elements relate activities and restraints of the same year. Many, if not most, of the elements in P will be zero. Non-zero elements of P exist mainly where $i = j$. Most of the elements will be positive where $i = j$, although some can be negative, as in the case for supply activities which provide water (i.e., dams which add to water supply) for irrigation, power, or flood control; for land treatment activities which provide soil conservation; and for capital activities which provide funds for construction of watershed treatment. Generally, there will be non-zero elements in the P_{ij} where $i = j + 1$, since these allow a product or service produced in one year to serve as a resource in another year. An example would be water stored in the fall months of one year and used for irrigation, recreation, or power in the next year. In this case, since the activity of one year provides a resource to be used in the next year, the non-zero elements of P_{ij} where $i = j + 1$ will be negative. In general, the elements of P_{ij} will be zero where $i > j + 1$, although there might be a few activities so defined that they add resource supplies beyond one year. An example would be a dam built in the ith year and providing water supplies in each succeeding year. Each P_{ij} will contain mn elements, relating the activities of a particular year to the resource restraints of a particular year. Hence, with k years, P contains (mk) x (nk) elements.

Production Possibility Equations

While somewhat awkward, the actual "simplex layout" for a dynamic watershed programming model might be best illustrated by the following set of production possibility relationships for n real activities per year, m resource or institutional restraints per year for k years. Returning to our original indication of years by the subscript t ($t = 1, 2, \ldots k$), there are mk = $\overline{m}$ total restraints and nk = $\overline{n}$ total activities over the k years. We use input-output or requirement coefficients $p_{ij(t)}$ which represent the quantity of the ith resource restraint used by the jth activity in the tth year. Hence, the third or t subscript is not a conventional index, but only serves to identify the year. Similarly, for an activity level $x_{j(t)}$ and a restraint $s_{i(t)}$, the second or t subscript serves to identify the year.

Simplex Layout for a Watershed Programming Model

$$p_{11(1)}\ x_{1(1)} + p_{12(1)}x_{2(1)} + p_{13(1)}\ x_{3(1)} + \cdots + p_{1j(1)}\ x_{j(1)} + \cdots + p_{1\bar{n}(1)}\ x_{\bar{n}(1)} \leq s_{1(1)}$$

$$p_{21(1)}\ x_{1(1)} + p_{22(1)}x_{2(1)} + p_{23(1)}\ x_{3(1)} + \cdots + p_{2j(1)}\ x_{j(1)} + \cdots + p_{2\bar{n}(1)}\ x_{\bar{n}(1)} \leq s_{2(1)}$$

$$p_{i1(1)}\ x_{1(1)} + p_{i2(1)}x_{2(1)} + p_{i3(1)}\ x_{3(1)} + \cdots + p_{ij(1)}\ x_{j(1)} + \cdots + p_{i\bar{n}(1)}\ x_{\bar{n}(1)} \leq s_{i(1)}$$

$$p_{m1(1)}x_{1(1)} + p_{m2(1)}x_{2(1)} + p_{m3(1)}\ x_{3(1)} + \cdots + p_{mj(1)}\ x_{j(1)} + \cdots + p_{m\bar{n}(1)}\ x_{\bar{n}(1)} \leq s_{m(1)}$$

$$p_{11(2)}\ x_{1(2)} + p_{12(2)}x_{2(2)} + p_{13(2)}\ x_{3(2)} + \cdots + p_{1j(2)}\ x_{j(2)} + \cdots + p_{1\bar{n}(2)}\ x_{\bar{n}(2)} \leq s_{1(2)}$$

$$p_{21(2)}\ x_{1(2)} + p_{22(2)}x_{2(2)} + p_{23(2)}\ x_{3(2)} + \cdots + p_{2j(2)}\ x_{j(2)} + \cdots + p_{2\bar{n}(2)}\ x_{\bar{n}(2)} \leq s_{2(2)}$$

$$p_{i1(2)}\ x_{1(2)} + p_{i2(2)}x_{2(2)} + p_{i3(2)}\ x_{3(2)} + \cdots + p_{ij(2)}\ x_{j(2)} + \cdots + p_{i\bar{n}(2)}\ x_{\bar{n}(2)} \leq s_{i(2)}$$

$$p_{m1(2)}x_{1(2)} + p_{m2(2)}x_{2(2)} + p_{m3(2)}\ x_{3(2)} + \cdots + p_{mj(2)}\ x_{j(2)} + \cdots + p_{m\bar{n}(2)}\ x_{\bar{n}(2)} \leq s_{m(2)}$$

$$p_{11(t)}\ x_{1(t)} + p_{12(t)}x_{2(t)} + p_{13(t)}\ x_{3(t)} + \cdots + p_{1j(t)}\ x_{j(t)} + \cdots + p_{1\bar{n}(t)}\ x_{\bar{n}(t)} \leq s_{1(t)}$$

$$p_{21(t)}\ x_{1(t)} + p_{22(t)}x_{2(t)} + p_{23(t)}\ x_{3(t)} + \cdots + p_{2j(t)}\ x_{j(t)} + \cdots + p_{2\bar{n}(t)}\ x_{\bar{n}(t)} \leq s_{2(t)}$$

$$p_{i1(t)}\ x_{1(t)} + p_{i2(t)}x_{2(t)} + p_{i3(t)}\ x_{3(t)} + \cdots + p_{ij(t)}\ x_{j(t)} + \cdots + p_{i\bar{n}(t)}\ x_{\bar{n}(t)} \leq s_{i(t)}$$

$$p_{m1(t)}x_{1(t)} + p_{m2(t)}x_{2(t)} + p_{m3(t)}\ x_{3(t)} + \cdots + p_{mj(t)}\ x_{j(t)} + \cdots + p_{m\bar{n}(t)}\ x_{\bar{n}(t)} \leq s_{m(t)}$$

$$p_{11(k)}\ x_{1(k)} + p_{12(k)}x_{2(k)} + p_{13(k)}\ x_{3(k)} + \cdots + p_{1j(k)}\ x_{j(k)} + \cdots + p_{1\bar{n}(k)}\ x_{\bar{n}(k)} \leq s_{1(k)}$$

$$p_{21(k)}\ x_{1(k)} + p_{22(k)}x_{2(k)} + p_{23(k)}\ x_{3(k)} + \cdots + p_{2j(k)}\ x_{j(k)} + \cdots + p_{2\bar{n}(k)}\ x_{\bar{n}(k)} \leq s_{2(k)}$$

$$p_{i1(k)}\ x_{i(k)} + p_{i2(k)}x_{i(k)} + p_{i3(k)}\ x_{i(k)} + \cdots + p_{ij(k)}\ x_{j(k)} + \cdots + p_{i\bar{n}(k)}\ x_{\bar{n}(k)} \leq s_{i(k)}$$

$$p_{\bar{m}1(k)}x_{1(k)} + p_{\bar{m}2(k)}x_{2(k)} + p_{\bar{m}3(k)}x_{3(k)} + \cdots + p_{\bar{m}j(k)}x_{j(k)} + \cdots + p_{\bar{m}\bar{n}(k)}x_{\bar{n}(k)} \leq s_{\bar{m}(k)}$$

In the conventional programming tableau, $\bar{m}$ variables for disposal activities would be added to turn the relationships to equalities, and an appropriate number of artificial variables would be added where the relationship represents a minimum restraint. Our equations illustrate only those with maximum restraints. With the relationship $PX \leq S$ stated in the above manner, it is obvious that the problem becomes of considerable computational magnitude as k includes many years. A set of m relations with n unknowns for each of the k years gives $\bar{m}$

equations in total and at least $\bar{m} + \bar{n}$ activity variables after slack activities are added. As mentioned previously, however, many of the coefficients for these variables will be zero. The $p_{ij(t)}$ associated with the $x_{j(t)}$ will generally be positive only where the year is the same for the activity and the restraint. These coefficients are zero where the activity is for one year and the restraint is for another year, with the exception of an activity in one year which adds to a resource supply in the next (a later) year. In the latter case, it will be negative. With n activities and m restraints for k years, a total of $nk = \bar{n}$ activities and $mk = \bar{m}$ restraints in k years, there are $nk \times mk$ coefficients $p_{ij(t)}$. There are $nk = \bar{n}$ activity variables in each of the relationships outlined above. But only the proportion k^{-1} of these relate activities of one year to restraints of the same year. Hence, we can expect that the proportion of non-zero $p_{ij(t)}$ coefficients will never be greater than k^{-1} proportion. This is true because only the k^{-1} proportion of activities can possibly have requirements for resource supplies in the same year, and while a few activities in year t will have negative $p_{ij(t)}$ coefficients with restraints in year $t + 1$, some of the activities within a year will not have requirements on resource supplies within this year (e.g., a dam at one location will not require land at another location).

In mathematical terms, a programming model can be formulated to consider most settings within which watersheds might be analyzed. As mentioned previously, the physical restraints within the watershed can be taken as fixed, while the capital required for development can be considered as variable. Using a criterion such as the plan which will maximize discounted net revenue (i.e., benefits), we could analyze the amount or scale of investment which is optimum and how this capital should be allocated between alternatives such as dams, channel improvement, farm-land treatment, forestry, or conventional farm investments. Or, we can take the amount of capital for watershed development as given and determine how it should be allocated among purely watershed developments. In the latter case, we would not let farm units and the watershed unit compete for the capital allocated for watershed purposes.

Computations for Solution

If the necessary activity, restraint, and price vectors can be defined and — the major empirical task — if the matrix of input-output coefficients can be collected, the usual steps in simplex computations can then be applied. Illustrated algebraically, they follow. The first step is to add mk slack variables or disposal activities to X to allow nonuse of particular restraints (under-attainment or over-attainment of maximum and minimum restraints in particular years). Problems may exist in watersheds where a restraint must be "exactly used" and the equality condition will eliminate the need for a disposal activity. However, this case will be unlikely. Hence, X now will contain $nk + mk = h$

variables whose levels or magnitudes are to be determined in specifying the optimum watershed program. The number of elements in C
also become h. An identity matrix of mk $= \bar{m}$ order is added to P,
causing it to conform with the h variables now in X and with the $\bar{m}$
equations relating to resource supplies in S. With h elements in X
and C, $\bar{m}$ restraints in S and P being a matrix of $\bar{m}$ x h, we eliminate
subscripts denoting time and use the conventional notation x_j, c_j, p_{ij},
and s_i, where j = 1, 2, ... h and i = 1, 2, ... $\bar{m}$. Hence, P allows a
nonsingular submatrix of $\bar{m}$ order to be formed. Redefining X, C,
and P in this manner, the programming restraints now take the conventional computational form.

$$PX = S \tag{13}$$

and

$$X \geq 0 . \tag{14}$$

For those who may wish to review the algebraic procedure in computing a watershed optimum through the simplex programming procedures, we repeat the following steps. First, we partition to obtain:

$$X' = [X'_s \ X'_o] \tag{15}$$

where X_s represents levels of activities (resources, farm products,
water control structures such as dams, and so forth, which are generally at non-zero level, while X_o represents those initially at zero level,
whose magnitudes are to be determined. Hence, X'_s includes, in the initial statement of feasible programs, the resource supplies for each
year. With C and P partitioned conformably into C_s and C_o and P_s
and P_o respectively, we can restate the matrix representation of the
production possibility equations as:

$$P_s \ X_s + P_o \ X_o = S \tag{16}$$

and the objective functions as:

$$f(X) = C'_s \ X_s + C'_o \ X_o . \tag{17}$$

From (16) we can derive:

$$P_s \ X_s = S - P_o \ X_o \tag{18}$$

by matrix subtraction. Now, by inverting P_s , we define the level of
variables in X_s as:

$$X_s = P_s^{-1} S - P_s^{-1} P_o \ X_o . \tag{19}$$

Substituting the value of X_s in (18) into the profit or objective equation
in (17), we obtain:

$$\pi = f(X) = C'_s(P_s^{-1} S - P_s^{-1} P_o X_o) + C'_o X_o . \qquad (20)$$

Multiplying and collecting terms gives:

$$\pi = C'_s P_s^{-1} S + (C'_o - C'_s P_s^{-1} P_o)X_o \qquad (21)$$

where π denotes net discounted revenue over the planning period of k years. With the definitions:

$$B = P_s^{-1} S \qquad (22)$$

and

$$R = P_s^{-1} P_o \qquad (23)$$

the objective function becomes:

$$\pi = C'_s B + (C'_o - C'_s R)X_o . \qquad (24)$$

We now have a criterion or choice equation whose elements represent marginal net returns of activities in X_o. It is:

$$\Delta = C'_o - C'_s R , \qquad (25)$$

and each element of the vector Δ indicates the amount by which net discounted income will be increased by a one-unit increase in the corresponding activity represented by an element in X_o. For positive elements in Δ, net discounted income will be increased. The largest positive element in Δ indicates the x_j which will add most to revenue per unit of activity (but not per unit of resource or watershed investment).

Given linear functions, the variable x_v in X_o, with the largest corresponding element in Δ, is increased to the maximum allowed by the system of production possibility equations defined in (16) and (19). Substituting the B and R into (19) and rearranging, we obtain:

$$RX_o = B - X_s, \qquad (26)$$

but elements in X_s can be driven to zero, to allow specification of activity levels in X_o for maximizing net discounted income. Hence, we have:

$$RX_o = B \qquad (27)$$

which, in terms of vector multiplication, becomes:

$$x_1 \begin{bmatrix} r_{11} \\ r_{21} \\ r_{31} \\ \vdots \\ r_{\overline{m}1} \end{bmatrix} + x_2 \begin{bmatrix} r_{12} \\ r_{22} \\ r_{32} \\ \vdots \\ r_{\overline{m}2} \end{bmatrix} + \cdots\cdots x_{\overline{n}} \begin{bmatrix} r_{1\overline{n}} \\ r_{2\overline{n}} \\ r_{3\overline{n}} \\ \vdots \\ r_{\overline{m}n} \end{bmatrix} = \begin{bmatrix} b_1 \\ b_2 \\ b_3 \\ \vdots \\ b_{\overline{m}} \end{bmatrix} \qquad (28)$$

We increase only one variable, x_v, from X_o at each computational step or iteration. Hence, its magnitude, in terms of the various restraints or competing activities in X_s or B, can be defined as:

$$x_v \begin{bmatrix} r_{1v} \\ r_{2v} \\ r_{3v} \\ \vdots \\ r_{\overline{m}v} \end{bmatrix} \leq \begin{bmatrix} b_1 \\ b_2 \\ b_3 \\ \vdots \\ b_{\overline{m}} \end{bmatrix} \quad \text{or} \quad \begin{bmatrix} x_v\,r_{1v} \\ x_v\,r_{2v} \\ x_v\,r_{3v} \\ \vdots \\ x_v\,r_{\overline{m}v} \end{bmatrix} \leq \begin{bmatrix} b_1 \\ b_2 \\ b_3 \\ \vdots \\ b_{\overline{m}} \end{bmatrix} \quad (29)$$

Expressing the latter as a system of scalar inequalities and dividing each by its corresponding r_{iv} , we obtain the set of inequalities indicating r magnitudes:

$$\begin{aligned} x_v &\leq b_1\,r_{1v}^{-1} \\ x_v &\leq b_2\,r_{2v}^{-1} \\ x_v &\leq b_3\,r_{3v}^{-1} \\ &\vdots \\ x_v &\leq b_{\overline{m}}\,r_{3v}^{-1} \end{aligned} \qquad (30)$$

by which x_v may be defined. The feasible level of x_v is equal to the smaller of the ratios $b_i\,r_{iv}^{-1}$ in (30) if the restraint in (14) is not to be violated. With the level of x_v so defined, we can compute the magnitude of variables from X_s , after x_v from X_o is increased to the level $b_i\,r_{iv}^{-1} = b_g\,r_{gv}^{-1}$, from similar modifications of the equation in (19). One variable or activity, x_g, in X_s will be driven to zero. The variable x_v is then transferred to X_s at level $b_g\,r_{gv}^{-1}$, and the variable x_g is transferred to X_o at zero level. The procedure or steps outlined above are then repeated until a criterion vector, Δ, is computed which has only negative d_j values. The optimum watershed program then will have been computed. The final vector X_s will contain elements indicating the magnitude of watershed activities, along with the usual farm activities or enterprises, for each year. These will be the practices or activities which maximize net discounted revenue for the watershed, given the restraints specified in the original S. The set of non-zero activities in the optimum program, the magnitude of the variables in the final X_s , will show these quantities for each year.

RESOURCE VALUATION AND THE DUAL OF PROGRAMMING

A by-product of the linear programming model which could have importance in analysis of watersheds is the "dual." With programming applied in the sense outlined previously, to define the maximum discounted revenue over the relevant number of years, a set of dual computations automatically results. These provide values, discounted over

the planning period, for the resources which prove to be scarce. Within
the limitations which exist for particular programming models, they
could indicate the value of additional public capital for the watershed,
if it has previously been appropriated in specific quantities. For two
dams of limited capacity which appear in the optimum program for the
watershed, the dual could indicate values per unit of limited capacity,
and hence suggest which might add most to return if added funds were
made available for the project. Or, where a dam uses land at a particular location, to provide irrigation of land at another location, the dual
could provide some insight into compensation to owners of the former.
If land in the first location proved to be limitational in water storage
and hence in irrigation at the second location, its value in contributing
to increased production of the irrigated area would be indicated. If
land in the first area did not prove limitational in providing water storage capacity for the second location, its value would be reflected only
as it contributes to crop production or related uses.

These resource valuations, or shadow prices, as they are sometimes called, are provided automatically in computations for a programming problem of the conventional type outlined above. They are
computed directly in the final Δ vector. The final positive values of
elements in Δ, corresponding to a resource supply or restraint in the
initial X_s vector, but now indicated as those at zero level in X_o, indicate the amount by which net discounted revenue over the period would
increase if the supply of the resource or restraint were increased by
one unit. These values could be computed directly, rather than as the
dual solution if there were any reason to do so.

In the programming model outlined previously, the task is to maximize discounted revenue subject to using no more of certain resources
and restraints than are physically available in the watershed or are
provided by legislation. With the objective stated in (6) the major programming restraint is expressed as $PX \leq S$. In resource valuation for
watersheds, the objective is to assign nonnegative values, w_i, for units
of the limited areas of soil at different locations, the limited rainfall
available, and so forth. This process is equivalent to determining the
increase in discounted net revenue for the watershed which would be
possible from a one-unit increase in a particular fixed resource or institutional restraint. We wish to compute elements for a column vector W, with elements w_1, w_2, ... $w_{\overline{m}}$. The objective now is:

$$\text{minimize } f(w) = S'W \tag{31}$$

$$= s_1 w_1 + s_2 w_2 + \ldots + s_m w_m$$

where S' is the transposed vector of resource restraints and W is the
vector of weights or values to be assigned the fixed resources. The
value of π so determined will be the same as π determined from the
approach starting with (20). But the restraint imposed on determining
the elements of W which minimize π now becomes:

$$P'W \geq C \tag{32}$$

where P' is the transposed vector of input-output coefficients explained earlier, W is the vector of values or weights for which values are to be assigned, and C is the vector of net prices for products or activities produced from the resources whose quantities are represented in S. Or, expressed as scalar relationships, the objective function is attained subject to:

$$p_{11} w_1 + p_{21} w_2 + \ldots + p_{\overline{m}1} w_{\overline{m}} \geq c_1$$
$$p_{12} w_1 + p_{22} w_2 + \ldots + p_{\overline{m}1} w_{\overline{m}} \geq c_2 \qquad (33)$$
$$\dot{p}_{1\overline{n}} w_1 + \dot{p}_{2\overline{n}} w_2 + \ldots + \dot{p}_{\overline{mn}} w_{\overline{m}} \geq \dot{c}_{\overline{m}}$$

and $w_1 \geq 0$, $w_2 \geq 0$, $\ldots w_{\overline{m}} \geq 0$. In other words, nonnegative values of the w_i, or values for individual limiting resources, are computed to minimize $f(w)$ so that the sum of these weights or values multiplied by the per-unit requirements of watershed activities are greater than the net discounted per-unit price of the watershed activities. Or, the value per unit of watershed activity is imputed to the resources which produce it. This is accomplished in computations by adding slack variables to convert the "imputational relationships" to equalities, adding artificial variables, and proceeding with the same computational steps outlined previously. The data and method are the same. Only the objective function and restraints are stated differently.

CHARACTERISTICS OF PRODUCTION FUNCTIONS

A major problem in applying programming models in determining watershed optima probably rests in the mathematical nature of the production function. The major products, particularly those which have an established price, will have a linear total revenue function. In the few cases where this might not be true for a small watershed and price is not a constant, the average revenue function will have a negative slope. Two procedures then could be used in computing a watershed optimum. One would be use of computing procedures which have been outlined for nonlinear objective functions.[3] However, these procedures are complex

[3] Kenneth J. Arrow and Leonid Hurwicz, "Reduction of Constrained Maxima to Saddle-Point Problems," *Proceedings of the Third Berkeley Symposium on Mathematical Statistics and Probability*, ed. by J. Neyman (Berkeley: University of California Press, 1956), Vol. V, pp. 1-20; Kenneth J. Arrow and Leonid Hurwicz, "Radiant Methods for Constrained Maxima," *Operations Research*, Vol. V, No. 2, Apr., 1957, pp. 258-65; E. W. Barankin and Robert Dorfman, "On Quadratic Programming," *University of California Publications in Statistics*, Vol. II, No. 13, Apr. 8, 1958, pp. 285-318; A. Charnes and C. E. Lemke, "Minimization of Non-linear Separable Convex Functionals," *Naval Res. Log. Quart.*, Vol. I, 1954, p. 301; George Dantzig, Selmer Johnson, and Wayne White, "A Linear Programming Approach to the Chemical Equilibrium Problem," *Management Sci.*, Vol. V, No. 1, Oct., 1958, pp. 38-43; Robert Dorfman, P. A. Samuelson, and R. M. Solow, *Linear Programming and Economic Analysis* (New York: McGraw-Hill, 1958), Chap. 8; M. Frank and P. Wolfe, "An Algorithm for Quadratic Programming," *Naval Res. Log. Quart.*, Vol. III, Nos. 1 and 2, 1956, pp. 95-110; H. O. Hartley, "Nonlinear Programming for Separable Objective Functions and Constraints," mimeographed report, 1958. Iowa State University.

and when used for a watershed with a broad range of possible activities and restraints, the computational burden may be prohibitive. An alternative would be retention of a linear objective function based on a "stair-step demand function" for those commodities or services of the watershed which do not have horizontal demand curves. But again, the computational burden would increase considerably, since additional activities would need to be defined for these "ranges of constant price." Again, these problems are the exception for small watersheds where the main or only products marketed are those from farms.

Hence, the appropriateness of a linear programming model for small watersheds perhaps rests more on the mathematical nature of the production functions for certain watershed activities. Given a production function:

$$y = \phi(z_1, z_2, \ldots z_j, \ldots z_n), \tag{34}$$

for a particular product, the model can be formulated in an operational manner under the condition:

$$\sum_{i=1}^{n} \frac{\partial y}{\partial z_j} \frac{z_j}{y} \leq 1.0 \tag{35}$$

which also supposes that $\frac{\partial y}{\partial z_j} \frac{z_j}{y} \leq 1.0$ for each factor. This condition does not require constant returns to scale or constant marginal productivity of any factor. It allows declining marginal productivity of resources. However, if this is true, activities must be defined so that their corresponding requirements or input-output vectors represent productivity coefficients, or resource mixes. If a sufficient number of vectors and activities are so defined for a particular product and its production function, programming can proceed as outlined previously. The result, as is well known, gives the equivalent of a production function composed of linear segments. The number of separate vectors — computed from a production function if it is known algebraically — and activities can be as small as is deemed practical for computations or as large as is deemed necessary in approaching a continuous nonlinear production function. The more complex problem arises when:

$$\frac{\partial y}{\partial z_j} \frac{z_j}{y} > 1.0 \tag{36}$$

or when increasing returns to scale exist for all resources increased together. It is not always possible to compute vectors of input-output coefficients for different mixes of resources, to designate a corresponding number of activities, and to incorporate them into the usual linear programming model and obtain sensible results. The reason is easily illustrated. Suppose that three resources are used in producing a particular product or service and, setting the resource inputs at various magnitudes and in various proportions, we compute requirement vector for three activities (three different ways of producing the same product as represented by different points on the production surface). The three vectors are represented in (37). In terms of revenue or profit criteria,

$$P_1 = \begin{bmatrix} p_{11} \\ p_{21} \\ p_{31} \end{bmatrix}, \quad P_2 = \begin{bmatrix} p_{12} \\ p_{22} \\ p_{32} \end{bmatrix} = \begin{bmatrix} .7p_{11} \\ .5p_{21} \\ .6p_{31} \end{bmatrix}, \quad P_3 = \begin{bmatrix} p_{13} \\ p_{23} \\ p_{33} \end{bmatrix} = \begin{bmatrix} .5p_{11} \\ .3p_{21} \\ .4p_{31} \end{bmatrix} \quad (37)$$

the activity with the requirements vector P_3 would enter the watershed program before those with P_1 and P_2. But it might enter at an activity level which is inconsistent with the elements of P_3. The level of output might be consistent only with input-output ratios of the magnitude in P_1 or P_2.

These types of problems would exist or be important for certain watershed activities. An example is a dam where activity level, measured by dam capacity, would have unit requirements for capital, land area, and other resources which decline with output. There is no simple computational method for overcoming them. While integer or "discrete" programming methods are now available, the computing routines are complex and perhaps too burdensome for the size of problems necessary for programming actual watersheds.[4] A more crude method for solving these problems would be this: First, for activities of this nature which have one or two clearly limiting resources such as water or area for a dam, define a constant average set of coefficients for a scale of the activity allowed by the most limiting resource. By average, we mean a quantity approaching the mean of input-output coefficients if they were computed over the scale range possible. Then compute the optimum program. If the activity comes into the program at the maximum feasible level, the plan is optimum for the restraints. If it comes into the plan at a level less than the maximum allowed by the crucial resource or restraint, it would still have entered the plan had declining requirement coefficients been considered — as long as the scale is not so small that the corresponding coefficients are larger than the average set described above. If the latter is not true, then the alternative considered below may be appropriately followed.[5]

---

[4] For example, see the following: G. B. Dantzig, "Solving Linear Programs in Integers," (Santa Monica: The RAND Corporation), RM-2209; A. Manne and H. Markowitz, "On Solution of Discrete Programming Problems," (Santa Monica: The RAND Corporation), P-711; R. E. Gomory, "Outline of an Algorithm for Integer Solutions to Linear Programs," *Amer. Math. Soc. Bul.*, Vol. LXIV, No. 5, Sept., 1958, pp. 275-78.

[5] Where the scale at which the activity enters the program is one with coefficients smaller than the average set used, one might reprogram the situation. The activity could now be entered with a set of coefficients at levels equal to or smaller than those consistent with the level of the activity for the first plan.

Linear programming which provides sensible answers is possible only with convex sets. In case of non-convex sets, we may "split" them into convex sets. This possibility has been illustrated elsewhere.[6] Practically, we might define input-output or requirement vectors consistent with several levels or magnitudes for the activity. With all other coefficients and variables the same, we could set up an equal number of programming problems, each containing a different one of these several requirement vectors. A dummy "scale" restraint would be introduced in each problem so that the activity used for each problem could not enter the plan at a level greater than consistent with the particular vector of coefficients defining this particular scale. Then, solutions could be obtained for each problem and the one with the greatest revenue would approximate the optimum scale. Or, we could first compute the optimum program for the problem when it has been defined with a requirement vector falling somewhere in the middle of the several sets. If the activity came in, but at a level inconsistent with (i.e., smaller than supposed by) this set of coefficients, we could substitute the vector with the "next higher" set of coefficients. If it came in at the maximum allowed by the dummy "scale" restraint, we could substitute the vector with the "next lower" set of coefficients. This procedure could be continued until our judgment and data suggest that refinement has gone sufficiently far. The degree of refinement attained will depend on the number of separate vectors and "scale" restraints used, the quantity of funds available for computations, and the degree of precision required for making policy recommendations. The important question in deciding on the degree of refinement is: Will there be serious errors in decisions or policy recommendations with the degree of refinement attained? This same question might even be asked in deciding whether to treat the production process as if it involved constant or declining coefficients as level of activity increases.

WATERSHED DETAIL

It appears to this writer that programming models for over-all analysis of small watersheds, or a series of small watersheds, could easily be possible from existing or prospective data. A watershed model soon gets large and complex if it is a dynamic one which includes a fair number of years. However, problems of data collection and preparation are not simple even for a programming model for an individual farm or for other methods of analyzing watersheds. A dynamic model which includes much intra-year detail and many years can easily overtax computing capacity and research funds. For example, a single model which retains identification of many individual farm restraints and activities, as well as those which are aggregate for the watershed,

---

[6] See Earl O. Heady and Wilfred V. Candler, *Linear Programming Methods* (Ames: Iowa State University Press, 1958), pp. 223-24.

would likely do so. Practical models might need to include activities and restraints which are quite highly aggregated. For example, rather than identify individual farm activities and restraints, we might identify separately only those in aggregate for major areas of important soil types. The computational burden would be lessened greatly. The effects of some activities which are secondary and tertiary to watershed planning might be left out of the computations, with their importance or value analyzed by other means and "added on" as a by-product of watershed development. Reducing the scope of the analysis by these means would generally leave a problem which is manageable in terms of data collection and computations. The main remaining problem would be in defining coefficients which appropriately express interrelationships in activities and restraints among years of the planning period. If this task became impossible, then a final alternative is to use a purely static model which supposes a single production period. The optimum plan, with various investment alternatives within the period and those required initially as multiperiod requirements, could be defined for this period which might refer to a time sufficiently far in the future to allow a complete transition from the present state of the watershed. Using this plan, as the "constant pattern" for all other future periods, we could discount revenues of this standard program of each future year back to the present, to see if their sum is greater than for alternative arrangements and uses of resources in the watershed.

Other degrees of "crudeness" also can be used, including a purely static determination of an optimum program for a "typical year of the future." In these cases, we would not identify activities and restraints by years. Certainly these models are possible with data now being used for other types of analyses and approaches in watersheds. They would simply be models applicable in terms of available data and computational facilities. But their results might be misleading, although no more so than for other or current approaches using the same data and related assumptions. Rather than focus entirely on defining models which are operational with existing data, some attention should be focused on improving data so that more appropriate models can be used. Also, thought needs to be given to application of stochastic models which consider variance in rainfall, crop yields, and other products of watersheds.

Robert Dorfman is Professor of Economics and member of the faculty of the Graduate School of Public Administration, Harvard University. He was Associate Professor of Economics at the University of California and has served as a consultant to the RAND Corporation. Earlier he was senior statistician for the OPA and operations analyst for the U.S. Air Force.

Chapter 14 — B

ROBERT DORFMAN

Mathematical Analysis: Design of the Simple Valley Project[1]

T HIS DISCUSSION will illustrate one of the methods of analysis that Dr. Heady recommended. It is a report on an attempt to apply the programming approach to a very simple artificial watershed problem. Most of the data are contained in Figure 1, which portrays a reach of the Simple River. The figures in braces give the mean flows in the river in two seasons of the year, the wet season and the dry. Thus, at the very top the flow is 3.3 million acre feet (to be abbreviated "maf" hereinafter) in the wet season, and 1.4 maf in the dry.

The first topological feature the river encounters is reservoir A, whose tidal range, or active capacity, is one of the unknowns of the problem. It will be denoted by Y. Since Y maf will be detained in the wet season and released in the dry, the flows just below the reservoir are 3.3 - Y maf in the wet season, and 1.4 + Y maf in the dry, as shown.

It should not be necessary to explain in full detail all the flows shown on the map, but a few more explanations of the hydrology are in

---

[1] This discussion is based on a very preliminary pilot study of a method of analysis that the Harvard Water Resources Program is considering. In working it out I have borrowed heavily from the work and ideas of my colleague, Professor Harold A. Thomas, Jr., but the responsibility for any errors is entirely mine. Much of the computation was performed by Mr. Peter Watermeyer, for whose intelligent assistance I am grateful.

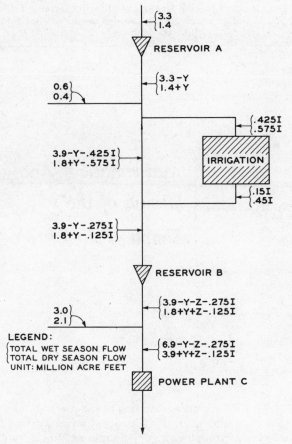

Figure 1. Map of Simple Valley.

order. Just below the confluence of the Simple River with its West Branch there is an irrigation diversion canal, taking off water to an irrigated area lying to the east. The total amount of irrigation water to be diverted, denoted by I, is the second unknown of the problem. The agricultural pattern of the region requires that, whatever I may be, 42.5 percent of it is required in the wet season, and 57.5 percent in the dry. Furthermore, the return flows from the irrigated area are 15 percent of I in the wet season, and 45 percent in the dry. These assumptions account for the flows indicated for the irrigation segment and for the river as it passes that segment.

The third variable to be determined is the usable capacity of reservoir B, to be denoted by Z. Retaining Z maf in the wet season and releasing it in the dry results in the flows shown just below reservoir B. The final variable is the energy output of the power plant at point C, to be denoted by E.

In short, we have constructed the problem: Determine the capacities of reservoirs A and B, the supply of irrigation water, and the output of energy from the power plant so as to attain the maximum possible net benefit from this system.

ECONOMIC AND TECHNICAL ASSUMPTIONS

Succinctly stated, we have to find values of four decision variables, Y, Z, I, and E, which (1) satisfy certain technological constraints, and (2) confer the maximum possible value on an "objective function" which will measure the net benefits derivable from the system. In this section we shall lay out the constraints and the objective function, beginning with the constraints.

The Constraints

The first group of constraints is simply that none of the four decision variables — Y, the capacity of reservoir A; Z, the capacity of reservoir B; I, the intake of irrigation water; and E, the output of electric energy — can be negative.

The second group of constraints states that the flows in all reaches of the system must be nonnegative. Reading these flows from Figure 1, we have:

$$3.3 - Y \qquad\qquad\qquad \geq 0, \qquad (F1)$$

$$3.9 - Y \qquad - .425I \geq 0, \qquad (F2)$$

$$1.8 + Y \qquad - .525I \geq 0, \qquad (F3)$$

$$3.9 - Y - Z - .275I \geq 0, \qquad (F4)$$

$$1.8 + Y + Z - .125I \geq 0. \qquad (F5)$$

The third group of constraints asserts that the flow at the power plant must be adequate to generate the amount of power that has been decided on in both the wet and the dry seasons. We shall now derive the wet season and dry season power constraints.

The technical relationship between flow and energy output is assumed to be:

$$E = 0.144 \ F$$

where:

E denotes energy generated in any period in billions of kilowatt hours (abbreviated bkwh); F denotes the flow through the turbines in maf in the same period. We assume also that half the energy generated will be required in the wet season and half in the dry. Thus, the two power constraints are:

$$F_W = 6.9 - Y - Z - .275I \geq \frac{0.5}{0.144} E = 3.47E ,$$

$$F_D = 3.9 + Y + Z - .125I \geq \frac{0.5}{0.144} E = 3.47E .$$

Rearranging terms, these can be written:

$$Y + Z + .275I + 3.47E \leq 6.9 , \quad \text{(W)}$$

$$- Y - Z + .125I + 3.47E \leq 3.9 . \quad \text{(D)}$$

This completes the discussion of constraints.

The Objective Function

We assume that the design sought is the one which, while satisfying these constraints, yields the greatest possible present value of net benefits. Thus, we write the objective function as:

$$\pi = B_1(E) + B_2(I) - K_1(Y) - K_2(Z) - K_3(E) - K_4(I)$$

where:

$B_1(E)$ is the present value of an output of E bkwh per year in millions of dollars,

$B_2(I)$ is the present value of an irrigation supply of I maf per year, in millions of dollars,

$K_1(Y)$ is the capital cost of building reservoir A to capacity Y, in millions of dollars,

$K_2(Z)$ is the capital cost of building reservoir B to capacity Z, in millions of dollars,

$K_3(E)$ is the capital cost of building power plant C to capacity E per year, in millions of dollars,

$K_4(I)$ is the capital cost of building the irrigation system to capacity I per year, in millions of dollars.

All six of these functions are given data. The first three capital cost functions are simple, and are as follows:

$$K_1(Y) = \frac{43Y}{1 + .2Y}$$

$$K_2(Z) = \frac{47Z}{1 + .3Z}$$

$$K_3(E) = 20.6E - E^2.$$

Each of these, it will be seen, reflects the effects of increasing returns to scale. $K_4(I)$, however, is a bit more complicated because we assume that up to 3 maf can be taken for irrigation without pumping, but that a pumping plant will be required if more than 3 maf of irrigation water is to be supplied. The assumed data, then, are these: The basic cost of the diversion works is $4.5 million, plus $44 million per maf of irrigation water. If more than 3 maf is to be supplied, a pumping plant must be constructed, the cost of which is $0.5 million, plus $20 million per maf of water to be pumped.

To express this capital cost function we introduce the following notation for discontinuous functions:

$$u^\dagger = \text{Max}(0,u), \text{ for any variable } u \, ,$$

$$u^\ddagger = \frac{u^\dagger}{u} \, , \, u \neq 0, \, 0^\ddagger = 0 \, .$$

For future reference, note that

$$\frac{d}{du} u^\dagger = u^\ddagger \, , \, u \neq 0 \, ,$$

$$\frac{d}{du} u^\ddagger = 0, \, u \neq 0 \, .$$

In terms of this notation:

$$K_4(I) = 4.5I^\ddagger + 44I + 0.5(I - 3)^\ddagger + 20(I - 3)^\dagger \, .$$

We now compute the benefit terms of the objective function, which consist in each case of four stages: first, deduce annual gross benefits as a function of scale (E or I as the case may be); second, deduce annual operating and maintenance costs as a function of scale; third, by subtraction compute annual net benefit; and finally, convert annual net benefit to present value by applying the appropriate present value factor. For this last stage we shall assume a planning period of fifty years and a discount rate of 2-1/2 percent, corresponding to a present value factor of 28.4. That is, under these assumptions the present value of a net benefit of $1 per year for fifty years is $28.40.

$B_1(E)$ is thus derived as follows. Energy is assumed to be worth 9 mills per kwh, so the gross benefit, in millions of dollars, is 9E. Operating and maintenance costs are taken as 0.2E. Thus, annual net benefit from electric power is 8.8E, and the present value of electric power operations (gross of capital costs) is:

$$B_1(E) = 250E \, .$$

The calculation of the present value of the net benefit from irrigation, $B_2(I)$, is considerably more complicated, partly because of the pumping plant and partly because the marginal value of irrigation water cannot be regarded as constant. Let us turn to gross benefit from irrigation first. The basic datum assumed is:

Marginal gross benefit $= 2.1 + \dfrac{3.2}{1 + .2I}$, in dollars per acre foot. Integrating this from 0 to I, total gross benefit in millions of dollars is found to be:

$$2.1I + 36.8 \log (1 + .2I) . \quad \text{(With log} = \log_{10}).$$

Operating and maintenance costs are assumed to be $0.5I + 1.06(I - 3)^{\dagger}$, giving an annual net benefit of:

$$1.6I + 36.8 \log (1 + .2I) - 1.06(I - 3)^{\dagger} .$$

Finally, applying the present value factor:

$$B_2 (I) = 45.4I + 1045 \log (1 + .2I) - 30.1(I - 3)^{\dagger} .$$

Now the objective function can be computed by adding its six components, and is:

$$\pi = 229.4E + E^2 + 1.4I + 1045 \log (1 + .2I) - 50.1(I - 3)^{\dagger} - 4.5I^{\ddagger}$$

$$- 0.5(I - 3)^{\ddagger} - \frac{43Y}{1 + .2Y} - \frac{47Z}{1 + .3Z} .$$

This concludes the set-up of the problem. The calculations necessary to obtain even fictitious data for this problem should remind us of the very tedious and expensive engineering, hydrologic, and economic estimating work that must precede the analysis of even the simplest watershed system.

SOLUTION

We now have the problem of maximizing the objective function, π, subject to the seven inequality constraints (F1, F2, F3, F4, F5, W, and D) and the restriction that none of the decision variables be negative. Since we have to maximize a function subject to inequality constraints (as distinct from equality constraints) we have a programming problem, and the straightforward methods of the differential calculus will not avail. Fortunately, it is a very small programming problem, and we can make it even smaller by using the following strategy. Let us assume values for Y and Z and then solve the two-variable problem of finding values of E and I that make the objective function as large as possible regarding the dam sizes as fixed at the assumed levels. This device, in effect, makes E and I functions of Y and Z. Thus, when we have found the maximum value of π possible with given Y and Z, we can differentiate it with respect to Y and Z and determine whether it would be advantageous to increase or decrease the dam sizes. We then change Y and Z in the indicated directions, and try again — and keep on trying until we find dam sizes from which no change is desirable.

Two remarks about this procedure seem worth making. First, the various derivatives that we shall compute are the dual variables that so often arise in programming problems (though computed here in an unconventional way). Second, the whole procedure, being guided by differential changes in the objective function, is an adaptation of the familiar method of steepest ascent.

Let us start by assuming Y = 1.5 maf; Z = 1.5 maf.

First Trial: Y = Z = 1.5

With these values of Y and Z the flow constraints become:

$$3.9 - 1.5 \qquad - .425I \geq 0 \quad \text{or} \quad I \leq \ 5.65 \quad (F2)$$
$$1.8 + 1.5 \qquad - .575I \geq 0 \quad \text{or} \quad I \leq \ 5.74 \quad (F3)$$
$$3.9 - 1.5 - 1.5 - .275I \geq 0 \quad \text{or} \quad I \leq \ 3.27 \quad (F4)$$
$$1.8 + 1.5 + 1.5 - .125I \geq 0 \quad \text{or} \quad I \leq 38.40 \quad (F5).$$

Of these, only F4, the strictest constraint, is effective. The power constraints are:

$$1.5 + 1.5 + .275I + 3.47E \leq 6.9 \quad (W)$$
$$- 1.5 - 1.5 + .125I + 3.47E \leq 3.9 \quad (D)$$

or, making the additions,

$$.275I + 3.47E \leq 3.9 \quad (W)$$
$$.125I + 3.47E \leq 6.9 \quad (D).$$

Inspection of the power constraints shows that if any positive pair —I, E — satisfy W, they will satisfy D *a fortiori*. In short, F4 and W are the only effective constraints. Without doing any further calculation it is clear that the dams, in the aggregate, are larger than optimal. For, by reducing the size of the dams we can (1) save money on construction costs, and (2) increase the output of power without decreasing that of irrigation by releasing more water in the wet season, when the constraint is binding at the expense of dry-season water which is in excess supply. Thus, it appears that we should try again with smaller dams.

Before acting on this suggestion we must dispose of one adverse possibility. If the optimal operating plan with Y = Z = 1.5 were to supply the maximum amount of irrigation water consistent with the flow constraints, then a decrease in the dam sizes might compel a decrease in irrigation supply and hence in net benefits. Thus, we must check to see whether I = 3.27 is optimal with Y = Z = 1.5.

To do this we compute

$$\frac{d\pi}{dI} = \frac{\partial \pi}{\partial I} + \frac{\partial \pi}{\partial E}\frac{dE}{dI}$$

at the point I = 3.27 (from F4), E = 0.865 (from W). From the formula for π :

$$\frac{\partial \pi}{\partial I} = 1.4 + \frac{90.8}{1 + .2I} - 50.1(I - 3)^{\ddagger} ,$$

$$\frac{\partial \pi}{\partial E} = 229.4 + 2E .$$

From constraint W:

$$\frac{dE}{dI} = -.0792 .$$

Substituting the numerical values for E and I:

$$\frac{d\pi}{dI} = 6.2 - (231.1)\,(.0792) = -12.1 < 0 .$$

Hence, the assumed irrigation supply is larger than optimal and the dam sizes can be reduced without sacrificing irrigation water.

Second Trial: Y = Z = 1.0

With these smaller dam sizes the flow constraints become:

$$2.9 - .425I \geq 0 \quad \text{or} \quad I \leq 6.82 \quad (F2)$$
$$2.8 - .575I \geq 0 \quad \text{or} \quad I \leq 4.87 \quad (F3)$$
$$1.9 - .275I \geq 0 \quad \text{or} \quad I \leq 6.91 \quad (F4)$$
$$3.8 - .125I \geq 0 \quad \text{or} \quad I \leq 30.40 \quad (F5).$$

The effective flow constraint is F3. The power constraints now are:

$$.275I + 3.47E \leq 4.9 \quad (W)$$
$$.125I + 3.47E \leq 5.9 \quad (D).$$

Obviously, the wet season power constraint binds for all positive combinations of E and I, so, just as before, the dam sizes should be reduced.

Third Trial: Y = Z = 0.5

With these dam sizes the flow constraints are:

$$3.4 - .425I \geq 0 \quad \text{or} \quad I \leq \ \ 8.00 \quad (F2)$$
$$2.3 - .525I \geq 0 \quad \text{or} \quad I \leq \ \ 4.38 \quad (F3)$$
$$2.9 - .275I \geq 0 \quad \text{or} \quad I \leq 10.55 \quad (F4)$$
$$2.8 - .125I \geq 0 \quad \text{or} \quad I \leq 22.41 \quad (F5).$$

The effective flow constraint is F3. The power constraints are:

$$.275I + 3.47E \leq 5.9 \quad (W)$$
$$.125I + 3.47E \leq 4.9 \quad (D).$$

This time it is not obvious at sight which power constraint binds, but the following Table shows that D is the effective one:

I	E from W	E from D
0	1.700	1.412
3	*	1.306
4.38	1.354	1.255

*Not computed.

We now use a process of trial and error to find the optimal combination of E and I for the assumed dam sizes. To do this we need the derivatives $d\pi/dI$, $\partial\pi/\partial I$, $\partial\pi/\partial E$, the formulas of which were found in the first trial. We also need dE/dI, as determined from constraint D. It is $dE/dI = -\dfrac{.125}{3.47} = -0.036$.

Let us first appraise the optimality of supplying as much irrigation water as possible, i.e., I = 4.38, E = 1.255. Substituting these values in the formulas:

$$\frac{\partial\pi}{\partial I} = -0.3 \quad \frac{\partial\pi}{\partial E} = 231.9$$

$$\frac{d\pi}{dI} = -0.3 + (-0.036)(231.9) = -8.7 < 0.$$

Thus, net benefit can be increased by providing less irrigation water and more electric power.

Now we try the pumping point, I = 3, E = 1.306. Here we meet a slight snag. Because of the discontinuity in the irrigation marginal cost functions, $\partial\pi/\partial I$ and therefore $d\pi/dI$ do not exist at this point.

Left-hand and right-hand derivatives do exist, however, and we compute them separately. For the right-hand derivative, relating to increases in I:

$$RH \frac{\partial \pi}{\partial I} = 1.4 + 56.7 - 50.1 = 8.0 \, ,$$

$$\frac{\partial \pi}{\partial E} = 232.0 \, ,$$

$$\frac{dE}{dI} = -0.036 \, .$$

Therefore

$$RH \frac{d\pi}{dI} = 8.0 + (-0.036)(232) = -0.35 < 0 \, .$$

Thus, increasing I above I = 3 will not increase net benefit. Turning to the left-hand derivative, which relates to decreases in I:

$$LH \frac{\partial \pi}{\partial I} = 1.4 + 56.7 = 58.1$$

and the other data are unchanged. Therefore

$$LH \frac{d\pi}{dI} = 58.1 - 8.4 = 49.7 > 0 \, .$$

This indicates that decreasing I below I = 3 will decrease net benefit. Thus, we have found the optimal output for the assumed dam sizes, viz., produce irrigation water just below the pumping point, I = 3, and subject to this produce as much electric power as possible, E = 1.306.

We now require $d\pi/dY$ and $d\pi/dZ$ in order to decide which way to change the dam sizes. The formulas are:

$$\frac{d\pi}{dY} = \frac{\partial \pi}{\partial E} \frac{dE}{dY} + \frac{\partial \pi}{\partial I} \frac{dI}{dY} + \frac{\partial \pi}{\partial Y} \, ,$$

$$\frac{d\pi}{dZ} = \frac{\partial \pi}{\partial E} \frac{dE}{dZ} + \frac{\partial \pi}{\partial I} \frac{dI}{dZ} + \frac{\partial \pi}{\partial Z} \, .$$

We have already found $\partial \pi / \partial E$ and $\partial \pi / \partial I$. The formulas for $\partial \pi / \partial Y$ and $\partial \pi / \partial Z$ come from straightforward differentiation of π. The dry-season power constraint, which is the effective one, gives

$$\frac{dE}{dY} = \frac{dE}{dZ} = 0.288 \, .$$

Finally, since I is fixed at I = 3 for this vicinity of dam sizes, dI/dY = dI/dZ = 0. Then, substituting I = 3, E = 1.306 in the formulas for the derivatives:

$$\frac{d\pi}{dY} = 232(.288) - 35.7 = 31.0 > 0 \,,$$

$$\frac{d\pi}{dZ} = 232(.288) - 35.6 = 31.1 > 0 \,.$$

Thus, both dams are now smaller than the optimum.

Final Solution

At this point it pays to use our heads. When the wet-season power constraint was the effective one, the dams turned out to be too large. When the dry-season power constraint was the effective one, we found the dams to be too small. This leads to the conjecture that when the dams are of optimal size both constraints will be effective.

This consideration does not completely determine the dam sizes, because there are many combinations of dam sizes for which both constraints will be effective for some pair of values of E and I. But we have found that the total capacity of the dams will turn out to be somewhere between 1 and 2 maf, and, if it is not too far from 1 maf we can expect that the optimal irrigation supply will be at the pumping point, I = 3.

To act on these conjectures, hold I fixed at 3 maf in constraints W and D and solve for the value of (Y + Z) at which both constraints are effective. Using this value of I the constraints are:

$$3.47E \leq 6.075 - (Y + Z) \,, \quad \text{(W)}$$
$$3.47E \leq 3.525 + (Y + Z) \cdot \quad \text{(D)}$$

If both are effective, the right-hand sides must be equal, giving rise to the equation:

$$6.075 - (Y + Z) = 3.525 + (Y + Z) \,,$$

whence

$$Y + Z = 1.275 \,.$$

We also find immediately from either constraint that E = 1.384.

With I, E, and Y + Z determined, it remains to determine Y and Z individually. The total cost of constructing the dams (we are assuming that the operating cost of the dams is negligible) is

$$\frac{43Y}{1 + .2Y} + \frac{47Z}{1 + .3Z} \cdot$$

Since the capacity of the two dams together has been determined, we have only to minimize this expression subject to the constraint that $Y + Z = 1.275$. This looks like a classical extremum problem, but it is not one because if the Lagrangean procedure is applied, it will yield the dam sizes corresponding to the maximum rather than the minimum cost for the prescribed total capacity. Thus, the optimum is either $Y = 0$, $Z = 1.275$, or $Y = 1.275$, $Z = 0$. Simple substitution shows that $Y = 1.275$, $Z = 0$ is the better, corresponding to a total cost of $43.5 million.

In summary, our solution is:

$$Y = 1.275 \text{ maf}$$
$$Z = 0.0 \quad \text{maf}$$
$$I = 3.0 \quad \text{maf}$$
$$E = 1.384 \text{ bkwh}.$$

It is left to the reader to verify that all permissible departures from this design reduce net benefits and that the resultant present value of net benefits is $\pi = \$490$ million.

CONCLUDING REMARKS

What have we learned from all this calculation, aside from the solution to a pat problem? One conclusion is that if a design problem is sufficiently simple, then quasi-linear programming (i.e., programming with linear constraints but an arbitrary objective function) can assist in the analysis. A second conclusion is that even in simple cases, quasi-linear programming demands a heavy amount of preliminary engineering and economic data-collecting, and even then is likely to present serious computational problems. How complex a contemplated watershed project can be before the computations required by the programming approach get out of hand is a question still to be investigated. Obviously, projects cannot become much more complex than the Simple Valley project without making solution by hand impracticable, but high-speed computing machines can solve such problems.

Third, we must call attention to the very strict simplifying assumptions invoked in this problem. It was of the essence of this example that a single year was treated in isolation. In practical watershed problems it sometimes happens that individual years can be studied separately (i.e., there is no need for over-year storage). In such cases the analysis is greatly facilitated. But when that does not happen, the programming approach requires some method that deals with single years or short periods of years in isolation from the rest of the life of the project. Otherwise, the problem will build up to unmanageable size. George Dantzig and Philip Wolfe of the RAND Corporation have recently developed a procedure of this type which can deal with a sequence of years linked only by the state of the system on each New Year's Eve. Some such procedure will be needed to keep the matrices that arise in programming problems down to the size that even the largest computing machine can cope with.

Finally, we must point out that this example has ignored stochastic aspects of the problem such as year-to-year variations in streamflow, year-to-year variations in demand for project outputs, and, above all, floods. No method that cannot contend with this aspect of reality is satisfactory, or even a reliable first approximation. But I am hopeful that programming methods can be devised that will permit the inclusion of random variation, droughts, and floods.

All that this exercise shows is that the programming approach has survived a simple test, like the Wright brothers' flying machine that flew just over a hundred feet.

Mark M. Regan is Assistant Chief, Land and Water Research Branch of the Farm
Economics Research Division, USDA. He has served on the staff of the Evaluation Standards Subcommittee of the Inter-Agency Committee on Water Resources
since its establishment in 1946, and with other governmental commissions on
water resources.

Chapter 15

MARK M. REGAN

Economically Desirable Institutional Arrangements and Cost-Sharing Requirements[1]

T HE TERM "institutional arrangements" as used here refers to a
complex of economic, social, and political characteristics influ-
encing organizations established for management of watershed
resources.

From an economic viewpoint, ideal institutional arrangements would
be those most effective in achieving the dual goals of: (1) optimum resource efficiency, and (2) socially desirable patterns of net benefit incidence. Obstacles to achieving optimum organizational arrangements
include: diversity of interests participating in programs with their
corresponding conflicts in viewpoints, lack of adequate information and
understanding by participating groups, limitations and conflicts in
powers available to the various interests concerned, differences in the
capacity of various groups to carry out assigned functions, and variations in the bargaining position of those affected. These obstacles have
frequently operated to reduce the effectiveness of local organizations.
They have led to project proposals of doubtful soundness and have resulted in pressures to shift an increasing share of the financial responsibility to the general public.

[1] The opinions expressed in this paper are those of the author and do not necessarily
represent official views.

Both the goals of watershed programs and the means available for their attainment are interdependent. The goals likely to be achieved depend at least partly upon the availability and acceptability of the necessary resource management authorities and powers. Both goals and means are subject to restraints imposed by economic, social, and political considerations. Ideally, the resource development process should start with the establishment of goals, which in turn indicate the various organizational attributes required. These include functions, authorities, and powers essential for an effective over-all resource management organization, and the distribution of responsibility for functions among participating groups. Functions need to be allocated according to performance capacity. Throughout, attention should be given the role of cost-sharing in implementing desired goals.[2]

ESSENTIAL RESOURCE PLANNING AND MANAGEMENT FUNCTIONS

The functions that need to be performed to achieve optimum development include: (1) establishment of over-all program goals and objectives; (2) planning and evaluation of specific projects and area programs; (3) devising and prescribing measures needed to induce participation; (4) installation, operation, and maintenance of projects and programs; (5) financing of project measures and distribution of financial responsibility; and (6) coordination and integration of authorities, powers, and responsibilities between national, regional, and local interests. Primary responsibility for certain functions falls logically at the national level, for others at the state and local level. The residual would become the joint responsibility of both.

Assignments to a central program agency might include responsibility for establishing national goals and standards including evaluation criteria and approaches. Administration of direct financial assistance might be a federal responsibility. A central agency could also obtain aid of various supporting national programs and undertake numerous integrating and coordinating activities.

State and local groups might best assume primary responsibility for the meeting of requirements for acceptable organizations and projects, administering project operation and maintenance, installing project features primarily of local concern, administering regulatory measures, and distributing local financial responsibility.

Most of the remaining functions would require varying degrees of joint participation by federal, state, and local agencies. Joint responsibility would appear to be necessary for project planning and evaluation, financial management and resource budgets, and the reconciliation of conflicts that might arise between local, area, and national considerations.

---

[2]A process for achieving effective operating arrangements is described in an article by Harry A. Steele and Mark M. Regan, "Organization and Administrative Arrangements for an Effective Water Policy," *Jour. Farm Econ.*, Vol. XXXVII, No. 5. Dec., 1955, pp. 886-96.

Local Organization Functions

Establishing resource program goals. Although the establishment of over-all resource policy goals is likely to be the primary responsibility of a higher level of planning, local organizations should be given opportunity to contribute to their modification and should be mainly responsible for establishing goals applicable to local resource conditions. The goals of watershed development might include:

1. The eventual optimum development and sustained use of watershed resources, with priority given projects expected to yield the maximum net social benefits.
2. A schedule for achieving the development desired, with sufficient flexibility to respond to changing conditions.
3. A socially desirable pattern of benefit incidence that is as widespread as is consistent with resource efficiency and with financial responsibility that will promote tenure objectives, conserve resources, and induce optimum participation.
4. The provision of information needed in choosing alternatives, with concerned interests afforded an opportunity to participate in choices.
5. The selection and use of that combination of economic incentives, directional measures, and administrative organization that will best accomplish the purposes of the program.

Achieving the policy goals would require local organizations to perform, either exclusively or jointly, a series of interrelated program planning and management functions.

Planning and evaluation. In addition to adapting general goals to particular areas and projects, the planning and evaluation function includes ensuring consistency in project formulation and selection; review and modification of project and program plans; provision of adequate basic data and analysis; and orderly scheduling of investigations and installations. Among the foregoing, local organizations would have primary responsibility for area goals, project selection, installation schedules, and program modification.

Implementation arrangements. Prescribing the types of measures and inducements required to assure the necessary extent of participation is an essential early phase in establishing a project. Provision is needed for available authorities and powers at appropriate levels sufficiently in advance of installation to permit effective program operations. Within the limits imposed by national program standards and legislative authorization, local districts should be responsible for utilizing the most effective measures available.

Program establishment and operation activities. Program installation activities include scheduling construction of improvements, establishing specifications, prescribing and administering regulations for contracts and force-account undertakings, acquiring needed property and easements, periodic supervision of construction under way, and approval of completed works. Such activities must be geared to planning schedules, and provision made for operation and maintenance. This includes establishing firm arrangements for assuring effective maintenance and obtaining optimum use of project services. Within central agency directives, primary responsibility for carrying out the bulk of such functions might appropriately be borne by local organizations.

Financial management. This function includes providing the financial resources necessary for project establishment and operations from taxation, credit, project revenues, grants, and other contributed resources. It includes the preparation of resource development budgets, provisions to meet annual maintenance costs, and the division of financial responsibility among purposes, interests, and beneficiaries.

Coordination. Coordination and integration activities include efforts to (1) utilize an effective combination of available institutional arrangements; (2) maintain a balance within and among measures, projects, and programs; (3) integrate the local program with related system and national activities at both planning and operating stages; and (4) reconcile conflicts between national, regional, and local levels of interest. Coordination activities at the local level could be the primary responsibility of local organizations, with such groups sharing in these activities for broader areas.

RESOURCE MANAGEMENT POWERS AND MEASURES

In order to carry out the functions that have been discussed, use must be made of the measures and powers available at different levels of government for implementing watershed resource programs.

Local Organization Powers

The powers needed by local organizations include planning, sponsoring, installing, operating, and maintaining improvement works and practices; authority to contract; authority to borrow, receive, and expend funds obtained from appropriations, grants, taxes, and charges or assessments for project services; power to acquire land and easements for reservoir sites and rights-of-way through purchase or eminent domain; and power to establish land use regulations to protect installed improvements.[3]

Administrative policy governing the Public Law 566 program requires that local sponsoring organizations have authority under state law to carry out, maintain, and operate authorized works of improvement. Aside from express powers of taxation, special assessments, eminent domain, and the regulation of land use, soil conservation

---

[3] Mark M. Regan and Harry A. Steele, "Recent Developments in Watershed Programs" in *Water Resources and Economic Development of the West,* Report No. 6, Conference Proceedings of the Committee on the Economics of Water Resource Development, Nov. 13-15, 1957.

districts frequently have most of the powers needed.[4] Accordingly, multiple sponsorship is often necessary in assembling adequate powers to meet full sponsorship requirements.

In addition to obtaining the necessary powers, local organizations need technical assistance, particularly in the financial management aspects of their operations.[5]

General Resource Management Measures

The operations of local organizations should be supplemented by the utilization of broader measures for directing resource use. The general measures may be grouped into three broad categories: (1) resource information and education, (2) incentives, and (3) regulatory measures. Although likely to be administered as parts of general resource conservation and improvement programs, the measures may be amenable to some adjustments for watershed conditions. Certain measures either encompass or overlap the more specific authorities and powers needed by local organizations.

Informational activities. These include technical training, development of effective media for communicating ideas, and an understanding of the issues that have a bearing on the interests of those participating in the watershed program. Recognition of the public interest in land and water resources would facilitate the application of regulatory measures and reduce the burden placed on incentive and voluntary measures.

Participation incentives. Most inducement and incentive measures represent an exercise of the government spending power to encourage voluntary participation in programs. As others have pointed out, this often involves involuntary tax or debt burdens placed on other segments of society.[6]

Participation incentive measures include technical assistance, cost-sharing, incentive payments, preference clauses, provision of project services, credit facilities, and differential taxes. Most have been used in one form or another as parts of the over-all farm program. Perhaps the most widely used in connection with watershed development are technical assistance, cost-sharing, provision of project services, conservation program incentive payments, and access to credit. All of them offer direct means of facilitating project development or encouraging wider application of recommended practices.

Problems involved in their application include capitalizing advantages

---

[4] John Muehlbeier, "Organizing for Watershed Development," S. Dak. Agr. Exper. Sta. Circ. 133, Jan., 1957, p. 7.

[5] Loyd Glover, "Organizing the Management of Small Watersheds for Multiple Uses — An Appraisal of Current Programs," in *Water Resources and Economic Development of the West*, Report No. 6, Conference Proceedings of the Committee on the Economics of Water Resource Development, Nov. 13-15, 1957.

[6] Harry A. Steele, Erling D. Solberg, and Howard L. Hill, "Measures to Facilitate Land Use Adjustments in the Great Plains," Great Plains Agricultural Council, Bozeman, Mont., July 29, 1958.

into land values and their appropriation by present landowners, designing measures so as to bring about the land use practices or changes desired, and the difficulty of achieving durable effects without a continuing incentive program.

Regulatory measures. Regulatory measures include laws governing property rights in resources, land use regulations, rural zoning, and public ownership and management.[7] Most involve the use of government police power. In general, the use of regulatory measures in establishing projects and obtaining the desired participation in watershed programs has been rather limited, particularly in relation to their potential contribution.

Modification and clarification of property rights in water, particularly in the eastern states, appear to merit consideration.

Soil conservation districts in most states are authorized to adopt land use regulations, but few have used the authority. The land use type of regulation has been applied more extensively to forest lands, grazing, wildlife, and oil, gas, and mineral production. Its effectiveness for agricultural land remains largely untested.

The potentials of zoning as a land use directional measure also seem to be promising, but again, they are relatively unexplored. Zoning might be used to advantage to reduce flood and drought hazards, encourage the conservation of resources, protect installed projects against excessive sedimentation, and perhaps for other watershed development objectives. The use of restrictive covenants as regulatory or control measures could have an effect on resource use similar to that of zoning.

Authority to acquire reservoir sites by local watershed organizations may need to be supplemented by more extensive public acquisition activities. This may be the only effective way of managing resources when complicated regulations and involved administration are necessary. Public acquisition provides a means of obtaining control for public management purposes, for consolidating or retaining certain rights, and, by excess condemnation, for capturing windfall gains resulting from resource development. Land passing through public ownership also offers an opportunity to retain easements at limited cost. An alternative to outright purchase would be the acquisition of easement rights. This would avoid certain management problems, but the sporadic or occasional exercise of such rights might become difficult.

The extent to which local watershed organizations should have express authority to administer measures of the broader types would depend upon the need for them in solving watershed problems, how effectively they were performed under other programs, whether the watershed organizational mechanism is adequate for effective administration, and the attitudes of the local organization membership.

---

[7] Comprehensive discussions of land use directional measures may be found in S. V. Ciriacy-Wantrup, *Resource Conservation; Economics and Policies* (Berkeley: University of California Press, 1952), Chap. 19; and Raleigh Barlowe, *Land Resource Economics* (Englewood Cliffs, N. J.: Prentice-Hall, Inc., 1958), Chap. 17.

EVALUATION CRITERIA AND COST-SHARING REQUIREMENTS

In addition to adequate authorities and powers, the successful performance of functions by watershed organizations depends also upon the use of a systematic set of evaluation criteria at all stages of the process of establishing the type of program likely to be most advantageous socially. Such criteria are essential in both selection of goals and arrangements for their attainment. While it would seem possible to achieve desired programs under a range of institutional arrangements and combinations, appropriate cost-sharing requirements can effectively promote both optimum resource efficiency and an acceptable pattern of incidence.

Evaluation Objectives and Approaches

Previous chapters have centered attention on the economic objectives and standards for watershed planning and development. Accordingly, attention here is limited to a discussion of some of the principal characteristics of customary evaluation criteria that may become controversial when applied to local level and cost-sharing aspects of programs.

Maximizing benefits. The most frequently accepted goal for the formulation of resource projects is that of maximizing net benefits.[8] The concept is applicable to the development of a comprehensive watershed program, as well as to its various constituent parts in the form of projects and measures.

In terms of either a project or program, each purpose that added benefits in excess of its costs would be included, and the scale of each would be extended to the point at which incremental benefits and costs were equal. In order to meet the conditions necessary for economic justification, a project or program must yield total benefits in excess of total costs; benefits from each separable project, purpose, or segment must be sufficient to cover the cost of its inclusion; and the costs involved must be less than those of available alternatives.

With the imposition of other than market price restraints, the maximization principle becomes applicable to the use of the limiting resource. Here the scale of development stops at the point at which the relationship of marginal returns to costs in the various uses are equal and net returns to the limited resource are maximized. In the case of programs, various projects and purposes would be formulated so as to equate their marginal returns. The same general principle would apply whether the most limited resource was water, land, reservoir sites or investment funds.

---

[8]The term "maximum benefits" refers to the resource efficiency goal considered preferable at the time resource commitments are planned. It is thus regarded as a directional or orientational guide rather than a specific position necessarily expected to be achieved. Its main purpose is to provide a framework for improving programs over those expected in the absence of reasonably systematic conceptual criteria.

The general objective of maximizing benefits would appear to be acceptable at all levels of participation. The difficulty arises in connection with the viewpoint and the standards used in measuring the benefits and costs considered appropriate.

To make the comparisons essential for maximizing project benefits, various types of effects must be measured from a common viewpoint and converted to a common value basis. Beneficial and adverse project effects arise initially in many physical forms. They accrue at different times, continue for varying periods, and arise under a variety of circumstances that influence the certainty of their occurrence. In order to obtain comparability, diverse effects must be expressed in common terms, appraised from the same viewpoint, and measured on the basis of similar standards.

Viewpoint. Federal participation in resource development infers a public interest in such activities. Projects that involve substantial federal investments accordingly should reflect an evaluation from a comprehensive national or public viewpoint. Emphasis should be placed on taking account of all significant effects, beneficial and adverse, to the fullest extent feasible.

Even before local interests are taken into account, the full-fledged application of such a viewpoint raises several difficult evaluation problems. The treatment of a wide range of intangibles constitutes one source of difficulty. This includes project effects that are difficult to measure even partially in monetary terms, such as contributions to national security, provision for future generations, improvements in health, scenic and aesthetic values, and so on. Similar difficulties arise in assessing different patterns of incidence on welfare. Furthermore, even though market prices are available, such prices may depart from those considered appropriate from a public viewpoint. Differences may result from various imperfections in market operations and their tendency to reflect a private rather than a public viewpoint. Such influences as tariffs, subsidies, price supports, and other forms of both government and privately administered prices all operate to reduce the effectiveness of market prices as measures of public values. Possibilities exist for overcoming some of these deficiencies; others defy treatment other than in qualitative terms.

An additional set of difficulties is encountered in applying a social viewpoint to local conditions. Economic justification from the public viewpoint excludes the value of various types of offsets accruing outside the area of project influence. This is the chief reason for excluding secondary benefits in determining project justification. Under an evaluation from a local viewpoint, account would be taken of all effects within the area, regardless of whether they were net from society's viewpoint.

The viewpoint that is applicable to planning and evaluation from the standpoint of society differs from that appropriate for purposes of compensation, reimbursement, cost-sharing, or evaluations from a local viewpoint. For most such purposes consideration is restricted to the incidence of project effects on specified areas (segments or subgroups), hence the applicable viewpoint is essentially local in nature.

Measurement standards. The selection of measurement standards that reflect the social interest is an essential part of an evaluation from a public viewpoint. From that viewpoint, the unit prices applied should reflect the expected purchasing power of goods and services at the time they are produced or used. The cost of a project to society is measured by the exchange value of the economic resources required at the time they are used, and benefits are measured by their exchange value at the time they are produced. Thus, measurement is in terms of real values as reflected in purchasing power. Excluded are effects resulting from changes in the general price level and transfers associated with market form or administrative intervention.

Problems similar to those related to commodity prices arise in the selection of interest and discount rates. Market rates may depart from those considered appropriate for an evaluation from a public viewpoint. The social cost of capital utilization is established by the productive opportunities that are foregone. The primary basis for the charge is the expected productivity of capital in other uses. Whether such productivity is best measured by market interest rates (often assumed to reflect private time preference), government bond rates (often treated as a measure of social time preference), or a rate somewhere between the two remains controversial. In any case, the rates customarily used in project evaluation depart from the rates payable by private participants.

Differences in the prices and interest rates used in project evaluation and those considered acceptable to participants constitute another source of divergence that bears directly upon cost-sharing requirements.

Period of analysis. The appropriate limit on the period of analysis when the public viewpoint guides evaluation is the expected economic life of the project. This may extend far beyond the planning horizons of most private participants, or even those of local watershed organizations.

Cost-Sharing Requirements

Because of the diversity of interests participating in watershed programs, conflicts may stem from either the evaluation criteria used or the resource management measures applied. These conflicts become obstacles to the achievement of optimum programs. Cost-sharing requirements offer a means of reducing conflicts and contributing directly in other ways to the attainment of project objectives.

The broad field of cost-sharing covers all aspects of the incidence of both project effects and impacts of implementation measures. It includes consideration of the distribution of impacts among regions, areas, groups, and individuals; the compensation required to allow all those affected to be as well off with as without the project; ways in which cost-sharing provisions may be used to adjust incidence; and the possibilities and limitations of alternative types of cost-sharing requirements. Attention in this section will center mainly on the use of cost-sharing requirements in (1) achieving an efficient allocation of resources, and (2) promoting incidence patterns consistent with public policy objectives and welfare criteria. Under ideal arrangements, any conflicts between the two would be minimized.

Relation of cost-sharing to efficient resource development and use. Cost-sharing requirements have a bearing on both the development of optimum projects and the utilization of the resulting project services. Ideal requirements for efficiency purposes would be those that would promote the type of project and program formulation and operation indicated as optimum by the evaluation criteria.

As indicated above, economic formulation should be such as to include all purposes that produced benefits sufficient to cover the costs of their inclusion, and the scale of each should be extended to the point at which marginal benefits and costs are equated. Cost-sharing requirements that favor certain purposes over others would be expected to influence — adversely — balanced resource development. Local organization plans might well propose extending favored purposes beyond their justified levels and curtailing the less favored short of optimum intensity. Variations in agency requirements might also influence the type of program selected, with the choice based on the most favored treatment rather than that most advantageous from an economic standpoint.

Similar disparities could arise from differences in the value standards acceptable to the various participants. If farmers participating in a program considered a 5 percent rate of return the minimum acceptable, the intensity of investments for which they were responsible might fall short of that considered desirable under a project evaluation interest rate of 3 percent. Prices used for evaluation that are based on purchasing power might also differ from those acceptable to participants. These differences might lead to plans and practices by local agencies and individuals that depart from those considered to be most advantageous socially.

To achieve optimum development under voluntary participation arrangements, it would seem necessary to provide that the marginal benefits from each purpose accruing to each participant be sufficient to cover the corresponding marginal costs borne by each. In such determinations, allowance would need to be made for differences in the value standards considered appropriate for the various participating groups. All net costs of extending the intensity beyond that considered justified by private participants would become a public responsibility. In the absence of means for obtaining the degree of participation desired, project formulation would need to be adjusted to reflect expected degree of participation without the necessary inducements.

The attainment of efficiency goals will be influenced also by the effect that cost-sharing through assessments and charges may have on the use of project services. The absence of any charge might induce waste of services and provide insufficient incentives for participation. Excessive charges could cause under-utilization of project services and a failure to realize potential benefits. The effect of charges on use depends partly upon whether the charges are fixed or variable, and whether or not the service is vendible.[9] At the planning stage, most costs may be treated as variable in the sense that they are still un-committed. Once the project was constructed, restrictions on the use of project services for flood control, drainage, and related purposes would be difficult to exercise. Irrigation, municipal water, and recreation would represent the main types of vendible services from watershed projects.

Substantial cost-sharing requirements may also provide an effective check on the reliability of the evaluation analysis. The willingness of local organizations and individuals to bear project costs or pay for project services is rather conclusive evidence of assured benefits. The existence of such requirements would reduce promotional activities and pressures for uneconomic projects that are locally supported largely because the general public is expected to bear the bulk of the costs.

Incidence and distribution aspects of cost-sharing. With adherence to appropriate evaluation criteria, achievement of reasonably advantageous resource development under a range of cost-sharing requirements would seem possible. An area for policy discretion on cost-sharing that would still allow the realization of acceptable efficiency levels is thus available.

The emphasis placed on cost-sharing for adjusting incidence depends upon how extensively such requirements are to be applied as positive instruments of public policy in promoting the attainment of benefit distribution objectives. Such objectives for resource programs include (1) stimulating area and regional development; (2) providing preferences for selected classes of owners, sizes of farms, and types of users; (3) promoting resource conservation, economic stability, and adequate levels of living; (4) minimizing windfall gains; and (5) generally encouraging distribution patterns considered to be equitable and in accord with such welfare criteria as avoiding adverse effects on any participant.

The justified extent to which cost-sharing may be modified to take account of these objectives is limited by expected impacts on efficiency and available alternative forms of control. No basic obstacle arises when the measures for attaining the distribution goal permit efficient resource use. Frequently, both can be served if a reasonably close association is maintained between the incidence of benefits and that of costs. The receipt of benefits gives rise to an increased ability to bear charges; and, in general, charges corresponding either to costs or to the value of service promote project efficiency.

---

[9] Various aspects of this problem are discussed by Michael F. Brewer, "Water Pricing by Small Groups," *Calif. Agr.*, Vol. XIII, No. 4, Apr., 1958; and S. V. Ciriacy-Wantrup, "Cost Allocation in Relation to Western Water Policies," *Jour. Farm Econ.*, Vol. XXXVI, No. 1, Feb., 1954, pp. 108-29.

In case the distributive goal and efficient resource use conflict, the decision becomes a matter of weighing the alternatives, based on a clear understanding of the extent and significance of the divergence. Thus, the costs of the efficiency foregone might measure the costs of choosing the distribution goal; or, the adverse effects of obtaining optimum efficiency on distribution might reveal the need for relaxing the efficiency requirements.

The effectiveness of alternative means of accomplishing distribution objectives may affect the reliance placed on cost-sharing for such purposes. Other means available for controlling or adjusting resource distribution patterns include various types of legislative preferences, land use regulations, rural zoning, public acquisition and management of land or easements, and application of required resource management practices. Other resource development programs, such as reclamation, have made use of the 160-acre limitation and associated anti-speculation provisions as incidence-control measures. Differential charges and graduated assessments are among the alternatives to acreage limitations that have been proposed.

The application of direct controls on resource use does not necessarily escape the incidence issue. If land use regulations, rural zoning, purchase, or other measures are used, the question arises as to whether or not compensation should be provided to adjust any adverse impacts resulting from their application. If property is acquired, sufficient compensation should be provided to allow those affected to become re-established in an equally advantageous position. If no compensation for regulations imposed is provided, the owners of the affected property would bear the brunt of any costs associated with controlled use. The economic justification for compensation for property acquired by purchase or eminent domain would appear to be applicable to property adversely affected by land use regulations and zoning.

Nor would the absence of adequate charges or assessments avoid significant aspects of the incidence problem. When project services are provided at less than their value, the advantages may be largely absorbed by present landowners. If a wide and durable benefit distribution pattern is desired, the ultimate aspects of incidence must be considered. In case benefits are subject to appropriation, it would be fair, in my opinion, that either the charge or assessment should be sufficient to limit windfall gains, or such gains should be obtained for the public through taxes or excess condemnation. The possibility of achieving and maintaining distribution objectives through law in the absence of project charges would be limited.

CONCLUSIONS

It is possible to indicate certain general characteristics of institutional arrangements and cost-sharing requirements desirable if local watershed organizations are to operate effectively in establishing advantageous programs. These organizations should be assigned functions sufficient to stimulate active interest and be in accordance with their capacities. To carry out assigned functions, they need to have the necessary authorities and powers to plan, install, maintain and operate, finance, and otherwise manage programs. Such authorities should be coupled with cost-sharing arrangements that will favor balanced programs, permit sharing of financial responsibility in accord with interests, and promote equitable assessments and charges among local watershed members and other beneficiaries. When advantageous, the organizations should be able to apply direct regulatory measures and establish corresponding compensation practices necessary to assure a harmonious program.

In practice, achieving even the minimum institutional arrangements considered desirable gives rise to certain dilemmas. Establishing a standard set of essential requirements as a condition for local organization qualification could result in delaying program operations in many states. Also, experience may not be adequate as yet to crystallize many aspects of potentially desirable arrangements. But allowing programs to get under way without adequate authorities and powers will make acceptance of more stringent requirements difficult. At the same time, expansion based on inadequate local organizations may operate to undermine program effectiveness and support.

The strengthening of cost-sharing requirements is particularly difficult. Improved procedures are essential for applying more systematic requirements. Groups need to be identified, bases for determining charges agreed upon, and techniques and mechanisms for assessment and collection established. The absence of a consistent national policy on resource development cost-sharing also operates to limit the establishment of improved requirements for particular resource development activities. The difficulties cited preclude easy or simple solutions, but do not yet represent insurmountable obstacles to progress in establishing more effective institutional arrangements and cost-sharing requirements. However, if prevailing trends continue, improvements are likely to become increasingly difficult to achieve.

WILLIAM L. GIBSON, JR. | *Comment*

THE BENEFIT-COST APPROACH involves many problems of benefit and cost evaluation and their incidence upon individuals and the public. To assign a speaker the job of clarifying some of the issues involved in these problems would not be an easy assignment. But to ask him "to lay out a framework within which an unrestrained ideal institutional setup for watershed development could be searched for" was to multiply many-fold the difficulties of his task. Yet there was a great need for this to be done, and we were fortunate that Mark Regan found it possible to accept this assignment.

As a point of departure, Regan defines ideal institutional arrangements as organizations which best serve "the dual goals of optimum resource efficiency and socially desirable patterns of net benefit incidence." He recognizes certain obstacles to achieving optimum organizations and states that "the goals likely to be achieved are at least partially dependent upon the availability and acceptability of the necessary resource management authorities and powers." Nevertheless, the ideal approach is a process which starts with the establishment of goals, followed by a consideration of the functions essential to achieving these goals in which emphasis might appropriately be placed on assignments to participating groups in accordance with expected performance capacity. I find no reasons for disagreeing with this process as an effective operating mechanism for resource planning and management.

Next, the essential functions for optimum resource development were enumerated, and assignments of responsibility for the functions were made. Absent from the enumeration is one important step, namely, the realization of the problem and the starting of action to do something about it. Benefit-cost analysis gives a criterion for allocation of scarce funds among projects to maximize net social benefits only if those watersheds where resource development is most critically needed are included. I suspect that to assume they are included may not always be a valid assumption. In other words, program formulation should provide for inclusion as well as exclusion of projects.

Regan presents a framework of general resource policy guides with five principal components which may be summarized as optimum development and sustained use of resources under a balanced and orderly schedule and with as widespread a pattern of benefit incidence as is consistent with resource efficiency. There must be provision for adequate information to explore and weigh the possible alternatives, as well as effective organization at the various levels of planning to accomplish the goals sought. Thus, problems of determining proper planning and

---

William L. Gibson, Jr., is Professor of Agricultural Economics at Virginia Polytechnic Institute, where he has been on the staff since 1934.

management functions and the distribution of these functions are of major importance. Regan discusses these problems, and his enumeration, appraisal, and distribution of the functions add clarity to many of the issues involved. He stresses the viewpoint that effective local programs can be achieved only if provision is made for establishing organizations with authority to perform all functions essential to the carrying out of their responsibilities. These include authority to sponsor, plan, install, operate, and maintain works of improvement; the authority to collect, borrow, or otherwise raise the necessary funds; and the authority to acquire property where needed and to establish land use regulations to achieve the objectives of the program and to protect any public investments made. At times, it is not clear whether Regan's reference to local organization means the state or some division of the state. I believe this distinction is important because more active state participation in planning is required for improved utilization of land and water resources. Local organizations below the state level, even where permissive powers coupled with provisions for planning assistance have been provided, frequently do not act until problems reach a critical and costly stage. Too often, local action arises from incentives offered rather than an awareness of a public interest in the utilization of land and water resources.

Successful performance of functions depends upon the use of a systematic set of evaluation criteria. Here Regan briefly outlines the framework for equi-marginal returns and proceeds immediately to an examination of a number of difficult evaluation problems which arise in connection with viewpoint and the standards used in measuring the benefits and costs. His analysis warrants careful study by all persons interested in the economics of watershed development. I should like to comment on only one point. A great deal has been said about the ability of economists to obtain reliable data for benefit-cost analyses of resource development projects. We are all familiar with the unmeasurable nature of some of the benefits and with other measurement problems arising when imperfections in market operations reduce the effectiveness of market prices as measures of public values. It is true that we need to seek diligently for data improvement, but we should not become so preoccupied with details as to overlook the possibilities of improving economic appraisals by focusing attention on a choice of plans. The framework which has been outlined will help determine when detail is necessary and, conversely, where costly detail will add little to the results of the analyses. Perhaps this is a main reason for having a framework for any analysis.

Lastly, Regan discusses cost-sharing requirements in relation to (1) achieving an efficient allocation of resources and (2) promoting incidence patterns consistent with public policy objectives and welfare criteria. In the former, the main problems are avoidance of situations whereby local organizations extend favored purposes beyond justified levels, disparities arising from differences in the value standards acceptable to the various participants, the effects of cost-sharing on waste or under-utilization of project services, and the use of cost-sharing as a check on reliability of the evaluation analysis. Here again, I am in agreement, and wish Regan had developed the latter more fully. Substantial cost-sharing at the local level as a requirement appears necessary if resources are to be developed on a basis of benefits and needs rather than a transfer of income from the general public to a local group. However, where benefits are so widely diffused that it becomes impractical to determine benefit recipients and assess costs accordingly, financial responsibility should rest with the general public.

In his discussion of promoting incidence patterns consistent with public policy objectives and welfare criteria, Regan says, "The economic justification for compensation for property acquired by purchase or eminent domain would appear applicable to property adversely affected by land use regulations and zoning." This statement raises an important question. Is zoning not a forward-looking measure primarily adapted to orderly development of land use rather than to correction of adverse land uses? If so, I believe property owners should not be compensated for restrictions imposed under zoning ordinances, except for the purchase of nonconforming rights.

Robert E. Lowry is a public administration analyst with TVA, where he has been on the staff since 1935, except for a two-year period with the naval military government. Earlier he was with the Ohio Institute and the National Reemployment Service.

Chapter 16

ROBERT E. LOWRY

Organization for Watershed Planning in the Public Interest

T HE WATERSHED PLANNER is constantly reminded that land and water resources are administered differently. Land programs are guided by broad national policies and administered as continuing operations. Water resource developments, on the other hand, are traditionally conceived as individual projects, each separately justified. Within specified beginning and ending dates the objectives of water projects are usually sought by an intensive effort temporarily applied.

Watershed activity has been generally organized into projects rather than programs. If separate watershed projects can be fitted into a cohesive continuing program, they serve more fully the national interest in water management and the state and local interest in economic development. Ways need to be found to preserve the desirable features of both project and program approaches to organization for watershed planning. An administrative theory is needed to incorporate land and water aspects of watershed improvements into a broad framework of national and state policy without sacrificing the values attached to local area development.

The national interest in watershed development began, modestly enough, as an upstream adjunct to river basin flood control programs. The Flood Control Act of 1944 authorizes the Department of Agriculture to intensify its national land treatment programs for improvement of runoff, waterflow retardation, and soil erosion prevention, concentrating them on the upper watersheds of eleven river systems. Over the next few years the Department of Agriculture, with the approval of Congress, gradually added engineering works to land treatment on the grounds that these were needed for more complete flood control.[1] Local development became the major objective with the passage of Public Law 566 — the Watershed Protection and Flood Prevention Act of 1954. Still more recently other phases of water conservation and use have been added to the flood control structures by amendments to Public Law 566. [2]

The evolution of land treatment programs of the Department of Agriculture into more comprehensive water control engineering and area development projects has not been unopposed. The House Committee on Public Works investigated in 1952 and recommended that upstream engineering works be returned to the Army Corps of Engineers.[3] The Second Hoover Commission agreed that the Department of Agriculture should leave flood control to the Army Engineers.[4] Both investigators took the position that the department should not engage extensively in water control engineering. In the background were questions as to whether the application of water management techniques to area development should be administered as primarily an agricultural problem.

In the view of many observers, watershed planning and development as presently organized fall short of achieving full status as a national program. In the language of Public Law 566, works of improvement are authorized to prevent erosion, floodwater, and sediment damages that "constitute a menace to the national welfare." The congressional intent is to advance the "conservation, development, utilization, and disposal of water," thereby preserving and protecting the nation's land and water resources. [5] Administrative shortcomings appear when the quest for these national objectives is diverted into detailed consideration of localized project-by-project results. A preoccupation with economic justification within restricted territorial limits has tended to obscure the broader interest as expressed in Public Law 566.

Three points relating to watershed planning and the public interest will be considered. One is that organization of the national watershed program according to local units, with the transient, temporary characteristics inherent in the project type of approach, tends to remove

---

[1] 85th Congress (House), Department of Agriculture Appropriations for 1959; Hearings (Washington: U.S. Government Printing Office, 1958), Pt. 1, p. 386.

[2] Public Law 1018, 84th Congress, 2nd Session, Chap. 1027.

[3] 82nd Congress (House), Committee Print No. 22, "The Flood Control Program of the Department of Agriculture" (Washington: U. S. Government Printing Office, 1952), p. 42.

[4] Commission on Organization of the Executive Branch of the Government, 1953, "Water Resources and Power," Recommendation No. 6 (Washington: U.S. Government Printing Office, 1955), Vol. I, p. 71.

[5] President Eisenhower's statement upon signing Public Law 566 (68 Stat. 666) adds that, "This legislation is significant because it gives new stimulus to local initiative and establishes for the first time a nationwide program of conservation practices based on the concept that farms, streams, forests, and towns are all interrelated parts of a watershed." *Congressional Record*, Vol. 100, p. A6165, Aug. 18, 1954.

watershed development from the normal channels through which most
public services are administered and financed — causing this activity to
be an appendage to public policy rather than an integral part of it. The
second point is that separate economic justification of watershed projects impairs opportunity to view in wider perspective the contribution
watershed planning can make to water management and economic development for nation and region. A third concern is what might be done
organizationally to establish watershed planning and development more
firmly as a national program within a framework of federal and state
policy.

FRAGMENTATION TENDENCIES

An important factor directing the national watershed program into a
project type of approach has been the heavy reliance upon federal-local
relationships. The Public Law 566 requirement of local participation
in watershed project planning has necessitated local organizations especially created for the purpose. New alignments are taking form outside the traditional structure of local government, and direct channels
of communication are opening up between local watershed districts and
federal agencies. Watershed development has clothed itself in much
the same organizational arrangements as flood control projects, although
intended to serve a more comprehensive purpose.

There has been a tendency toward removal of individual watershed
projects from their setting in a larger water region. Much of the national interest in watershed development originated from the fact that
watersheds are subdivisions of the nation's river valleys. As early as
1936 TVA was advising the Congress that "In a general program for
the unified development of the Tennessee River system, the small tributary rivers with drainage areas of 25 or 50 square miles up to 300 to
600 square miles play an important part."[6] On a national scale the
interrelation of upstream watersheds to downstream water control
within major river systems is declared or implied in the flood control
acts of 1936, 1938, and 1944, and in executive orders and administrative
directives.[7]

In spite of pronouncements that watersheds are a part of comprehensive river basin planning, the trend has been toward separate and
independent watershed project status. The Pilot Watershed Act of 1953
was the first to authorize watershed projects divorced from major
river flood control plans. A year later the 1954 statute, requiring local

---

[6] Tennessee Valley Authority, "Report to the Congress on the Unified Development of the
Tennessee River System," 1936, p. 47.

[7] Executive Order 10584, prescribing rules and regulations for the administration of
Public Law 566, directs that "The Secretary of Agriculture shall submit plans for installation of works of improvement under the Act to the Congress through the President only if
the Secretary is satisfied that such works constitute needed and harmonious elements in the
comprehensive development of the river sub-basin or river basin involved." 3CFR, 1954,
Suppl., p. 98.

sponsorship of projects, made the separation of watershed from river basin more complete. A 1956 amendment to Public Law 566 eased requirements for review of watershed plans by federal agencies responsible for river basin planning.[8] Spokesmen for the Department of Agriculture were able to testify by 1958 that "upstream detention structures must be integrated in place and time with soil and water conservation measures applied on watershed lands."[9] The manual of instructions for use of the Soil Conservation Service watershed workplan parties[10] makes little provision for relating watershed problems to either river basin or other external conditions. An economics guide for preparing workplans[11] omits altogether any specific reference to the river basin and the region in the formulation of watershed plans. Workplans for national watershed projects are required to give at best only perfunctory notice of conditions outside the immediate watershed area.[12]

A separatist tendency is found also in the relation of watershed projects to the states. Most small watershed projects are entirely within and — in a geographic sense — are subdivisions of states. More than five years have elapsed since Senator Mundt complained that state governments were being ignored in local requests to the federal government for watershed planning assistance. Over the years some progress has been made in strengthening the role of the states.[13] There is growing recognition that national-local relationships bypassing the states were at variance with a truly federal system of government.[14] To most eastern states, however, water management and watershed development have had little appeal. States in general have authorized direct federal-to-local arrangements for watershed planning with minimum controls or supervision. The over-all financial position of states (36 in the nation had deficit spending in 1958) has not been conducive to their embracing a new and costly governmental function.

The passive attitude of most state governments toward watershed planning contrasts with the increasing concern states are showing for

---

[8] Public Law 1018, *op. cit.*

[9] 86th Congress (House), Department of Agriculture Appropriations for 1960; Hearings (Washington: U. S. Government Printing Office, 1959), Pt. 2, p. 1059.

[10] Soil Conservation Service, *Watershed Protection Handbook*, USDA, July, 1957.

[11] Soil Conservation Service, *Economics Guide for Watershed Protection and Flood Prevention,* USDA, Dec., 1958.

[12] In the Tennessee Valley, however, provisions for consultation between SCS and TVA are set forth in Executive Order 10584, and are implemented by a memorandum of understanding negotiated in 1958. Cooperation between the two agencies has been good. The legal basis for TVA interest in Public Law 566 projects in the Valley rests in Section 26a of the TVA Act, which directs the TVA Board to review plans for all works on the Tennessee River and tributaries that may affect water control operations and federal facilities.

[13] The Tennessee Valley states participate in field investigations, approve watersheds for planning, and enact enabling legislation for local sponsoring district organizations. Kentucky contributes financially to planning of Public Law 566 projects. The Mississippi Forestry Commission, by agreement with the U. S. Forest Service, undertakes the forestry phases of Public Law 566 developments in the state. In all Valley states except Kentucky the state interest is represented by the state Soil Conservation Committee. In Kentucky it is the Department of Conservation.

[14] See L. L. Durisch and R. E. Lowry, "State Watershed Policy and Administration in Tennessee," *Public Admin. Rev.*, Vol. XV, Winter, 1955, pp. 17-20.

over-all economic planning. Economic conditions are nearly as important a political issue in gubernatorial campaigns as in presidential elections. Nearly every state of the Southeast has recently reorganized or revitalized its programs for industrial, economic, and resources development. State capitals and universities are studying the basic causes of growth in manufacturing, trade, and agriculture. Water as a factor important to economic expansion has been increasingly recognized by southeastern state leadership.[15] It is surprising that most states have not yet associated watershed development more closely with their own economic interests. Perhaps it is because watershed project planning has given too little consideration to these interests.

Support of watershed activity by state and local government is inhibited by the high level of project expenditures. Planning alone has been reported as costing $52,000 for a typical watershed.[16] The installation of Lick Creek watershed in Tennessee is estimated to involve outlays in excess of $6 million. These obligations, even with their offsetting benefits, are considerably beyond the normal level of financial capability of government in most rural sectors of the Southeast. Costly watershed developments for limited local objectives are not yet accepted as an obligation of general government by either the states or the counties. If and when watersheds become an integral part of state economic planning, this situation will probably change.

Because it originated in the Department of Agriculture, national watershed planning has been directed mainly to rural problems. Limitations upon the size of watershed units (250,000 acres) generally have the effect of excluding important nonrural interests from watersheds, since they are selected primarily because of recurrent flood damages to crops, erosion and sedimentation of soils, demands for agricultural water, poor forest and farm management, and inadequacies in land treatment practices. Yet we see the cities and urban industry of the Southeast mushrooming in size and economic importance.[17] Strategically located rural lands face the early prospects of urban settlement, accompanied by urban-type problems. The dependence of cities upon their watersheds is coming to be as firmly established as the importance of water management to rural lands.[18] Careful examination of long-term urban and industrial requirements would add greatly to multiple-purpose concepts of watershed planning, but such examination is difficult when watersheds are organized on a project basis.

Watersheds organized as separate projects are excluded from the normal economic and political associations that are characteristic of other governmental activities. Watershed areas are bounded by natural topographic lines that may have little coincidence with economic

---

[15] Within the past five years, all of the Tennessee Valley states have created water study commissions or taken similar action to strengthen state interest in this field.

[16] Department of Agriculture Appropriations for 1959, *op. cit.*, p. 417.

[17] Over the past 25 years population of metropolitan areas in the Tennessee Valley states has increased 85 percent, while farm population has declined 40 percent.

[18] As evidence of growing municipal interest in water, see "Water Resources of Top Concern to Tennessee League, 1957-59," *Tennessee Town and City*, Vol. 8, Mar., 1957, pp. 6-7.

structure. They are, as a rule, not closely identified with the governmental and community organizations that exercise formal or informal control over public activity at the local level. As a result, watershed district leaders must find their own channels of education and mutual understanding in order to build public confidence in watershed objectives. Watershed districts, where organized, are not yet accepted as fully accredited members of the family of local governments. What powers of taxation or eminent domain the districts possess are carefully contained and sparingly used. Acceptance of responsibility for watershed development by district organization provides a formal compliance to federal requirements, but there is little assurance that works planned under district leadership will give optimum service to the general public within their jurisdictions. Organizations created to sponsor public works have yet to prove their capacity as permanent bodies for day-to-day operation and maintenance of facilities.[19]

Within a project organization there is sometimes a temptation to overlook the established political leadership in favor of the technical, professional competence required in watershed planning. Engineering, economic, forestry, agricultural, agronomic, soils, and other skills are brought to focus in depth obviously beyond the resources and understanding of those local organizations officially responsible for watershed projects. The necessity for technical help, vital though it is, poses a limiting condition upon local leadership. Outside assistance — both planning and financial — takes on an overriding importance and, in fact, becomes a mechanism of informal control. The nominal watershed leaders, facing unfamiliar programs within unfamiliar territorial boundaries, often can do little but intuitively accept or reject the improvements offered them by the watershed practitioners. Too often the workplan fails to set forth alternative courses of action in understandable terms. In many states the facilities of agricultural extension and other educational agencies have not been used to the fullest in bridging the hiatus between technical and political leadership at the watershed level.[20]

These are some of the organizational factors that tend to divert watershed activity from the main stream of public affairs. They limit also the effectiveness of watershed planning in achieving its full potential for comprehensive area development.

---

[19] In the Tennessee Valley states, Mississippi continues to operate under old drainage district enabling legislation, amended to include work authorized by Public Law 566. Soil conservation districts are the watershed project sponsors in Georgia. Other Valley states have or are seeking comparatively new special district organization: watershed districts in Tennessee and North Carolina; water conservancy districts in Alabama and Kentucky; water improvement districts in Virginia. In most states the lack of a state program to effectively supervise and assist watershed district organizations has been a handicap.

[20] The use of watersheds as resource program demonstrations deserves more exploration than it has received. This educational device has been applied in selected areas within the Tennessee Valley. Durisch and Lowry, *op. cit.*

SEPARATE PROJECT JUSTIFICATIONS

Local project benefits have become the key factor in evaluating the national interest in watershed activity. National interest — and the federal investment that reflects national interest — are determined by favorable economic findings within small hydrographic units. Benefits calculated for justification of projects are usually direct and definable, measurable in the same dollar units as costs are measured. The benefit base tends to be narrowly prescribed. Instructions to watershed planners advise that agricultural benefits from flood control works shall be determined either as flood losses prevented or as land enhancement.[21] This type of benefit generally accrues to landowners operating in flood plains, not to the whole watershed public. In some instances fewer than ten landowners may be benefited, with little or no cost-sharing required of them.[22]

There is no disposition here to question the technical competence of benefit-cost analysis. One can accept the fact that ratios of benefits to costs provide an objective scale for justifying individual watershed projects. It is important to note, however, that watershed workplan preparation rests on the premise that nearly all direct benefits are to be found within the watershed itself, and that they are measurable in the same coin and quantitative terms as costs are measured. If benefits are thus identifiable and measurable, presumably they are also assessable, though cost-sharing arrangements avoid this logic. Moreover, the selection of watershed projects and decisions between alternative improvements within projects, when made by findings of local benefits, may not weigh sufficiently the contributions such projects will make toward national and state program objectives. Those concerned with public policy might well ask why criteria for the selection of watershed projects should not give at least equal consideration to "preserving and protecting the nation's land and water resources" — as stated in the federal authorizing legislation — that they give to local land enhancement.

Many observers are convinced that a too rigid requirement of economic justification on a project-by-project basis can seriously compromise the public quality of watershed program objectives. It is conceded that nationally the conservation of water and related land resources must rest upon a broad base of economic benefit — fhat, by and large, resources are conserved, developed, or otherwise made available for economic use. It is more difficult, however, to apply this general principle separately to each watershed project. Let us suppose that a search for a favorable economic return in watershed X is successful. Sufficient

[21] While local cost-sharing for land enhancement values of water projects is required under Bureau of the Budget Circular A-47, it is not required under interpretations of Public Law 566; thus, land enhancement resulting from flood prevention in Public Law 566 watersheds is, in effect, financed by federal appropriations. Department of Agriculture Appropriations for 1959, *op. cit.*, p. 408.

[22] As of November, 1957, the estimated federal share of construction costs for approved Public Law 566 projects was about 93 percent of total estimated costs. (From data presented in Department of Agriculture Appropriations for 1959, *op. cit.*, p. 343.)

project benefits to flood-plain landowners are found that are direct, identifiable, and measurable. The question still remains whether such favorable findings from a select group of beneficiaries make the case for a publicly financed activity. Certainly the distinction between justified public investment and prudent private investment becomes obscure if identical forms and amounts of economic return are controlling in both instances.

A widely held belief is that pinpointing of benefits within projects attracts forceful political support and public appropriations for water-related programs. Political support for the program as a whole is often a compelling reason for the attention paid in watershed planning to direct and localized benefits. Yet a precise blueprint of local results may sometimes only add to the upstream-downstream controversies between economic and geographic interests that smolder within watershed communities. How often has an upland farmer refused easements for a detention reservoir mainly on the grounds that such works would protect holdings of landowners on the flood plains below? To assure public support, the essentially public nature of watershed activity must be clearly and vigorously shown.

This leads to the proposition that government needs to search out additional public benefits of watershed programs — values that must be ascribed as public because they cannot be stated in dollar amounts — and desirable results that are indirect, secondary, and in many instances remote from the area of impact.[23] These findings would be drawn in part from project workplans, but would embrace larger issues than the local problems of each watershed. It seems reasonable to believe that public policy on watershed development, as in education, health, and other fields also of genuine public concern, could rest upon decisions more inclusive than a determination of what group or groups gain by each local improvement, how, and by what amounts. The economic purpose of watershed development, its importance undiminished, would emerge as a public policy judgment on the state and national scene rather than confined to benefit values within hundreds of localized settings.

The total public stake in this nation's watersheds and its land-water resources eludes the slide rule. No completely satisfactory way has been found to measure in dollars the importance of sound water management to the national security and welfare, nor to assess all of the values of soil restoration and prevention of soil losses, the public health benefits from abatement of pollution, the easing of fears of floods, the lasting advantages of forest and pasture cover, the human and aesthetic satisfactions from parks and recreation and from fish and wildlife

---

[23] The Soil Conservation Service in its *Watershed Protection Handbook* recognizes the existence of secondary benefits but warns: "Secondary benefits will not be used for economic justification but may be used for establishing equitable cost-sharing arrangements." *Op. cit.*, Sec. 6, p. 10. A contrasting view stated by the Committee on Public Finance is that: "The role of government in the total pattern of economic organization must be justified in terms of social as well as economic values." Committee on Public Finance, *Public Finance* (New York: Pitman Publishing Co., 1959), p. 31.

sanctuaries, and the intangibles that go to make up a better, safer, and more enjoyable life. Benefits of watershed development may accrue in unforeseeable ways to future generations, or to distant peoples. To a few of these benefits a price tag may be ingeniously attached. However, it is inadmissible that those values without price should be overlooked, discarded, or supplanted by less socially desirable but more easily identified results. Is it sound public policy that each watershed project should require specific proof of its value by a dollar yardstick before it is regarded as "justified?"

A larger view may be extremely useful to supplement economic measures of costs and benefits within individual watershed projects. Have such projects been fitted into an over-all water resources policy for this nation and its major river valleys? Have they been tested against basic economic and land use goals of a state or region? Water control improvements in a particular area are designed either to hold water back or to carry it away faster. How does this engineering decision conform to judgments on downstream economic growth or future water demand?

The urbanizing trend should be more fully recognized in watershed justifications. Do watershed improvements now designed mainly to protect rural land also meet urban-industrial needs, and are they adjusted to future prospects of population explosion and redistribution confronting the nation and its major economic regions? There are many regions of the nation that stand now at an agricultural-industrial crossroad. Their future may lie in either direction. Can we separate the rural and urban benefits of watershed development in an age of growing interdependence and merging of these historic divisions?

All this is to say that watershed planning needs special effort if it is to be really foresighted and comprehensive. Statistical measures are essential as one tool in selecting projects; policy decisions must continue to have this kind of economic support. However, we must face up to the fact that benefits of watershed projects are diffused, and not all are purely economic. Economic values are themselves diminished by an over-zealous effort to compact them within project boundaries.

ORGANIZATION FOR PROGRAM PLANNING[24]

Responsible public action comes in part with sound organizational arrangements. This leads to the third and most controversial point, directed to the question of organization for watershed planning and development.

On this subject, agency lines have been firmly drawn. Few areas of politics and administration in the resources field have provoked as

---

[24] No effort is made here to even touch the enormously complicated problems of organization common to all aspects of resource development and conservation. A brief but excellent summary of these by Dr. Gilbert White is contained in Resources for the Future, *Perspectives on Conservation* (Baltimore: Johns Hopkins Press, 1958), pp. 205-26.

much controversy as has the jurisdictional debate regarding national watershed operation. A federal organization is obviously needed to administer a national watershed program. But watershed activity is so comprehensive, at least potentially, that no single agency is ideally fitted for this multi-function type of work on a national scale. The question can be fairly raised whether the federal establishment is organized for area development in the form envisioned by national watershed legislation.

A few principles of program organization for watershed development are suggested here in general terms. As a basic proposition, it seems appropriate that watershed organization should take account more fully of the dominant federal interest in water and land resources management and the dominant state-local interest in economic development. Both are close to the ultimate objectives of watershed programs.

A key question is one of leadership and responsibility for watershed work. State government seems to this observer to be the focal point in our federal system for decisions affecting particular watersheds. The present inadequacies of most states in the field of water management from the standpoint of organization, financing, and staff are admitted by the states themselves, through their Council of State Governments.[25] There is room for optimism, however, that the interest and the competence of states in watershed policy and administration will grow in response to public pressure, just as the state interest in economic development has grown.

It is possible to make a case for a stronger state role in watershed project decisions by reference to other programs. The interstate highway and urban renewal programs are quite different from watershed activity in important respects. Yet they have features of federal-state relationships worth study. Like watershed development, urban renewal and interstate highways are national programs. They originate and take final form essentially as engineering projects. Unlike watershed development, they require that projects be fitted into larger plans and long-range economic trends.[26] The highway program establishes the state as the principal agency for planning and administration, with the national interest protected by federal performance standards and activated by federal grants. The urban renewal program is presently a federal-local undertaking like the national watershed program, but recent studies of the program have urged greater state participation.[27]

---

[25] Council of State Governments, "State Administration of Water Resources," Chicago, 1957.

[26] Thus, S. 57 before the 86th Congress would amend the 1954 Housing Act as follows: "The Administrator is further authorized to make grants to state planning agencies for statewide comprehensive planning including research and coordination directly related to urban needs."

[27] "States, no less than the Federal Government, have a major stake in the success of urban renewal efforts.... State action... permits a degree of flexibility in urban renewal programs not likely to be achieved in a purely federal-local effort.... The job to be done is so vast that it requires the combined action of all levels of government...." Joint Federal-State Action Committee, Second Report to the President of the United States (Washington: U.S. Government Printing Office, 1958), pp. 62-63.

State responsibility for watersheds should include financing. The superior financial resources of the federal government, however, suggest that grants-in-aid might be used to equalize state differences in need for watershed improvements and in fiscal capability. Grants-in-aid are no cure-all for financial difficulties, and separation of fiscal from administrative responsibility has not always turned out well. But possibilities of grants should at least be explored. State and local financing might be helped by at least partial recovery of land enhancement values that result from watershed projects and that enter into calculations of project benefits.

Professional competence required in watershed programs is particularly available within the highly specialized agencies at the federal level. Use of this planning assistance by the states should be continued and even expanded. However, there is a need for regional diversity in watershed management, and state-by-state experimentation. Watershed program organization should encourage further technology and research within states and state institutions.

Organization for watershed planning should — more often than it now does — recognize the mounting urban and industrial interest in water and related land resources. This suggests that the area for planning and decision-making includes cities as well as rural lands. Plans should consider industrial as well as agricultural development. Watershed leadership, advisory services, and planning bodies should have urban as well as rural representation. Differences in flood problems according to rural and urban land use must be taken into account. Urban financial sources should be tapped.

Multiple-use planning is one of the evolving features of watershed programs. It complicates both administrative and political decisions. Multiple-use plans are especially difficult where areas for planning are small and only direct benefits are counted. To accomplish multiple uses, we need to consider possibilities of hydrographic units for planning much larger in area than 250,000 acres, areas large enough that the typical southeastern state might have 10 to 15 such divisions. Comprehensive water resource plans for these areas would be a function of state leadership, with priorities established according to the urgency of water problems. Area plans could be incorporated into state-wide economic planning if and as the state so desired. Areas could also be subdivided into small watershed projects for more detailed planning, but the place of each proposed structure or improvement in a larger area development picture should be given recognition.

Multiple-use planning, whether of watershed or larger hydrographic subdivisions, creates its own problems of state organization. All resource purposes have their professional alignments and agency jurisdictions. Mechanisms are needed for coordination among numerous program agencies, but need to be applied in a way that gives reasonable freedom for final decision and action. Moreover, devices are needed for education and interpretation of technical planning directed to political leadership. Plans should be prepared with reasonable alternatives that invite decision by responsible public authority.

This suggests that principal responsibility for comprehensive or multipurpose watershed planning might best be accomplished through an organization not directly attached to operational divisions of state government.

Such an organization would represent the state in all phases of watershed program development. Its structure and responsibilities would vary with differences in over-all state organization, but might include: (1) preparing plans for watersheds or other hydrographic divisions of the state, either directly or by arrangement with other agencies; (2) coordinating plans with interested state agencies into a workable state watershed program; (3) getting review and approval of this program by the state authority legally qualified to do so; (4) exercising necessary supervision over local watershed organizations; (5) acquiring easements and rights-of-way where necessary; and (6) acting for the state in dealing with the federal government in the watershed field.

At the local level, states would encourage the formation of special district organizations, again according to watersheds or larger hydrographic divisions. The structure and duties of the local organizations naturally would vary from one state to another. They would presumably hold hearings on the need for planning assistance and on the local acceptability of alternative plans of action. They would serve mainly as a bridge between the technically correct and the politically feasible. Education in watershed purposes would perhaps be the most important job of the local organizations. In most cases agricultural extension could assist the district leadership in reaching the rural sectors.

Agencies for multipurpose development of river basins can be helpful to states in their watershed planning, and in any case should have opportunity for review of state plans that affect their river basin jurisdictions. In addition to planning functions, river basin engineering organizations, where they operate, could assist the states in the design, installation, and maintenance of watershed facilities. The states would decide if these functions would be undertaken directly by their own agencies or through sources of assistance available to them.[28]

While details need more study, the proposal in broad outline is that attention be given to a federal-state organization that would combine watershed projects within subdivisions of states into a workable state program, geared to state economic plans and long-range aspirations. Such state programs would be given federal help to the extent they are found to advance national policy and national water- and land-management objectives. An important feature is that decisions regarding individual projects would be made by the state governments; federal review of

---

[28]Various forms of river basin planning organizations have been proposed from time to time. Among the more recent, the Presidential Advisory Committee on Water Resources Policy in 1955 recommended water resources committees composed of representatives of the federal agencies and the states of the region. H.R. 3704 in the 86th Congress would declare congressional policy on multipurpose water development and establish water resource commissions in river basins to coordinate all plans and activities for water resource development.

projects would be in the context of proposals for state programs. As a corollary, provision would be made that watershed project plans contribute positively to planning and water management within the nation's major river valleys.

Of course, the willingness and capacity of states to take on additional watershed responsibilities would be a crucial factor. States like California and Ohio perhaps are ready to do so now. Others will need more time. Some states may never voluntarily accept new watershed responsibilities. Grants-in-aid from the federal government, if they are authorized, must be conditioned on state performance; but inaction by any state should not bar its watersheds from needed development. One solution may lie in the states exercising an option; at some designated date to be agreed upon, each state wishing to do so would take over responsibilities for a state-wide program of watershed area development under a plan of operation the state would devise with federal advice and assistance. The amount of over-all federal expenditure on watershed work in each state need not be increased or diminished by the state's decision on program administration.

SUMMARY AND CONCLUSIONS

With water and related land resources increasingly vital to the national welfare, the public interest gives watershed planning a high order of importance. The public interest suggests that watershed programs be planned in relation to such factors as long-range water management conditions, state and regional economic trends, and urban-rural developments. The broader purposes of watersheds tend to be obscured when programs are fragmented according to projects selected through local economic justifications. Alternative forms of organization might knit projects more closely into a state and national watershed program having values greater than the sum of separately conceived projects. Key elements of a watershed program might be identified as follows:

1. Comprehensive multipurpose planning according to major hydrographic units of states, under state leadership.
2. A strengthened state organization for supervision of plans and for incorporating them into a state program.
3. Federal review directed to workable state programs rather than specific projects. (A more precise national watershed policy for guidance is implicit in federal review.)
4. Cost-sharing by federal grants-in-aid to states, and by at least partial capture of land enhancement values of projects.
5. Coordination of watershed development with river basin planning, state economic goals, and national land and water resource purposes.
6. More attention to education and local understanding of watershed objectives.

Changes in organization are outlined here in only the most general terms. A great deal of detailed study is needed before the best possible action for watershed development can be recommended. The broad outline of a plan of organization must rest upon a solid conviction that the development of the nation's watersheds serves a genuine public purpose.

The task ahead is to get maximum public value from watersheds comprehensively planned and economically developed. There is no greater challenge in the entire field of resources administration. The vision of watersheds as the focal point for a sustained attack on land and water problems calls for realistic political and administrative decisions — many of which are still to be made.

FRED A. CLARENBACH | *Comment*

SOME YEARS AGO Walton Hamilton said that the solution of an economic problem involves making choices among conflicting and incommensurable values. Watershed planning is part of a process of choosing among alternative values in local resource development. The processes are usually complex, often obscure, sometimes misrepresented, and necessarily political in character. Determinations of who gets what, when, and how from watershed projects — and who pays what, when, and how — are made primarily through agencies of government and not primarily through the market. Whether the results of such fairly direct political decision-making are on the whole better or worse than outcomes primarily market-determined is itself a matter of value judgment. But whatever may be one's answer to that question, we seem to be irretrievably committed to heavy reliance on rather direct political methods for making many choices concerning land and water development. Yet it is abundantly clear to Robert Lowry and to practically every other observer of these processes that our relevant political institutions have many shortcomings, and the idea of this symposium reflects concern and hope that improvement may be possible.

Lowry's thoughtful and constructive paper is properly concerned with "fragmentation tendencies" in watershed development and with some of their causes. He suggests, however, that "Only minimum changes in the present approach should be required... to knit together a national program that would have values greater than the sum of its now separately conceived units." Now, I submit that the seven guidelines

Fred A. Clarenbach is Professor of Political Science at the University of Wisconsin. He has been on the staff of Cornell University, the University of Connecticut, the USDA, and the U.S. Department of the Interior.

presented by Lowry involve far more than "only minimum changes."
These well-conceived guidelines, in fact, point toward thorough re-
orientation of programs and restructuring of major parts of the governmental system relating to resource development. If the indicated arrangements were made, strong state economic development agencies
would have a central role, and watershed work would be incorporated
into state developmental programs. Federal agencies would be concerned mainly with "workable state programs" and with the relation of
projects to plans for larger basin areas. Divisions within states would
be big enough for comprehensive multipurpose planning covering both
urban and rural areas. The corresponding special district organization
would be sufficiently endowed with legal authority, powers, and staff to
permit it to function effectively in planning, in promoting public understanding and consent, and in other essential activities such as operation
and maintenance of facilities. These changes make up a big order and
would not be easy to achieve, however desirable they might be.

Moreover, the new dispensation within the national government
would seem to require not only a reorganization or firm coordination
of the several federal agencies, but also a fairly drastic remodeling of
processes within Congress itself. As Wantrup has pointed out (p. 10)
the federal water resources program may be thought of as the collection
of projects whose proponents were able to muster the necessary congressional support. And intertwined with the congressional committees
and with the separate agencies are such facts of life as the Rivers and
Harbors Congress, the National Watershed Congress, and other important organizations which do not readily consent to changes in the rules
of the game if their interests are not thereby promoted. Lowry does
point out that "practical difficulties" confront those who would convert
principles into procedures and action.

Early in the paper Lowry suggests that the kinds of improvements
outlined might be thought of as falling within the framework of present
policies. But he also points out that many present difficulties are traceable to vague and conflicting policies embodied in statutes, regulations,
and the less formally established behavior patterns of the federal agencies. In fact, at some points, policy — in the sense of stable and consistent principles for the guidance of water resource development — is
virtually nonexistent. It seems to me, therefore, that the most significant improvements in organization and in planning processes must be
related to changes in and authoritative clarifications of water policies.
And, since policies are sometimes secreted in the interstices of agency
procedures, we need not only the verbal proclamation of more appropriate policies, but also effective machinery in the executive branch to
see that operating agencies do not seriously distort or drift away from
or ignore the stated policies when pressures rise in particular situations.

A key issue of policy, just emphasized by Mark Regan and William
Gibson, concerns cost-sharing. This question is closely related to the
problem of local responsibility, local organization, and a viable pattern

of intergovernmental relations. Irving Fox has stated one issue in this way: "Can efficiency in water resources development be attained when the direct beneficiaries pay such a small share of the cost?" While recognizing that efficiency might be theoretically possible even if all costs were borne by Uncle Sam, Fox nevertheless points toward a practical answer in the negative with the further query: "But are our institutions capable of achieving this goal when many benefits are local and specific, when the task of analysis is so complex, and when responsibility for bearing the cost is diffused over the entire population instead of borne by those who benefit directly?" [1]

My observation is that the Soil Conservation Service, operating according to law and under its environmental limitations, is frequently not very successfully promoting either efficient development of water resources or responsible local government. Much of the watershed work boils down to local real-estate improvement projects at national expense. If the local landowners can, in fact, often obtain such benefits at almost no cost and with a bare minimum of local government responsibility, the stage is naturally set for a considerable display of local irresponsibility — and the play is in progress. In short, our governmental arrangements are not operating satisfactorily under the strategic handicap of faulty cost-sharing policies. The Soil Conservation Service, however, is not likely to cast great blame on this policy goat, possibly because of some connection with the creature's birth and growth.

To conclude: I like the alternative governmental arrangements indicated by Lowry, and especially his emphasis on the importance of responsible participation in watershed development by strong state and local governmental agencies. I hope that the idea, shared by many others, may prove to be not simply utopian.

---

[1] Irving Fox, "National Water Resource Policy Issues," *Law and Contemporary Problems*, Vol. XXII, No. 3, Summer, 1957, pp. 508-9.

Harold H. Ellis is an agricultural economist with the Land and Water Research Branch of the USDA. He holds bachelor's degrees in law and science from the University of Illinois, and a master of science degree from Michigan State University. He maintained a private law practice in Illinois during 1948 and 1949.

Chapter 17

HAROLD H. ELLIS[1]

Relationships Between Water and Other Property Rights and Small Watershed Development in the Eastern States

RELATIONSHIPS between water and other property rights and small watershed development are explored in this chapter.[2] Primary attention is given to Public Law 566 projects, which constitute a substantial part of small watershed development in the 31 states east of Texas and the Dakotas. Watershed development projects, in addition to providing flood protection and other benefits, may reduce the severity of water rights problems in the eastern states by enlarging available water supplies. But there remain a variety of water and other property rights questions.

COURT DECISIONS REGARDING WATER RIGHTS

There has been considerable state legislation affecting water rights.

---

[1] Opinions are those of the author and do not necessarily represent official views. As research regarding all matters covered herein has not been completed, no definitive conclusions are presented.

[2] See also Wells A. Hutchins and Harry A. Steele, "Basic Water Rights Doctrines and Their Implications for River Basin Development," and Frank J. Trelease, "A Model State Water Code for River Basin Development," *Law and Contemporary Problems*, Vol. XXII,

But the bulk of the law is still embodied in the court decisions of each state. The general rules of law described herein vary from state to state and may be modified by legislation, contractual arrangements, prescriptive rights, or other complicating factors.

A watercourse is often defined as a stream that flows along a definite channel, with a bed and banks, for a sufficient time to give it a substantial existence. This may include streams that dry up periodically, or springs which flow through or along the lands of two or more owners.[3] The riparian doctrine is commonly applied by eastern courts to the use of water in natural watercourses.[4] This doctrine provides that owners of lands that adjoin watercourses — riparian owners — have certain rights to the use of water that accompany their ownership of such lands. Riparian owners have rights to obtain water from a watercourse by some reasonable method of diversion for use on their adjoining lands for "domestic" or so-called natural purposes. These purposes include water for household needs and the watering of at least a few head of cattle for home use.[5] In a number of states, each riparian owner along a stream may use all the available water he reasonably needs for such purposes, even though he thereby exhausts the total flow. But the rights to use water for farm irrigation, manufacturing purposes, and other so-called artificial purposes stem from one of the following two doctrines:[6]

1. The "natural flow" doctrine permits a riparian owner to take water for artificial purposes only if (a) there is more than enough to satisfy the domestic-use requirements of lower riparian owners, and (b) such use does not substantially lower the water level or impair the quality of the water.
2. The "reasonable use" doctrine, the one more generally followed, permits a riparian owner to use water for artificial purposes as long as the use is reasonable, considering all circumstances at the time. All riparian owners along the watercourse may have such rights, the rights of each qualifying those of the others. Reasonable use is determined by such factors as: (a) size and character of the watercourse, (b) location and type of use, (c) amount of water returned, and (d) rights and reasonable requirements of other riparian owners.

Spring, 1957. River basin development, not considered herein, often may involve interstate compacts or international treaties and construction of dams and other improvements by federal agencies.

[3] Omitted from the discussion will be consideration of: (1) instances in which a dam may be located in a normally dry, intermittently flowing draw, gully, or ravine where questions may arise as to whether this constitutes a natural watercourse or diffused surface water; and (2) instances in which a dam may be located in an *artificial* water channel or a natural channel that has been artificially improved to an extent that special considerations may apply.

[4] In all eastern states except Louisiana this doctrine has its historical roots in court decisions. In Louisiana the Civil Code has provided its principal basis. See L. S. A. — Civil Code Art. 661.

[5] In some states, family (but not commercial) recreational uses may be treated as domestic use, although a number of courts have said that domestic use includes only such uses as are necessary to the sustenance of the family.

[6] There are various shadings between these two doctrines in several states.

Under either doctrine, priority in time of use is usually of no importance, and riparian rights are not lost simply by failing to exercise them. But, particularly under the reasonable use doctrine, one riparian owner may find courts reluctant to enjoin another's use unless he thereby may suffer imminent damage.

Overflow waters that will naturally return directly to the watercourse are generally considered a part of it and subject to riparian rights. A landowner may make use of overflow waters that will not so return as he sees fit, as long as his use does not cause damage to adjoining lands.

A number of state courts have not precisely defined riparian land, nor have they decided about the use of water on other land. Several courts have held that to be riparian to a watercourse, land must be contiguous to it and lie within its watershed. Some courts have added that it may consist of no more than the original ownership tract when acquired from the government, and that a conveyance of any part of the original tract that does not touch the watercourse results in the loss of riparian rights with respect to that part, unless otherwise provided. Municipal or other nonriparian use often is not permissible. But a limited use of the water on nonriparian land, subject to riparian rights, is permitted under the reasonable use rule in a number of states.[7]

The riparian doctrine described above usually applies to both navigable and nonnavigable watercourses, but riparian rights in navigable watercourses are more subject to public use and regulation. In a few states, except for their access to such watercourses, riparian landowners may have no better rights than the general public to use the waters.[8]

Constructing a Dam on a Watercourse

In constructing a dam[9] on a stream it may be necessary to obtain the right to flood the lands inundated by the reservoir and to use land upon which to build the dam. In the case of nonnavigable streams, the

---

[7] See, e.g., Virginia Hot Springs Co. vs. Hoover, 143 Va. 460, 130 S.E. 409 (1925); Stratton vs. Mt. Hermon Boys School, 216 Mass. 83, 103 N.E. 87 (1913). In a few states, nonriparian owners who have obtained legal access to a stream may obtain fairly substantial rights. For example, the Vermont Supreme Court has stated: "The fact that such [persons] were taking the water to their nonriparian lands did not per se make their use unreasonable. But that fact, together with the size and character of the stream, the quantity of water appropriated, and all the circumstances and conditions, might make their use unreasonable." Lawrie vs. Sillsby, 82 Vt. 505, 74 Atl. 94, 96 (1909). See also Griswold vs. Town School Dist., 117 Vt. 224, 88A 2d. 829 (1952); and Gillis vs. Chase, 67 N. H. 161, 31 Atl. 18 (1892).

[8] But this question is not clearly settled in most such states. I will not go into the several variations and complications that arise in applying state and federal tests to determine the navigability of a watercourse for various purposes. The navigability of a particular watercourse or portion thereof may depend largely on the circumstances. State courts usually consider its navigability for either (1) commercial purposes or (2) recreational purposes.

[9] Several of the legal problems discussed in regard to multiple-purpose dams also may apply to single-purpose dams, but the latter are not as apt to detain water during low-flow periods or to give rise to problems regarding nonriparian use and transportation of water.

lands generally are owned by the adjoining landowners. General rules
of law do not permit the deliberate flooding of another's land with an
impoundment. Privately owned land, or easements to flood such land,
may be acquired by donation, purchase, or condemnation.[10]

The bed of a navigable stream is often owned by the state. If the
dam is to be erected for a public purpose, the state may give its consent
to erecting the dam on the bed it owns, provided it has taken necessary
measures to protect the public interest in such a stream.[11]

In addition to obtaining flooding easements and land upon which to
build the dam, there may be such problems as possible liability (1) to
upper landowners for obstructing their drainage; (2) to upper or lower
landowners, or the public, for obstructing the passage of fish or boats,
particularly if the watercourse is classed as navigable; (3) to lower
landowners or the public for cutting off or reducing the streamflow;
(4) to lower or adjoining landowners for casting floodwaters upon their
lands in the event of a breakthrough, negligent operation of a dam, etc.;
or (5) for contributing to stream pollution problems.

In operating the dam, as long as reasonable precautions are taken,
there normally would be no liability for damages caused by unusually
severe floods. Stricter precautions may be required, however, to avoid
liability for obstructing navigation or causing stream pollution.

An efficient flood control structure normally would be operated to
permit continuous and controlled release of the water impounded during
a flood stage or high-flow period. Usually it would be entirely released
within a few days, except for water retained in the sediment pool. During low-flow periods the streamflow may at times be retained in such a
pool, to replace evaporation and seepage losses.[12] (But this might be
partly or entirely offset by the re-entry into the stream of seepage or
related ground waters resulting from such impoundments.) In a number
of small watershed projects water is stored in a permanent pool for
irrigation, municipal, or industrial water supply. To the extent that
the streamflow is reduced by impoundment, liability to lower landowners
might arise. Under the reasonable use rule, such liability is more
likely to occur from impoundment during low-flow periods. Liability
especially may arise from injuring preferred domestic uses of a small
stream. There also may be problems with competing upstream water
uses.

The prohibitions or limitations on municipal and other nonriparian
use must be considered. While much water used by municipalities is
returned to the stream, its quality may be impaired, its return delayed,
or it may be returned far downstream from the intake point. The use
of water on nonriparian land may require rights-of-way and raise questions concerning the transportation and allocation of the stored water.

---

[10] Often it may be less expensive and otherwise easier to acquire flooding easements than
complete ownership, particularly easements to flood periodically the outer edges of the detention reservoir during the larger but infrequent floods.

[11] Public Law 566 provides that if small watershed projects are to be built on federal lands,
appropriate federal agencies shall be contacted.

[12] Considerable retention may occur in the initial filling up of a reservoir, but we are concerned here with the long-run effects of the structures.

Additional storage capacity may be added to flood control structures to supplement the natural streamflow in low-flow periods. This could benefit lower landowners. However, it may present additional problems. Transportation of stored waters results in a mixing of the stored water with the natural streamflow. Some courts have indicated that riparian rights of lower landowners may attach to the stored as well as to the natural water, once it has been released from the dam. But riparian and other rights in such mixed water may vary, depending on the arrangements made.

Public rights in navigable streams, including commercial navigation, pleasure boating, and fishing, may need to be considered.[13] Rights for installing structures on some streams may be granted by a state or local agency, and may relieve project sponsors of certain types of liability.[14] In addition, permission from appropriate federal agencies may be needed where commercial navigation is involved.[15] Even though a stream is nonnavigable, placing an impoundment on it may adversely affect the use of a lower navigable portion of the stream.[16] The state agency responsible for approving Public Law 566 projects presumably shall endeavor to safeguard state and public rights.[17]

Employing Condemnation Powers

Public Law 566 provides that those who undertake small watershed projects shall "acquire, or provide assurance that landowners or water users have acquired, such water rights, pursuant to state law, as may be needed" to construct and operate the works of improvement. Whether liability under the reasonable use rule may result from project activities depends on the circumstances. The uncertainty of liability of those who build and operate dams tends to be balanced by uncertainty as to the rights of others. Considering the benefits to be received from a

---

[13] But in some states, riparian landowners may hold more or less exclusive rights to fish, etc., in navigable streams, subject only to public rights of commercial navigation and certain related rights.

[14] Some state statutes expressly (1) require fish passageways in dams (see, e.g., Ark. Stat. Ann., sec. 21-1301 *et seq.*), and (2) give the state's consent to the building of authorized dams on beds which it may own (see, e.g., Ark. Stat. Ann., *op. cit.;* Va. Stat. Ann., sec. 62-94.10). Riparian landowners may have pleasure-boating rights in some nonnavigable streams. Each may have the exclusive right (at least along with an opposite owner) to boat and fish in waters adjoining his land, but may have no right to boat or to walk along or over other lands (except by acquiring such a right). Hence, it may be necessary to deal only with the rights of landowners adjoining the dam and reservoir in this regard.

[15] Congress has granted the Corps of Engineers, U. S. Army, certain regulatory authority over the construction of dams and alteration of the course or capacity of navigable waters. (30 Stat. 1151; 33 U.S.C.A., secs. 401 and 403.) Similar regulation regarding the Tennessee River Valley by the Tennessee Valley Authority is also provided. (49 Stat. 1079; 16 U.S.C.A., sec. 831y-1.)

[16] This paragraph constitutes a simplified discussion of a subject complicated by legislation and constitutional provisions.

[17] And in certain projects the recommendations of certain federal agencies shall be obtained. See 16 U.S.C.A., sec. 1001 *et seq.*

small watershed project,[18] such uncertainties may encourage a mutual accommodation of interests through voluntary arrangements. The participation of municipalities in such projects may encourage such accommodation of rural-urban water-rights conflicts that may arise. Moreover, possible liability to riparian landowners far downstream or along a connecting stream may be remote, because intervening additions of water to the stream may make it difficult to prove that damage has resulted.[19]

It often may be difficult to acquire all possible rights that might conceivably be infringed, but acquisition of rights that are most likely to be infringed and cause substantial damage would greatly mitigate risk of further liability. If such rights cannot be voluntarily acquired, condemnation may be considered. If it is, consideration may need to be given to the scope of a district's or agency's authorized condemnation powers.[20] In general, eminent domain may be exercised only for a public purpose, and it requires the payment of just compensation. There are several variations in the methods used to determine compensation. Some common basic rules are:

1. If land is taken, compensation will be at its fair market value immediately prior to the condemnation, or if there is any adjoining land of the condemnee remaining after the condemnation, the difference in the fair market value of the entire tract of land held by the condemnee before, and of the part remaining after, such condemnation.
2. If no land is taken, but associated water or other rights are condemned or the land may be otherwise damaged, the difference in the fair market value of the land before and after such condemnation will determine compensation.[21]

In determining compensation in a number of states, land taken or flooded may have to be paid for in full without reference to any benefits received from the project, although a landowner may be required to pay taxes or other charges for benefits received.[22] But if the landowner

---

[18] Depending on a particular landowner's location and other factors, such benefits may include flood protection and related benefits and water supply for various purposes.

[19] Particularly in local watershed projects that are not carried out under the federal Watershed Protection and Flood Prevention Act and are not subject to its requirements, certain additional factors may be worth considering. For example: (1) Insurance might be acquired to cover certain liability risks, particularly for direct damage to others' property. (2) In some states, if a district has condemnation powers and is later sued over rights it could have condemned but didn't, it has the right to have "permanent damages" assessed (similar to delayed condemnation) and continue to maintain the structure or uses in question, although subject perhaps to certain limitations that the court may impose. See 18 Amer. Jur., *Eminent Domain*, sec. 385; and Harold H. Ellis, "Some Legal Aspects of Water Use in North Carolina," *The Law of Water Allocation in the Eastern United States*, ed. Haber and Bergen (New York: The Ronald Press Co., 1958), pp. 351-54. (3) Depending on applicable state laws, persons who attempt to sue a district, agency, or other political entity may sometimes be faced with complicated questions concerning possible governmental immunity from suit for all or certain types of actions, and limited liability of governmental officials.

[20] These condemnation powers usually are based on statutory and constitutional provisions, as interpreted and augmented by the courts.

[21] See 18 Amer. Jur., *Eminent Domain*, secs. 242, 243, 252, 265.

[22] *Ibid.*, secs. 243, 294, 297, 301, 303. 3 Nichols, *Eminent Domain*, (1950), secs. 8.6204(1) and 8.6206.

will still be able to make use of the property, this may reduce the amount of compensation awarded.[23] In several states, benefits to any remaining adjoining land of the condemnee may be considered,[24] but such benefits often must be of a "special" nature.[25]

LEGISLATION REGARDING DAMS AND IMPOUNDMENTS

The discussion thus far has centered on problems under the riparian doctrine as developed by the eastern courts. Consider now: (1) questions that may arise under statutory permit systems and related legislation, and (2) impacts of small watershed development in the formulation of state water-law systems.

Both general and special-area state legislation have influenced small watershed development. Some legislation has served to safeguard public interests and to clarify rights regarding the impoundment of stream waters and the use of watercourses. Other legislation has led to confusion regarding its intended application without substantially clarifying any water rights.

Considerable eastern legislation has dealt with the impoundment and obstruction of stream waters, dating from early milldam statutes in the colonial period.[26] The milldam statutes often provided that permission be obtained from some local court to build a milldam across a stream, and they required that other riparian landowners, whose lands would be flooded, be compensated for any damages (akin to condemnation).[27] A number of these acts are still in effect, and some have been amended to apply to dams used for a variety of manufacturing and other purposes.

Legislation regarding the construction, improvement, or repair of dams has been enacted in a number of states. Several appear to be designed primarily to enforce standards of construction for public safety, usually through a permit from a state agency, rather than to regulate the use made of the impounded water or otherwise regulate water rights. Even so, it is uncertain whether some of these statutes free the permittee from possible liability to other persons in the event of a breakthrough, although the permit may be of evidential value — as in the question of negligence in the dam's construction.

Some statutes use the permit requirement for protection of a variety of other public interests other than public safety.[28] Some combine

---

[23] 18 Amer. Jur., *Eminent Domain*, sec. 251.

[24] *Ibid.*, secs. 297, 299, and 301.

[25] Special benefits are often defined as those accruing to particular properties because of their advantageous location in regard to the structure for which condemnation is employed, as contrasted to general benefits which may accrue to the surrounding area or community. See 3 Nichols, *Eminent Domain* (1950), secs. 8.62, 8.6203(1) and 8.6207; 18 Amer. Jur., *Eminent Domain*, secs. 297, 299, 301, 302.

[26] See Head vs. Amoskeeg Mfg. Co., 113 U.S. 9 (1855).

[27] Some have, in effect, permitted permanent or temporary condemnation for such purposes, although the court might deny or modify the application on certain grounds.

[28] See Yang-Ch'eng Shih, *American Water Resources Administration* (New York: Bookman Associates, Inc., 1956), Vol. II, p. 684.

regulation of impoundments with regulation of water use.[29] Except for the milldam acts, these statutes usually do not require that compensation be paid by the permittee to others who may be damaged. Several are vague about permits having any effect on the permittee's liability to others. Conversely, the acquisition of various rights by donation, purchase, or condemnation generally would not avoid the necessity of obtaining a permit. Several statutes include important exceptions. For example, small dams for domestic or farming uses and uses begun prior to passage of the legislation may be excepted.

Legislation To Facilitate Storage From High- to Low-Flow Periods

Some states have recently enacted statutes to facilitate the storage of water during seasons of high flow for later use during seasons of low flow.[30] In states where rights to do this would otherwise be in doubt, this is a helpful part of a system of water rights, especially if it also facilitates multiple-purpose structures. However, there are a number of problems related to these statutes.

A Virginia statute provides that any riparian landowner may apply to an appropriate court for permission to impound and store waters in excess of the "average flow" in a nonnavigable watercourse. After receiving the recommendations of the appropriate state agencies concerned, the court may grant permission — subject to certain mandatory limitations and prohibitions.[31] Arkansas and Indiana statutes require that such permission be obtained from a state agency. The Arkansas statute allows permits to be issued to any person, municipality, public or private corporation, or state or local governmental agency. An impoundment permit may be issued as long as the applicant either owns or "has a right to occupy" the land on which the impoundment is located.

Such statutes usually are vague regarding the degree of security afforded the permittee. It appears unlikely, for example, that the permittee is freed from possible liability to others for causing their lands to be flooded. The statutes apparently are intended at least to free the permittee from possible liability to others who suffer no real damage from the impoundment.[32] Moreover, the hearing held by the court or

---

[29] See, e.g., Iowa Code Ann., sec. 455A.1 *et seq.*; Miss. Code Ann., sec. 5956.01 *et seq.*

[30] See especially Va. Code Ann., sec. 62-94.1 *et seq.*; Ark. Stat. Ann., sec. 21-1301 *et seq.* See also Burns Ind. Stat., sec. 27-1401 *et seq.*; Ky. Rev. Stat., sec. 262.680 *et seq.*

[31] No such permission shall be granted, for example, if the Water Control Board states that the reduction of pollution will be impaired or made more difficult.

[32] Permits issued under the Arkansas statute, *op. cit.*, have included the proviso that "this permit does not authorize any injury to private property nor invasion of private rights, nor any infringement of federal, state, or local laws, ordinances, or regulations...." This proviso is not expressly required by the statute. The Virginia statute, *op. cit.*, has been interpreted by the Virginia Attorney General to mean that, once permission has been granted to build an impoundment (subject, of course, to possible reversal on appeal) others may not prevent the permittee from doing the authorized acts. (Va. Atty. Gen. Op. dated August 23, 1956.) The statute provides, however, that the permittee shall agree to abide by certain mandatory conditions, including " ... that there will be no damage to others." (Secs. 62-94.3 and 62-94.4.)

agency issuing the permit and the minimum streamflow requirements included in the permit should help avoid results that might give rise to liability.[33]

When two or more impoundments are placed on the same stream, there may be enough water to fill all reservoirs during periods of highest streamflow, but it may be advantageous to refill the reservoirs shortly before low-flow periods. At such times there may not be enough available streamflow to refill all reservoirs. There also may be danger of causing loss to other interests. In general, the higher the minimum flows established, the less likelihood there will be that anyone will be damaged by such impoundment, except for competing permittees.

Maintaining Minimum Streamflows

Provisions for minimum streamflows are an important development in eastern water legislation.[34] The specific purposes for such provisions are usually not stated. Among other things, minimum streamflows may be maintained for the benefit of nonwithdrawal uses — such as fish life, recreation, pollution carriage, and navigation. In some states (e.g., Virginia and Arkansas) minimum streamflow provisions are included in legislation regarding impoundments, while in others (e.g., Florida, Mississippi, and Iowa) they apply also to direct withdrawals of stream waters. Some statutes include detailed provisions for establishing minimum streamflows. In some states these may be mandatory.[35] Other statutes simply enable such provisions, by implication, under a general power to include conditions of use in issuing permits.

Minimum-flow requirements for a reservoir usually necessitate installation of devices capable of passing along the entire natural flow when necessary. Probably the easiest minimum-flow legislation to administer would be that allowing administrators to establish the minimum streamflow to be maintained below a dam whenever the incoming flow equals or exceeds such minimum flow; and to require an amount equivalent to the incoming flow to be released whenever it is less than the established minimum flow. Under this arrangement, the higher the

---

[33] The permit also may be of some evidential value in the event of a lawsuit. Under the Virginia statute, *op. cit.*, an application shall be denied if it appears to the court that other riparian owners will be damaged. Furthermore, a permittee shall agree (a) not to damage others, (b) not to impound water when the flow doesn't exceed the average flow, (c) that no part of the dam or impoundment will rest on another's land, and (d) that the structure will be maintained in a safe and serviceable condition. The impoundment's construction shall be approved by a registered civil or agricultural engineer.

[34] In some states, legislation also or instead provides expressly for the establishment of lake levels. See, e.g., Wis. Stat. Ann., sec. 31-14 *et seq.*; Minn. Stat. Ann., sec. 105.37 *et seq.*; Mich. Stat. Ann., sec. 11.211 *et seq.*

[35] See Virginia, Arkansas, Iowa, and Mississippi statutes, *op. cit.*; Fla. Stat. Ann., sec. 373.071 *et seq.* (However, the Virginia and Arkansas statutes do not require anyone to obtain a permit, but are permissive in this respect.) Most such statutes would appear to apply to dams built in whole or in part to store water for beneficial purposes.

established minimum flow, the shorter would be the period of permissible impoundment.

The Virginia legislation does not permit such broad discretion in setting the minimum flow, but it provides greater uniformity of application in that permittees may impound water only when the incoming flow is in excess of the "average flow." They must release an amount equivalent to the average flow at other times. The average flow is defined as "the average discharge of a stream at a particular point" and "may be determined from actual measurements or computed from the most accurate information available." The statute defines waters in excess of this as "floodwaters." In practice, the courts commonly have employed streamflow data obtained at an established stream-gaging station to estimate the average discharge at the location of the proposed impoundment.[36] Recent Florida and Iowa legislation spells out minimum flow requirements in terms of historical experience.[37]

Other considerations concerning minimum streamflow requirements pertain to (1) possibly altering minimum flow with changing conditions, after it has been established for a particular permittee, and (2) coordinating minimum-flow requirements with pollution-control laws. The establishment of a relatively high minimum flow may tend to afford protection to polluters at the expense of consumptive water users, and vice versa, although minimum-flow requirements also benefit nonconsumptive users.

Nonriparian Use

Several statutes are vague as to whether impounded waters shall be used only on riparian land. Apparently the Virginia statute is intended to facilitate only riparian use, but it employs a liberal definition of riparian land which appears to permit a nonriparian owner to purchase adjoining riparian land and thereby make the entire tract riparian land for this purpose, providing it all lies within the watershed.

It will be recalled that rules of law adopted by a number of state courts permit nonriparian use under certain circumstances, although on only a more or less temporary basis until it is needed to satisfy riparian requirements.[38] The extent to which permissible nonriparian use on a more permanent basis might be desired may depend on such factors as: (1) the size of the stream, (2) the amount of riparian land and prospective riparian use, and (3) the physical, economic, and legal

---

[36] Information supplied by H. B. Holmes, Jr., Virginia Commissioner of Water Resources, who is required by the statute to supply data on average flow to the court.

[37] See Fla. Stat. Ann., secs. 373.081(4) and 373.141; and Iowa Code Ann., secs. 455A.1 and 455A.18.

[38] Under eastern legislation of various types, administrators and attorneys general have tended not to authorize such use if not clearly intended by the statute. See Harold H. Ellis, "Some Current and Proposed Water-Rights Legislation in the Eastern States," *Iowa Law Rev.*, Vol. XLI, No. 2, Winter, 1956. The Florida, Arkansas, Mississippi, and Iowa statutes include provisions suggesting that at least some limited nonriparian use may be permissible.

availability of ground water or other alternative sources of water on the nonriparian lands. Moreover, constitutional safeguards against impairment of vested riparian or other property rights without compensation may limit nonriparian use. It would appear easiest to justify permitting extensive nonriparian use of stream waters if the waters are impounded during high-flow periods.

Questions Concerning Preferences

Although some statutes are silent on the relative rights of competing impoundments, the Virginia legislation provides that "Priority to the right to store ... will go to upstream riparian owners."[39] The early milldam acts and the Iowa, Mississippi, and other legislation give a permittee a preference over *later* permittees — whether upstream or downstream — similar in this respect to the prior appropriation doctrine.[40] An alternative approach, more compatible with the riparian reasonable use rule, might include provisions for sharing or rotation among competing permittees when water is in short supply.

Consideration might be given to providing preferential treatment for different types of impoundment. However, it may be questioned whether preferences should be of absolute or exclusive nature. They might apply as between competing applicants, competing permittees after issuance of their permits, or between an applicant and existing permittees. They might apply against applicants for direct water withdrawals in a state in which both storage and direct withdrawals are regulated. Under type-of-use priority provisions in western statutes, courts have held that compensation would need to be paid if preferential permits damage a prior appropriator.[41] Such a requirement may be particularly appropriate for impoundments that involve substantial sunk costs.

A general preference list might look something like this:

1. Impoundments that serve to increase low streamflow.
2. Impoundments that do not increase low streamflow, but that otherwise increase available water supplies without damaging others during the period of impoundment or decreasing the flow during low-flow periods.
3. Impoundments that increase available water supplies through storage of high flows, but also reduce low streamflows.
4. Direct withdrawals of water for consumptive purposes during low-flow periods.

---

[39] This could mean that a later upstream permittee may have some kind of priority over an earlier downstream permittee, but this isn't clear.

[40] Subject to domestic and certain other types of uses that may be excepted or given preferential treatment by the legislation.

[41] See Wells A. Hutchins, "A Comparison of Riparian and Appropriative Rights," mimeographed report, Production Economics Research Branch, ARS, USDA, 1955.

A system of preferences for different purposes of use might be superimposed on such a preference list. However, except for certain types of domestic use, perhaps even more caution should be exercised before any such preferences are established — because of varying needs throughout a state and the limited available information regarding future needs. Except for domestic uses, few preferences have been included so far in eastern water legislation.[42]

Duration of Permits

Some statutes leave the duration of each permit for the administering agency or court to decide.[43] Some include guidelines and, occasionally, mandatory requirements. An Arkansas statute provides that the duration of a permit shall be "not less than that found ... to be necessary to permit amortization of reasonable indebtedness, if any, incurred in connection with the construction of the dam, but in no event in excess of fifty years ... " subject to renewal.[44] An alternative approach might be to substitute "investment" for "indebtedness." The Iowa legislation, applicable to direct withdrawals as well as impoundments, limits the duration of permits to 10 years, subject to renewal. A Minnesota statute provides that permits shall remain subject to "cancellation by the commissioner [of conservation] at any time if deemed necessary by him for any cause for the protection of the public interests," without including any provision for compensating a permittee.[45]

To encourage desired investments in permanent-type dams and reservoirs which involve sunk costs, permits might be issued for a longer duration and made less subject to cancellation than would be permits to make direct withdrawals of water with, e.g., portable and salable irrigation pump and sprinkler equipment. Relatively meager information is available on the degree of security of investment needed to encourage various types of water development. But decisions as to what to do about duration may also turn on what is regarded as "equitable" and on flexibility considered necessary to take care of future requirements and protect the public interest.

It would seem desirable to encourage impoundments that will increase water supplies during low-flow periods. However, there are problems of coordinating with the numerous other facets of the development and use of water — surface and underground.

---

[42] An Arkansas statute provides that "reasonable preferences" shall be given to different water uses in this order: "(i) sustaining life, (ii) maintaining health, (iii) increasing wealth." (Ark. Stat. Ann., sec. 21-1308.) Domestic, municipal, and manufacturing uses of water are given the highest priorities in Ohio conservancy districts. (Page's Ohio Rev. Code Ann., sec. 6101.24.)

[43] Some statutes also include time limitations for beginning and completing construction and provisions regarding nonuse and abandonment.

[44] See Arkansas statute cited in footnote 42.

[45] Minn. Stat. Ann., sec. 105.44.

IMPACTS OF WATERSHED DISTRICTS ON WATER RIGHTS SYSTEMS

Consider the impacts of watershed districts on a system of water rights. State statutes enable the creation of various types of water resource districts having a variety of designations, purposes, and powers, ranging from limited to comprehensive functions. Some enabling acts permit districts to impound water and control the allocation and use of the developed waters. Less frequently, they provide for control over the allocation and use of natural streamflows. But these activities are subject to the existing system of water rights. Needed rights to develop and allocate water must be obtained by donation, purchase, condemnation, or the securing of permits from appropriate agencies or the courts.[46] Subject to the existing system of water rights, however, districts may assess costs for water development and allocate the resulting supply, even over the objections of a protesting minority of district landowners.

Some enabling acts include general regulatory powers over the use of natural watercourses or other water sources. But few of these regulations have been invoked in small watershed projects. To the extent that such regulation over water allocation, without compensating riparian owners or acquiring their rights, is invoked by a district, it would constitute a new component in a state's water-rights system. Some statutes that provide for "regulation," however, may mean simply *physical* regulation through the operation of dams, rather than authority to require water use permits or otherwise adopt water use regulations.[47] At any rate, some of the statutory regulatory powers are so general or so vague that districts may hesitate to employ them.[48]

RELEVANT FUNCTIONS OF STATE AGENCIES

The role of state agencies may range through data gathering and dissemination; planning; advising; making recommendations; coordinating functions; regulation; and financing, construction, operation, and maintenance of improvements.[49]

Recent Florida legislation includes two provisions of interest in connection with the extent of state versus local regulation. Certain regulatory powers of the State Board of Conservation may be (1) exercised only within areas in which regulation is shown to be necessary by

---

[46] See, e.g., sec. 212 of S. B. 588, as enacted by the Maryland legislature in 1959, regarding public watershed associations; and Page's Ohio Rev. Code Ann., sec. 610.24, regarding conservancy districts.

[47] See, e.g., New York legislation regarding river regulating districts. McKinney's Consol. Laws of N. Y. Ann., Conservation Law, sec. 430(8).

[48] Moreover, such statutes might be held to be unconstitutional delegations of authority to such districts and/or to violate constitutional provisions against the taking of private property without compensation or due process of law.

[49] In Louisiana, for example, the Department of Public Works has constructed a number of dams and reservoirs. See also Page's Ohio Rev. Code Ann., sec. 1523.01 *et seq.*

evidence in a public hearing,[50] and (2) delegated to a water management district to administer within its boundaries.[51] In states where regulatory powers are granted both to state agencies and to local districts or governmental subdivisions, coordination problems may need to be worked out between state and local regulatory functions, as well as between various local regulatory bodies.

ROBERT H. MARQUIS | *Comment*

THE CHAPTER written by Mr. Ellis, in addition to providing a clear statement of relationships between water rights and small watershed development, serves to emphasize the complexity of water problems and the extent to which decisions concerning any one water problem may produce "side effects" not originally contemplated.

Small watershed development is related to a number of water problems besides water rights. One involves the controversy between advocates of so-called big dams and little dams. Fortunately, there is increasing recognition that each type can produce important benefits, that the benefits from each are basically different, that neither is a substitute for the other, and that the job ahead is to coordinate planning so that both can make the largest possible contribution towards achievement of over-all goals.

Another problem to which small watershed development is related concerns the measurement of benefits, the identification of beneficiaries, the extent of the contribution which beneficiaries should be expected to provide towards the cost of projects, and the manner in which the federal, state and local governments which have advanced money for the construction and operation of projects should obtain whatever contribution is determined to be appropriate. With a number of federal agencies constructing projects in different areas, the desirability of uniform standards for determining contribution seems evident. Further,

---

[50] Fla. Stat. Ann., sec. 373.171. The area to be regulated shall be designated a "water development and conservation district." For a similar approach to the regulation of ground water by a state agency, see Burns Ind. Stat. Ann., sec. 27-1301 *et seq.;* N.J. Stat. Ann., sec. 58:4A-1 *et seq.* An Illinois statute enables water authorities to be created by special election to regulate groundwater use in local areas. (Smith-Hurd Ill. Stat. Ann., Ch. 111 2/3, sec. 223 *et seq.*)

[51] Fla. Stat. Ann., sec. 373.141(1b). Another approach is to require the approval or recommendation of certain local districts or agencies before the construction of a dam or other works or water uses may be authorized by a state agency in their locality. See, e.g., Miss. Code Ann., sec. 5956-20.

Robert H. Marquis came to the Division of Law of TVA in 1939, and is now Solicitor. From 1936-38 he was in private practice, and from 1938-39 was a Special Attorney, U.S. Department of Justice.

at a time when projects must be critically examined in relation to the over-all requirements of the federal budget, increased local responsibility in the planning and construction of such works and increased contribution from individual beneficiaries may prove necessary.

Still another problem concerns the extent to which governmental funds should continue to be expended for flood control projects unless assurance is given that their completion will not encourage industrial, commercial, and other building construction to move down into the partially protected lower-level flood plains, thus creating new flood problems. If flood control projects are really to serve the purposes for which they were intended, land use regulations restricting such construction would seem to be imperative. Further, in many cases adoption of land use regulations now would obviate the necessity for new projects altogether.

Even in relation to water rights, the impact of small watershed projects may differ widely according to their particular setting. Problems may be particularly difficult, for example, where projects are located on a stream or on tributaries of a stream which has already been partly developed, and where the new project may affect the existing development. Many different interests and parties are involved. These include, among others:

1. The federal government, in relation to its authority under the commerce clause and other sections of the Constitution.
2. Beneficiaries of federal stream development efforts. The benefits may be direct, as in the case of owners of lands protected from flooding; or indirect, as in the case of those benefited by the general economic gains which result from flood protection and the enhancement in property values in which it results.
3. States in which developments are located, particularly as new projects may relate to any general over-all plans which they may have for development of water resources.
4. Riparian owners whose lands may be adversely affected.

The extent to which small watershed developments are related to other water problems and the wide variety of interests they may affect emphasize the need for cooperation in planning. This need includes cooperation between federal agencies, between federal and state agencies, and between both federal and state agencies and local communities and citizens.

Robert C. Otte is Head, Water Utilization Section, Land and Water Research Branch, USDA. He was an instructor in the Department of Agricultural Economics at the University of Wisconsin, and received his doctorate there in 1956.

Chapter 18

ROBERT C. OTTE[1]

State District Laws As They Affect Watershed Development

WITHIN our highly developed social and economic organization, most of the coordination made necessary by division of function is accomplished through the price system. However, considerable control of labor and other resources occurs outside the market place. Development involved in small watershed projects has been largely of this type and has been carried out through local, state, or federal governments.

Reasons for this are not hard to find. The market place does not give the stimuli necessary to bring forth investment in such development. No way exists for a farmer to collect from the off-site beneficiaries of his land treatment measures. Ordinarily he goes no further in the installation of such measures than he believes will be profitable to him as an individual. No investor would consider building a flood control structure and then selling benefits to people below the dam. A similar situation exists regarding drainage. Often commercial irrigation companies have found to their sorrow that, although they have the power to withhold water in case of nonpayment, usually they have no other customers if irrigators fail to buy. The bargaining advantage may lie with

---

[1]Opinions are those of the author and do not necessarily represent official views.

the landowners who can wait out the company and make an advantageous purchase of either the water or the structures. Municipal and industrial water supplies come nearer to being adapted to private development, but, in most instances, they must be regulated as a public utility.

There is little wonder that, over the years, many governmental devices have been created for the control and development of water resources. It was at the local level, with powers and authorities asked of and granted by the states, that the first of these governmental devices appeared. The state and federal governments came on the scene later.

It is to the local general governmental units — the counties and cities — that citizens turn first to demand a service not forthcoming in the market place. The next step may be to request the state legislature to provide for the creation of a special district with jurisdiction more nearly coterminous with the problem area and with the specialized authorities and legal powers deemed necessary.

In the 100-plus years since the first resource protection and development districts appeared, hundreds of pieces of legislation have been passed providing for the creation of such special districts and modifying existing acts. The 1957 Census of Governments reported 5,543 special districts in the natural resources field, plus another 662 "multiple-function" districts, many of which are engaged in supplying irrigation, municipal, and industrial water.[2] This includes only those districts that meet the census definition of "independent." Many other dependent districts are active in this field.

An inventory of the myriad state laws that have a bearing on the small watershed program is beyond the scope of this chapter. Even if assembled, these laws would defy classification. Almost every conceivable combination of authorized functions can be found incorporated in some district enabling act. California, for example, has more than 30 general water-district enabling acts, and in 1955 it had 40 specially created water districts.

In addition to special districts, counties and municipalities in many states have various authorities and powers in the field of water development and control. The creation and operation of many districts is so closely integrated with county and municipal governments that the districts are difficult to examine and classify apart from the parent government.

Both counties and special districts have been called the "dark continent of American politics."[3] In any exploration of two dark continents simultaneously, the best one can do is to point out a few landmarks.

The following four sources of information are used as a basis for describing the present situation regarding state district enabling legislation: the 1957 Census of Governments; *American Water Resources Administration*, by Yang-Ch'eng Shih; *Progress in State Legislation*

[2]U.S. Bureau of the Census, *Governments in the United States*, 1957 Census of Governments, Vol. I, No. 1, pp. 30-31.

[3]John C. Bollens, *Special District Governments in the United States*, (Berkeley: University of California Press, 1957), p. 1.

Relating to the Watershed Protection and Flood Prevention Act, 1955-57,
by Kirk M. Sandals and L. M. Adams; and a survey made in 1955 and
1956 by the Office of the General Counsel, U. S. Department of Agriculture. In the latter study, a survey was made to determine for each state
what local organizations could act as sponsors of Public Law 566 projects. Synopses were made of the provisions of 166 district enabling acts.

SPONSORS OF PUBLIC LAW 566 PROJECTS

A variety of types of local government serve as sponsoring organizations for Public Law 566 projects. Table 1 shows the pattern of this
sponsorship.

Table 1. Sponsors of Public Law 566 Projects[a]

Soil conservation districts only	62
Soil conservation districts + general governmental units	31
Soil conservation districts + multiple-purpose districts	28
Soil conservation districts + single-purpose districts	8
Soil conservation districts + soil conservation subdistricts	7
Soil conservation districts + special districts + general governmental units	11
State agency only	3
Other[b]	4
Total	154[c]

[a] Soil Conservation Service, *Status of Watershed Protection (P. L. 566) Program*
(Mimeographed), Washington, Apr. 1, 1959.

[b] Includes one project sponsored by a soil conservation district plus a state
agency, one by a single-purpose district only, one by a local unit of government only,
and one by a soil conservation district plus a state agency plus a local unit of government.

[c] Total projects approved for installation of works of improvement as of Apr. 1,
1959.

Soil conservation districts are sponsors of practically all projects.
They are the only governmental entities that have the facilities for planning and obtaining the agreements for carrying out the land treatment
measures required by the act. One or more soil conservation districts
make up the most common type of local organization.

Soil conservation districts in cosponsorship with counties or cities
is the next most frequent, and cosponsorship with multiple-purpose districts is a close third. The single-purpose districts are usually flood
control, drainage, or irrigation districts.

Cosponsorship is common. Almost two-thirds of all projects have
two or more sponsors. About one-sixth have four or more, with the
number running as high as seven. There are two main reasons for cosponsorship. First, one governmental entity alone may not have all the
necessary powers and abilities. Second, the watershed may lie in two
or more counties or soil conservation districts. For example, the
Abbotts Creek project in North Carolina lies in four counties and has

seven sponsors — three soil conservation districts, two cities, a county, and a drainage district.

Some projects involve local governments that are not listed as sponsors. They may be performing a specialized function in the project. Also, as a project progresses, additional sponsors may be brought in. Thus, Table 1 may not give a complete picture of local organization participation.

WATERSHED ASSOCIATIONS

The skeleton formed by enabling legislation is only one element affecting the success or failure of a watershed development project. No matter how complete the legal framework may be, without a thorough and effective educational and planning program and without intelligent, forceful leadership, this legal framework will remain only a skeleton.

At the beginning of any group attack, local people need an informal organization with which to start. A formal organization presupposes some knowledge and decisions regarding the nature of the problems and of possible solutions. This need has evidenced itself all over the country in the formation of watershed associations. Such an association can discuss its problems, call in technicians, and make further plans. The informal watershed association may be adequate to handle simple watershed problems.

The actions of individual farm operators and other residents of the watershed, with technical, material, and minor financial assistance from state and federal agencies, may provide the solution to other, simpler problems.

However, a more comprehensive program will require formal organization. Expensive structures, valuable sites, and relocation of highways and public utilities will involve costs beyond the means of individuals. Necessary actions may injure some while benefiting others, so that means must be provided for reimbursing the injured and assessing costs to those benefited. Situations of this kind require a formal organization having the necessary legal and administrative powers. The larger the project, the less amenable it is to planning and decision-making by the town-meeting process.

TYPES OF DISTRICTS

In addition to the types of local government found as sponsors in the present Public Law 566 program — soil conservation districts and subdistricts, multiple-purpose, flood control, drainage, and irrigation districts, and general governmental units — there are others, such as water supply, sanitation, park, and forest districts, that have potential roles in watershed development. Table 2 shows the number of districts of various types reported by the 1957 Census of Governments.

Table 2. Special Districts in the United States:[a] 1957.[b]

Type of District	Number of States Reporting	Number of Districts
Soil conservation	38[c]	2,285
Drainage	31	2,132
Irrigation and water conservation	20	564
Flood control	22	209
Multipurpose	25	217
Irrigation and/or flood control and water supply	14	96
Irrigation and/or flood control and electric light and power	6	12
Fire and water supply	19	111
Sanitation and water supply	23	144
Urban water supply	33	787
Parks and recreation	18	316

[a] Continental United States exclusive of Alaska.

[b] 1957 Census of Governments, Vol. I, No. 1, pp. 30-31.

[c] Soil conservation districts in 10 states are not classified by the Census of Governments as independent districts because they are closely integrated with county or state governments or fail in some other way to meet the census definition of an independent government. The Soil Conservation Service reports a total of approximately 2,800 districts.

Soil Conservation Districts

All states except Connecticut have statutes enabling the creation of soil conservation districts. In Connecticut the authorities and powers ordinarily granted soil conservation districts are vested in the Commissioner of Agriculture. All districts except those in Arizona have authority to carry out works of improvement. All are expressly authorized to engage in soil conservation activities. Districts in 20 states have express authorization for flood control, in 23 states for drainage, and in 28 for irrigation. In connection with the Public Law 566 program, attorneys general in a number of other states have rendered opinions that the soil conservation districts have authority to engage in works of improvement for flood control, drainage, and irrigation. These opinions cover flood control in 20 states, drainage in 17, and irrigation in 11.[4]

Soil conservation districts in general have the powers necessary to permit them to engage in watershed development projects. Most of them can acquire and dispose of land; make contracts; sue and be sued; make investigations; and carry out, operate, and maintain works of improvement. However, only five of the state soil conservation district enabling acts allow the eminent domain power.[5] The absence of this power indicates an important limitation of the soil conservation district. Without

---

[4] USDA, Office of the General Counsel, "Functions and Powers of Soil Conservation Districts Relating to Public Law 566, 83rd Congress, as Amended," prepared for the Soil Conservation Service, Jan. 1, 1958.

[5] *Ibid.*

it, any district alone is unlikely to prove to be an effective local agency
for carrying out a sizable project that requires land acquisition by
means other than acceptance of donations or genuinely voluntary sale.

Soil conservation districts have limited financial powers. Most depend upon grants from counties and states. Some have rather sizable
incomes from operation of district-owned equipment. However, soil
conservation districts in only one state — Colorado — have power to levy
taxes. Two states — Colorado and California — empower districts to
levy special benefit assessments. Three states — California, Colorado,
and Oregon — authorize soil conservation districts to borrow money, but
none provide for the issuance of bonds.[6] A number of the states grant
express authority for expanded functions and general and financial
powers to subdistricts of soil conservation districts that are not given
to the parent district.

Soil Conservation Subdistricts

Ten states — Virginia, Kentucky, Illinois, Iowa, California, Missouri,
Nebraska, New Mexico, West Virginia, and Alabama — have provided for
the creation of subdistricts of soil conservation districts, all with power
to carry out, operate, and maintain works of improvement of the types
possible under Public Law 566. These subdistricts are designed to be
used in connection with the soil conservation districts, and, in effect,
the powers granted to the subdistricts are additions to the powers of
the districts.

Special-purpose districts similar in many ways to subdistricts of
soil conservation districts are provided for in Idaho, South Dakota, and
New York. Idaho watershed improvement districts can be established
under the supervision of the State Soil Conservation Commission; they
are governed by three directors, two elected and one appointed by the
commission. In the creation of South Dakota watershed districts, the
soil conservation district receives the initiating petition and supervises
their establishment. New York law authorizes the county boards of
supervisors to create county small watershed protection districts for
Public Law 566 projects.

In general, subdistricts have the benefit of the same powers as the
parent district. That is, the subdistrict is either granted the same
powers, or in the operation of a project the parent district may exercise the powers. In addition, four states — Kentucky, Nebraska, New
Mexico, and Oklahoma — grant subdistricts (but not the parent district)
power of eminent domain. Idaho watershed improvement districts,
South Dakota watershed districts, and New York county watershed districts are empowered to exercise eminent domain.

Colorado law has a provision which in operation is similar to the
subdistrict device. A soil conservation district may levy taxes or

---

[6] *Ibid.*

assessments on real property in a part of the district for a watershed
project.

Eight states — Virginia, Kentucky, Illinois, Iowa, California, Missouri, Nebraska, and New Mexico — give subdistricts power to levy
taxes. Four states — Virginia, Kentucky, New Mexico, and Alabama —
authorize both borrowing and issuing of bonds. Nebraska gives subdistricts the power to borrow. Idaho watershed improvement districts
and South Dakota watershed districts may levy taxes, borrow, and
issue bonds. New York watershed protection districts may levy special
benefit assessments.

Multiple-Purpose Districts

Some states have laws that enable the creation of special districts
with authority to engage in a number of functions in the water resource
and related fields. Multiple-purpose districts can be divided into two
main categories — those authorizing several specific related functions,
and those granting a carte blanche in the general field of watershed development. An example of the first type is the water-storage district
enabling act in California which provides for storage and distribution
of water, concomitant drainage and reclamation, and incidental distribution of power. An example of the latter type is the Kansas Watershed
District Act, which authorizes districts to conserve soil and water, retard floods, and develop the water resources of the district.

The first of the conservancy or watershed-type district enabling acts
was the Ohio Conservancy Act, passed in 1914. There are two well-
known examples of Ohio Conservancy Districts — The Miami and the
Muskingum. The Miami is essentially a flood control project. It is
probably the largest in the United States with completely local financing
which utilizes flood retarding dams.

The Muskingum Valley Conservancy District, which covers 8,038
square miles, has 14 reservoirs constructed under the Federal Works
Program. Of these, four are single-purpose flood control reservoirs
without dead storage, and the rest have flood control capacities with
dead storages varying from 420 to 3,550 acre feet. More than 20,000
acres of adjoining hill lands have been reforested by the district. The
Corps of Engineers operates all the reservoirs, and the district man-
ages the recreational facilities on the 10 reservoirs with dead storage.[7]

Six states — Tennessee, Nebraska, Kansas, Minnesota, North Dakota,
and Nevada — provide for the creation of watershed districts, all with a
broad range of authorized functions. Six states — Ohio, Indiana, Oklahoma, New Mexico, Nevada, and Colorado — have statutes enabling the
creation of conservancy districts, which also have broad authorities in
water resources development and control.

---

[7] Yang-Ch'eng Shih, *American Water Resources Administration* (New York: Bookman
Associates, Inc., 1956), p. 991.

A number of other states provide for districts that are authorized to engage in two or more different single-purpose enterprises, and some states enable the creation of districts that are slightly more limited in the scope of their activities than are the watershed and conservancy districts — for example, the water conservation districts of Oregon and California.

A summary of the functions and powers of 39 multiple-purpose district enabling acts in 22 states shows that 5 are authorized to engage in works of improvement for soil conservation, 23 for flood control, 22 for drainage, and 29 for irrigation. Of these districts, 35 have the power of eminent domain, 29 the power to levy taxes, 31 to levy special benefit assessments, 26 to borrow, and 32 to issue bonds.[8]

Flood Control Districts

There are two general types of flood control districts: those providing for levees and dikes only, and those providing for all kinds of flood control devices, including dams. Levee districts are most common in the lower Mississippi area, where they originated about 1850; but some other states also provide for their formation, sometimes in combination with drainage district enabling legislation. The survey by the Office of the General Counsel, U. S. Department of Agriculture, showed that levee districts in 9 states were qualified to act as sponsors of Public Law 566 projects. Four of these laws were of the optional drainage-levee district type.

Levee districts were designed originally to build levees as a completely local undertaking, but the flood control districts, which are of broader scope and most of which have come into being since 1930, have the predominant function of assisting in federal projects through the provision of rights-of-way and maintaining and operating works after their completion. Also, in general, the organization of levee districts is controlled by county authorities or local courts, while flood control districts are usually controlled by state authorities. The 1957 Census of Governments reported flood control districts in 22 states. Apparently, this includes levee districts.

As a rule, levee and flood control districts have a full array of general and financial powers. A study of 12 such districts showed that all have power of eminent domain, 8 may levy taxes, 9 may levy special benefit assessments, 1 may borrow, and 8 may issue bonds.[9]

Drainage Districts

Practically all states provide for drainage organizations with

---

[8]Robert C. Otte, "Local Resource Protection and Development Districts," Agricultural Research Service, ARS 43-48, Washington, D.C., Apr., 1957, p. 5.

[9]*Ibid.*, p. 5.

governmental powers. Most of the states provide for the creation of districts, and the rest make greater use of the county governmental structure. A study of 55 drainage district enabling acts in 37 states shows that 47 may exercise eminent domain, 42 may levy taxes, 53 may levy special benefit assessments, 27 may borrow, and 50 may issue bonds.[10] Most of the county drainage projects may also make use of these powers.

Irrigation Districts

Laws enabling the creation of irrigation districts are found in all of the 17 western states, plus several eastern states. Some states have two or more kinds of irrigation districts. In most states, districts are engaged in irrigation only or with concomitant drainage. However, some states permit additional activities. Water-improvement districts in Texas may "furnish water for domestic, power, and commercial purposes." Nebraska irrigation districts are authorized to generate hydroelectric power, and California irrigation districts may furnish water for any beneficial purpose.[11]

Irrigation districts also have broad powers. Of 14 irrigation district enabling acts in 12 states, 14 granted power of eminent domain, 10 the power to levy taxes, 13 to levy special benefit assessments, 7 to borrow, and 13 the power to issue bonds.[12] Although some irrigation districts have power to levy taxes, their primary source of revenue is from assessments.

Other Single-Purpose Districts

Several other types of single-purpose districts are authorized to engage in functions that would be a part of many comprehensive watershed development programs. A number of states provide for special districts to supply water for domestic and municipal use, sometimes as the sole enterprise and sometimes in conjunction with sewage disposal (see Table 2). Such districts are usually formed by petition or referendum and are empowered to levy general taxes, special benefit assessments, service charges, or a combination of these. Ordinarily, they are permitted to issue bonds of either the revenue or general obligation type.

At least 8 states have general laws providing for the creation of park districts. Some others have created such districts by special legislation. The 1957 Census of Governments reported 316 park and recreation districts in 18 states. Such districts can be created in Illinois by order of the county judge upon petition of 100 voters; in North Dakota

---

[10] *Ibid.*, p. 5.
[11] Shih, *op. cit.*, pp. 949-50.
[12] Otte, *op. cit.*, p. 5.

by ordinance of a city or village, apparently at the discretion of the governing body; and in Washington by a city council either on its own initiative or upon petition by 15 percent of the city voters. Districts in Washington may include areas within the city and contiguous areas.

After approval by referendum, Illinois park districts may levy taxes and issue bonds. North Dakota districts may levy either special benefit assessments or special ad valorem property taxes, or both, and may issue bonds. In Washington such districts may levy a special ad valorem property tax and incur indebtedness. They may also levy special benefit assessments for improvements of a local nature. General park district laws are also found in New York, Minnesota, Ohio, California, and Oregon.[13]

Oregon provides for improvement districts that have reforestation as their primary function. These districts can be established by county courts upon petition by a majority of owners of logged-off or burned-over land. They may use county funds and may issue bonds after popular approval.

A few states have water conservation districts, and water conservation is an authorized function of many multiple-purpose natural resource districts. Water conservation districts in California are created by popular vote and may levy special taxes. The Santa Clara Valley Water Conservation District includes an area of 133,000 acres. It has constructed five storage reservoirs, water-spreading works, and a number of structures by which water is diverted to canals over gravel areas where it is percolated underground. Texas law provides for water control and preservation districts to control salinity.[14]

Counties and Municipalities

A number of states empower counties to engage in navigation improvement works which may serve incidentally the purposes of flood control. About one-fourth of the states authorize counties to construct flood control works, some specifying all kinds of flood control works such as dams, levees, floodways, and channel improvements, and some specifying only levees and dikes. In addition, some states empower counties to construct flood control works to protect or to facilitate the construction of county roads and highways.[15]

Municipalities in about one-fourth of the states are expressly authorized to undertake flood control works. In another one-fourth of the states, municipalities may clear, deepen, straighten, revet, alter, change, or otherwise improve the channels of streams within their jurisdictions.[16] Some counties and municipalities may go outside their boundaries to construct works of improvement.

---

[13] Shih, *op. cit.*, pp. 983-85.
[14] *Ibid.*, pp. 988-89.
[15] *Ibid.*, pp. 870-72.
[16] *Ibid.*, pp. 887-88, 897-98.

About one-third of the states have laws enabling county drainage enterprises. In most instances these enterprises are authorized after petition by a certain number of affected landowners, followed by a public hearing and, in some states, by an investigation and a public hearing. Usually, assessments are made on the basis of benefits. Many of the county drainage enterprises are almost indistinguishable from drainage districts except that they do not have corporate status or the qualities of an independent governmental unit. A few states enable counties to undertake irrigation enterprises.

Municipalities in all states are authorized to engage in urban types of drainage, but only a few have authorities in the field of agricultural drainage. Agricultural irrigation by municipalities is authorized in four states — New Mexico, Wyoming, Nevada, and Washington. Some municipalities in other states are furnishing water for irrigation enterprises, even though this is not expressly authorized by state law.[17]

A few states grant counties some general authorities for water and soil conservation. During the drought of the 1930's, ponds and wells were constructed in Kansas with federal funds under county sponsorship. An Ohio statute provides for counties and city governments in connection with highway and bridge construction to create various kinds of catchments to conserve the water supply of the state. Some California counties have undertaken projects for artificial recharge of underground aquifers; Nassau County, New York, has built seepage basins to recharge underground water supplies with sewer effluents.[18]

Practically all municipalities are authorized to supply domestic and industrial water and are engaged in doing so. Sewage disposal enterprises ordinarily belong to cities and special districts, but some states authorize counties to perform this function.

About two-thirds of the states authorize counties to establish county parks. Counties in about one-fourth of the states have express authority to establish county forests. County governments in some states may develop and conserve forest resources on other public lands and on private lands; in some states they may undertake the work of fire prevention and control. Several states provide for county conservation and development of fish and wildlife.[19]

This discussion has applied mainly to express authorization for the various functions. In addition, there are many situations in which a county or municipality engages in a given function in the absence of express prohibition.

Counties and municipalities have several financial limitations. Many are subject to mill levy and debt limits with most of their taxing and borrowing potential committed. Ordinarily, they are prohibited from taxing only a part of their jurisdiction. Thus, any funds allocated to watershed projects come from the county or municipality as a whole.

---

[17] *Ibid.*, pp. 901-2.
[18] *Ibid.*, p. 884.
[19] *Ibid.*, pp. 877-82.

Also, while many have authority to engage in various functions relevant to watershed programs, few have power to levy special benefit assessments for such activities.

Dependent Districts

Some districts are so closely tied to other governments that they are not generally considered as independent units of government. They lack fiscal independence or administrative autonomy, or both. Some that have popularly elected governing bodies of their own may rely on other governments as a source of funds. Others may have an independent source of revenue and still be administratively dependent.[20]
There is no clear-cut distinction, and in reality dependent districts are part of a spectrum through which general government shades into special-function districts.

The Census of Governments lists the types of dependent districts provided for by the laws of each state, but does not make a count of the number in existence. Table 3 is a tabulation of the number of states providing for dependent districts authorized to engage in functions having importance in watershed programs.

Table 3. Number of States Providing for Dependent Districts: 1957.[a]

Authorized Function	Parent Local Government		
	County	Municipality	Township
Flood control	7	3	-
Drainage	16	5	3
Irrigation	1	-	-
Water conservation	2	1	-
Water supply	9	13	5
Sanitation	17	19	5
Park and recreation	8	6	3

[a]From U. S. Bureau of the Census, *Local Government Structure*, 1957 Census of Governments, Vol. I, No. 3. Data is a tabulation of selected types of districts listed as "Subordinate Agencies and Areas."

STATE LEGISLATIVE RESPONSE TO PUBLIC LAW 566[21]

From the time of passage of Public Law 566 in 1954 through the 1957 legislative sessions, 38 states passed new or amendatory legislation to further cooperation between state and local agencies and the U. S. Department of Agriculture under Public Law 566. This legislation

---

[20]Bollens, *op. cit.*, p. 228.
[21]Much of the information in this section is taken from Kirk M. Sandals and L. M. Adams, "Progress in State Legislation Relating to the Watershed Protection and Flood Prevention Act, 1955-57," SCS-TP-135, Washington, D.C., Jan., 1958.

either provides for the creation of new districts or modifies legislation
pertaining to existing local governments of the following types: soil
conservation districts, subdistricts of soil conservation districts,
multiple-purpose districts, flood control districts, drainage districts,
counties, and other local units of general government. In addition,
three states created districts by special legislative act, and a number
provided for state participation in small watershed projects.

Broadened Authorities and Powers of Soil Conservation Districts

As of January, 1958, 18 states had broadened the expressly authorized functions of soil conservation districts to include flood prevention,
15 to include irrigation, and 13 to include drainage. As districts in
some states had express authorization to engage in drainage and irrigation prior to the passage of Public Law 566, this made a total of 18
states expressly authorizing flood prevention, 21 authorizing irrigation,
and 26 authorizing drainage. Typical of recent legislation is Ohio's.
Here the powers of soil conservation districts were extended to include
flood prevention and the agricultural phases of the conservation, development, utilization, and disposal of water.

Three states — Illinois, Oklahoma, and Wisconsin — granted soil
conservation districts the power of eminent domain. Colorado gave
districts power to levy a tax or assessment on real property in a portion of the district, upon a favorable vote of qualified voters, for installation, maintenance, and operation of flood prevention and watershed
improvement measures.

Subdistricts of Soil Conservation Districts

All of the subdistrict enabling acts discussed previously have come
into being in response to Public Law 566. Ten states have provided for
subdistricts as such, and four more have passed legislation that in operation would be very similar to subdistricts.

Multiple-Purpose Districts

Minnesota, Tennessee, and Nevada passed new legislation enabling
the creation of watershed or conservancy districts, with Nevada providing for one of each. Kansas, Nebraska, Oklahoma, and Indiana have
amended their watershed or conservancy district acts. Nevada watershed districts have power to levy taxes but not power of eminent domain
or power to levy special benefit assessments, borrow, or issue bonds.
The others have all of these powers, with the limited exception of Tennessee watershed districts, which have no express authority to borrow

but may issue bonds, and Nevada water conservancy districts, which have express authority to borrow but not to issue bonds.

Arkansas amended its Irrigation and Drainage District Act to include watershed improvement; authorized plans developed under Public Law 566 to be adopted by districts; and provided that construction costs may include costs of works for the purposes, *inter alia*, of the prevention of erosion, floodwater, and sediment damages and the conservation, development, utilization, and disposal of water.

Flood Control Districts

Both Connecticut and Wyoming have passed acts enabling the formation of flood control districts. Both granted the powers of eminent domain, taxation, and issuance of bonds. Connecticut districts may levy special-benefit assessments, while those in Wyoming may not do so. Neither has express authority to borrow.

Drainage Districts

Delaware amended its drainage law to define drainage as water management to remove or control excess surface and subsurface waters, and provided that drainage organizations may engage in such works. Mississippi authorized drainage districts to cooperate with the United States under Public Law 566 in constructing, operating, and maintaining works of improvement for the prevention of erosion, floodwater, and sediment damages, and for the conservation, utilization, and disposal of water, exclusive of irrigation.

Local Units of General Government

Eight states — Maryland, Mississippi, Nebraska, New York, Wisconsin, Arizona, Iowa, and West Virginia — have expanded the powers of counties so that they may assume some part of the local responsibility for Public Law 566 projects.

Maryland authorized the Board of County Commissioners of Worcester County to carry out, maintain, and operate works of improvement under the act. Mississippi authorized the board of any county to make contributions to any soil conservation district located entirely or partly within the county. Nebraska empowered counties to levy ad valorem taxes and appropriate money for flood control programs, and to employ the services of any nonprofit corporation or organization that has as one of its principal objectives the promotion or development of flood control upon any river or its tributaries within the county.

New York authorized the appropriation and expenditure of county funds to protect public and private property from floods and conserve soil from erosion. Wisconsin provided that counties and townships may raise and expend funds for watershed protection. Arizona gave authority to Graham and Gila Counties and the towns of Safford and Thatcher to cooperate with the Secretary of Agriculture under Public Law 566 in constructing, maintaining, and operating works of improvement for flood prevention.

Iowa authorized counties to participate in, and to construct, operate, and maintain on certain lands under their jurisdiction, projects for flood prevention or for the conservation, development, utilization, and disposal of water, and to furnish financial and other assistance to such projects. Also, when structures are constructed on county roads, all or a part of the cost is to be a cost of road construction. When projects are installed on private lands under an easement granted to the county, maintenance costs alone may be assumed by the county. Projects built on private lands for county use are to be maintained, as is other property owned or controlled by the county. Actual direction of such projects and work done in connection with them is to be assumed by soil conservation districts, their subdistricts, or the federal government.

West Virginia authorized towns, cities, and counties to expend money for construction, improvement, operation, and maintenance of watershed projects (even if the structures are located in another state), and to levy and collect taxes for this purpose. Soil conservation districts, towns, cities, and counties may give assurances, to be valid and binding for not to exceed 50 years, to agencies of the United States and others for the construction, improvement, operation, and maintenance of such works of improvement.

SUMMARY

Taken in total, the United States would appear to be well equipped with governmental devices designed to cope with comprehensive watershed development. However, a number of states do not grant to any one local governmental entity the broad range of authorities and powers necessary for such development. In a few states, even a combination of local governmental units may not have all the authorities and powers needed. Eleven states have either conservancy or watershed districts with broad authorities and powers. Another 12 states provide for districts with fairly comprehensive powers. Only soil conservation districts have the facilities for planning and obtaining agreements for carrying out needed land treatment measures under Public Law 566.

In 13 states, subdistricts of soil conservation districts may be created (10 in addition to the 23 having multiple-purpose districts), all of which have broad authorities, but which in some instances are more limited in their legal and financial powers.

Thus, cosponsorship is a necessary and common practice on projects of larger scope. This may create problems of coordination, and lack of agreement among sponsors may result in a stalemate. Soil conservation districts and subdistricts tied closely together and often with interlocking boards would seem, prima facie, to be one of the better alternatives for cosponsorship. Another possibility would be the creation of an "umbrella" or coordinating agency. Iowa and Texas have used informal local steering committees to perform this function. However, to make it effective in complex projects involving diverse and conflicting interests, the coordinating agency would need to be granted some authority over the cosponsors. This might be more feasible in the case of special districts than when counties or municipalities are involved as sponsors.

Thus, most states make provision for watershed development via local government. Few states provide for organizations that would be considered ideal by most standards. Even the ideal district law — granted that such could be written and enacted — would be no guarantee of a good project. Too much depends upon unanimity of interests or resolution of conflicting interests, upon a thorough and effective educational and planning program, and upon able, vigorous, and sincere leadership. Although a local group can make a project function within an organization that lacks many important powers, and a project may fail even with an ideal legal framework, the probability remains that more projects will succeed, given an adequate governmental structure.

STEPHEN C. SMITH | *Comment*

A THOROUGH REVIEW of state legislation enabling the use of public districts for watershed development has been presented by Dr. Otte. Primarily, the approach has been to comment on the variety of legislation. I should like to emphasize that the complexity of intergovernmental relations is often lost sight of because the focus is upon the written law rather than upon the "law-in-action."

The point is correctly made that in natural resource economics the government frequently plays a decisive role. But I wonder if today's citizens always "turn first to local government to demand a service not forthcoming in the market place." This ordering implies that citizens turn second to the state, and third to the federal government. This may be the case in some historical sense, but even here it depended upon what service was sought. In our pluralistic society, government is more

Stephen C. Smith is Lecturer and Associate Specialist in the Department of Agricultural Economics at the University of California. Previous positions as an agricultural economist were with TVA, the University of Wisconsin, and Willamette University.

complex. The various levels of government are utilized in combination
to provide a highly varied product. A plausible case could be made that
citizens damaged by floods from small streams turned to the federal
government "first" in order to finance this service, and in my own state
of California you might say they turned to Sacramento "second" to pick
up the bill for rights-of-way rather than assume this responsibility
locally. Such a lack of local investment may be a cause for concern in
assuring prudent use of public funds.

Conventionally, we think of a federal interest-finding expression at
the local level, but it might be instructive to reverse this thinking. For
the watershed program, we might inquire how local interests are reflected at the federal level. What federal officials contact the local
people? To what extent do local groups have a voice in establishing
the initial program goals, or are they generally handed a plan with a
perfunctory request for comment? What is the working relationship
between the local cosponsors and the federal agency?

As one link in the chain of representation, the watershed association — or some similar type of organization — may play a more important
role than Otte indicated at the first of his paper. He hinted, however, at
its possible use as an "umbrella" in the conclusions. He correctly
stated that an organization bearing this label lacks the ability to shoul-
der the usual financial responsibility of maintenance. Yet, where there
is a multiplicity of interested groups, such an association may play an
important role in determining the direction of the program and in coordination. It might be particularly important in the 54 percent of the
projects having cosponsors. As I understand the usual procedure, serious objections from an important affected group will quickly stall the
approval of a Public Law 566 project. If the objections are not raised
until the administrative machinery is well along the road, expenditure
of public funds may have been misdirected. I believe that in some of
the Public Law 566 projects, as well as in some of the Tennessee Valley Authority's experience in this field, local participation was not
initiated soon enough.

Too frequently the early watershed meetings are formal presenta-
tions to local representatives. A professional planning job is completed
with little more than occasionally touching base with the local community until it is requested to approve a completed package. Serious objection at this point may irreparably stifle action or seriously slow
down momentum. In these situations watershed associations may be
effective coordinators.

In obtaining local representation in a federal program, the positive
role of thorough economic analyses should not be overlooked. By
frankly discussing these analyses, the values and objectives of the local
representatives may be clarified and the economic feasibility of their
proposed plans tested.

One problem involved in making a competent appraisal is that the
project is small and that accompanying budgets for economic analysis
are also small. While balance must be achieved, enough care must be

exercised so that the public is accurately apprised and reviewers of reports can clearly see the justification for the conclusions.

As a minimum, it would seem that reports should state their method of calculating benefits which accrue from the reduction of agricultural crop damage and establish the relationship to specific crops. Do the reports meet this standard, and do they fulfill this role? Do the reviewing state agencies work as an effective counterbalance? Although federal procedures call for state review, to what extent does the district enabling legislation provide for review at the state level before it can assume financial obligations, either through the issuance of bonds or by assuming a contractual obligation with other governmental units?

Otte's observation that "more projects will succeed given an adequate governmental structure" is hardly to be questioned. But how do we know when we have "an adequate governmental structure"? Upon what objective basis can alternative structures be tested? Do we have research in progress that will yield answers on this point?

Conclusions are only prima facie depending upon the basis for reasoning. To illustrate, the argument could be made that prima facie the soil conservation district-subdistrict is not adequate for many situations. This argument would rest upon the fact that in many local situations a complex set of interests is involved and that all of these interests are not adequately reflected in an organization that emphasizes land treatment and flood control. I am cognizant that other activities are acknowledged by the Soil Conservation Service. These include drainage, pond building, and assistance in the recreational management of wildlife. Yet, in many parts of the West the flood problem is highly seasonal and frequently does not originate in areas of cultivated farming. In California, housing is one of the main "crops" to be protected in the winter when the floods come since other crops are as yet unplanted except for those similar to orchards, vines, and hay. Both the urbanite and the farmer may be interested in capturing floodwater for drinking, manufacturing, recreating, or irrigating. Can these interests be most ably represented through the soil conservation district-subdistrict organization? The argument could well be made that water resources development, rather than watershed development, should be the focus of our attention.

This is suggestive of two points. First, the organizational requirements for water resource planning and development are not uniform throughout the United States. Consequently, institutional flexibility is needed in a geographic as well as a time sense. Second, research should be formulated to test hypotheses about the day-to-day operations of differing types of arrangements. The results from this should aid in creating "an adequate governmental structure" in the future. Research effort is needed so that we can go beyond the prima facie basis of reasoning.

Milton S. Heath, Jr., is Assistant Director of the Institute of Government and
Associate Professor of Law and Government at the University of North Carolina.
He has previously served in the Division of Law of TVA and on the Governor's
Counsel's Office of New York State.

Chapter 19

MILTON S. HEATH, JR. | *Model Watershed District Act*

INTRODUCTION AND SUMMARY

THIS CHAPTER presents a model enabling act for watershed district programs. Its scope is essentially that of the typical conservancy district or watershed district legislation — embracing
the machinery for creation of districts; possible variations in forms of
district organization; district functions, financing, and administration;
and relationships with other governmental units. It also deals with
some aspects of water rights.

In summary, the act provides for (1) creation of districts upon
landowner petitions filed with a state water agency, public hearings,
and referendum approval; (2) the functions of districts — including flood
and erosion prevention and control, water conservation, drainage improvement, low-flow regulation, flood-plain zoning, promotion of water
recreation, and related land treatment measures and land use controls
— and incidental powers to enter contracts, acquire property (through
exercise of the power of eminent domain or otherwise), and so forth;
(3) administration of district affairs through an elected board of trustees; (4) financing of district activities by assessments against benefited lands; and (5) limited supervision of district activities by a state
water agency.

Two additional alternative methods of prosecuting or assisting

295

watershed programs are included — through ordinary county governmental processes supported by countywide ad valorem taxes, and through watershed membership corporations having all powers of watershed districts except the governmental powers of eminent domain, taxation, and regulation.

With respect to water rights, the act (1) requires the district to take title to real property (including water rights) in the name of the state, thus facilitating possible future changes in water law; (2) makes clear that no modification of existing water rights is intended and that watershed districts are granted no special privileges to use or dispose of water; and (3) requires the state water agency to pass upon workplans for district projects and, in so doing, to consider whether construction and operation of the proposed works will appreciably diminish downstream flows.

Many policy choices are inherent in these provisions. For example, districts might be created in administrative or judicial proceedings without referenda. Petitions to create districts might be addressed to soil conservation district supervisors rather than to a state water agency, at least where only Public Law 566 programs are involved. District functions might be broadened to include, for example, public water supply and electric power production. The power of eminent domain might be omitted, or an appointive governing board might be provided. These are illustrative of the policy choices to be made in any watershed district act. It is hoped that this chapter will furnish less an ideal conception than a framework for consideration of available alternatives, and some of the legal and practical issues they pose.

Finally, a word of caution that this act not be used as a guide for new laws or changes in existing laws in any particular state without careful attention to the need for dovetailing its language and procedures with the laws and practices of that jurisdiction.

A WATERSHED DISTRICT ACT

Article I, Watershed Districts

§ 1. Title.

This act shall be known and may be cited as the "Watershed District Law."

§ 2. Purposes of Watershed Districts.

Watershed districts, comprised of one or more counties, or parts of one or more counties, may be formed to prevent and control floods, erosion and sedimentation; to provide for low-flow regulation of streams; to improve drainage and to reclaim wet or overflowed lands; to carry out related land treatment measures and land use controls; to promote water recreation; to develop and conserve water resources and related land, forest, and wildlife resources; and to further the conservation, utilization, and disposal of water. Their objectives may be sought directly or through contract; in cooperation with any person, the United States, the state of _____ or any other state, any county or municipality or other political subdivision, or any of their respective agencies; through regulations or through mutual agreements among their members, or otherwise.

A watershed district may be formed for all or any one or more of the foregoing purposes and, when so formed, shall be a body politic and corporate. It is the intention of the legislature that the territory of a watershed district shall normally comprise all or part of a single watershed, or of two or more watersheds tributary to one of the major drainage basins of the state, or all of a major drainage basin, but exceptions to this policy may be permitted in appropriate cases.

§ 3. Petition to Establish District.

Any 100 owners of land lying within the limits of a proposed watershed district, or a majority of such owners if their total number be less than 200, may file a petition with the state board asking that a watershed district be organized to function in the area described in the petition. The petition shall set forth:

(a) The proposed name of the watershed district;

(b) That the said district appears to hold promise of administrative, engineering, and economic feasibility, and the reasons therefor;

(c) A description of the area proposed to be organized as a watershed district, so presented (by map, metes, and bounds, or otherwise) as to convey an intelligent idea as to the location of the area, and the names and addresses of the landowners therein who are known to petitioners;

(d) That the area described in the petition consists of contiguous territory and in what watershed or watersheds such area lies;

(e) To the extent feasible, a description of any proposed works of improvement of the said district, together with an explanation of the effect which said works will have upon lands in the proposed district;

(f) That none of the land within the proposed watershed district lies within the boundaries of any other watershed district;

(g) A request that the area described in the petition be organized as a watershed improvement district; and

(h) The amount of the maximum annual assessment that may be levied against the landowners of the proposed district, as provided in section 10.

Not later than five days after the petition is filed the state board shall notify the petitioners whether the petition complies with the requirements of this section as to form. The notice shall specify any formal particulars in which the petition is deficient.

§ 4. Notice and Hearing on Petition: Determination of Need for District and Defining Boundaries.

(a) The state board shall set the time and place for public hearings on the petition, to commence within 60 days after the filing of a petition meeting the formal requirements of section 3, and shall publish notice thereof once a week for two consecutive weeks. All interested persons shall have the right to attend the hearings and to be heard. During the hearings or thereafter the state board may recommend that the purposes of the proposed district or its proposed boundaries be changed.

(b) In passing upon the petition the state board shall consider whether:

(1) The area proposed to be organized as a district consists of contiguous territory, none of which lies in any other watershed district;

(2) Any land or structure has been included in the proposed district which cannot be served or benefited by the proposed works of improvement and which could be excluded from the boundaries of the proposed district without substantially impairing the effective purpose of the proposed works of improvement; and

(3) The proposed district appears to hold promise of administrative, engineering, and economic feasibility.

(c) If, in the judgment of the state board, there is substantial compliance with these requirements, it shall issue an order setting dates and places for a referendum concerning creation of the district (and for registration of voters therefor) to be held, after publication of the order as herein provided, among the qualified voters residing within the proposed district. The state board shall publish such order once a week for two successive weeks in the manner provided by this act for publication of notices. The state board shall also send to the board or boards of elections of each county wherein any part of the district lies a copy of the order, together with a request that the said board or boards conduct the referendum within their respective counties on the date set out in the order. If (in connection with a district that lies in more than one county) the state board determines that only a single voting place shall be used or that all voting places should be located within one county, the said order and request shall be sent only to the election board of the county containing such voting place or places. The referendum, and registration therefor, shall be conducted in accordance with the provisions of section 13, and the board or boards of elections shall certify the results of the referendum to the state board. The state board may not approve the petition unless a majority of the votes cast in the referendum were in favor of creation of the district and (such requirement being met) shall approve the petition.

(d) After completion of the referendum the state board shall enter a final order approving or disapproving the petition, and shall record such order in its official minutes. The state board shall by personal service or registered mail serve a copy of the final order upon every person who attended the hearings and signed a roster provided for that purpose, and shall publish notice of such order once a week for two successive weeks. Any order of approval shall declare the district to be duly organized; shall specifically define the boundaries of the district; and shall be certified by the state board to the clerk of the court of the county or counties wherein any part of the district lies for recordation in the special proceedings docket thereof. If a petition is disapproved, subsequent petitions covering the same or substantially the same territory may be filed after six months have elapsed from the date of the order of disapproval, and new proceedings held thereon.

§ 5. Board of Trustees: Selection and Tenure.

(a) Each watershed district shall be governed by a board of trustees to be composed of three members, all of whom shall be residents of the district, and shall be selected in the manner provided in this section.

(b) Within 30 days after it has entered a final order under section 4 declaring the organization of a watershed district, the state board shall appoint an interim board of trustees for the district to serve until their successors are elected and qualified. Such interim board shall have all of the powers and duties of, and be subject to all of the provisions of this act concerning, the board of trustees whose election is provided for in this section.

(c) At the next general election occurring not less than 180 days after the appointment of said interim board, there shall be elected three members of the board of trustees of the district. At each succeeding general election one member of said board shall be elected.

(d) Nominations in all cases shall be by written petition signed by any 25 owners of land lying within said district, or one third of such owners if their total number be less than 75. Such petitions shall be notarized and shall be presented to the board not later than 120 days before the date of the general election. The board shall examine the petitions, determine their validity, and, not later than 90 days before the date of the general election, shall certify to the board or boards of election of each county wherein any part of the district lies the names of the candidates thus nominated, together with a request that these candidates be presented to the voters at the next general election.

(e) The said board or boards of election shall conduct the election, and registrations therefor, in accordance with the provisions of section 13, and shall certify the results of the election to the board.

(f) Of the trustees first elected, the one receiving the largest number of votes shall serve a term of six years, the one receiving the second largest number of votes shall serve a term of four years, and the one receiving the third largest number of votes shall serve a term of two years. Their successors in every case shall serve terms of six years.

(g) Members elected to the board of trustees shall qualify and enter upon the duties of their offices on the first Monday of December next succeeding their election. Appointed members shall qualify and enter upon the duties of the offices not later than the second Monday next succeeding their appointment. All members shall take the oath of office prescribed by the state constitution before some person qualified by law to administer oaths.

(h) Vacancies in the membership of the board of trustees occurring otherwise than by expiration of term shall be filled by appointment to the unexpired term by the board.

§   6. Board of Trustees: Organization and Compensation.

(a) The interim board of trustees at its first meeting shall select a chairman, vice-chairman and secretary-treasurer to serve until their successors are selected. The elected board at its first meeting shall select corresponding officers to serve two-year terms. All official acts of the board shall be entered in a book of minutes to be kept by the secretary-treasurer. A majority of the membership of the board shall constitute a quorum. The board shall meet in regular session at least quarterly and may meet specially upon the call of the chairman or any two members, and upon at least three days notice of the time, place, and purpose of the meeting.

(b) Members of the board of trustees shall receive the same per diem allowance and expenses as are provided for _____ .

§   7. Corporate Powers.

In addition to all other powers conferred by this act, each watershed district created hereunder shall be authorized:

(a) To sue and be sued in its own name, to adopt an official seal and alter the same, and to maintain an office at such place or places as it may designate;

(b) To make contracts incidental to the performance of its functions, and to employ and fix the compensation of such officers, employees, agents, or consultants as it deems necessary, including attorneys, accountants, engineers, and construction and financial experts;

(c) To acquire, undertake, construct, develop, improve, maintain, and operate the projects and systems herein provided for and incidental facilities;

(d) To fix and revise from time to time and to collect rates, fees, and other charges for the use of or for the services or facilities furnished by any project or system operated by the district;

(e) To acquire, hold and dispose of such real and personal property as it deems necessary or convenient in the performance of its functions. All condemnation proceedings are to be in accordance with the provisions of _____ . Title to all real property (including water rights) shall be taken in the name of the state and such property shall be entrusted to the district as agent of the state to accomplish the purposes of this act, as amended from time to time;

(f) To adopt bylaws for the regulation of its internal affairs and rules and regulations not in conflict with common or statutory law to implement the provisions of this act, including:

> (i) Regulations concerning the development, conservation, utilization, and control of the water resources and related land, wildlife, and forest resources of the district;
>
> (ii) Regulations to promote and encourage water recreation, including requirements concerning public access areas and facilities, and rules respecting the use of reservoirs and waters, picnic sites, and other recreational areas;
>
> (iii) Such other bylaws, rules, and regulations as may be needful in the performance of its functions.

Regulations adopted hereunder shall be filed with the state board and shall become effective 30 days thereafter unless previously withdrawn or disapproved by the state board;

(g) With the approval of the state board, to undertake measures incidental to its principal purposes for the prevention of fires or the promotion and protection of public health;

(h) In the performance of its functions, to cooperate with; to accept grants, loans, and other assistance from; to act as agent for; and to enter agreements with any and all federal agencies; and to exercise all necessary or convenient powers in connection therewith;

(i) To perform any functions delegated to it by the state board;

(j) To do all acts or things necessary or convenient to carry out the provisions of this act. Nothing contained in this act is intended to authorize or approve the withdrawal of water from a watershed or stream except to the extent or degree now permissible under the existing common and statute law of this state; nor to change or modify such existing common or statute law with respect to the relative rights of riparian owners or others concerning the use or disposal of water in the streams of this state; nor to authorize the district, its officers, or any other person to utilize or dispose of water except in the manner and to the extent permitted by the existing common and statute law of this state.

§ 8. Flood-Plain Zoning.

(a) The board of trustees may establish zones or districts in those areas deemed subject to seasonal or periodic flooding or other natural disaster, and such regulations may be applied therein as will minimize danger to life and property and secure to the residents thereof eligibility for flood insurance under Public Law 1016, 84th Congress, known as the Federal Flood Insurance Act of 1956, or subsequently enacted laws or regulations promulgated thereunder. The regulations applied shall be uniform for each class of building throughout each zone or district, but may differ from one zone or district to another. They shall be made in accordance with a comprehensive plan and with reasonable consideration, among other things, as to the character of the zone or district and its peculiar suitability for particular uses, and with a view to conserving the value of buildings and encouraging the most appropriate use of land throughout the watershed district.

(b) For such purposes, the board of trustees may establish zones or districts; adopt regulations and restrictions applying thereto; provide methods of procedure; make changes; appoint a zoning commission to recommend the original boundaries and appropriate regulations to be enforced therein; hold public hearings and make preliminary and final reports; provide for appointment of a board of adjustment; and employ remedies to enforce such regulations; all as provided by _____, with respect to zoning regulation by municipal governing bodies. A zoning board of adjustment appointed hereunder shall have all of the powers and duties of municipal boards of adjustment under _____, and the procedure in such matters shall be as therein provided.

§　9. Benefit Assessments: Classification of Lands.

(a) The expenses of a watershed district under this act shall be assessed in the manner hereinafter provided against lands within the district specially benefited by the activities of the district.

(b) As soon as practicable after the organization of a district and the formulation of plans for construction of works of improvement, the trustees shall examine and classify the lands in the district (and from time to time may reclassify them) into as many classes as they deem necessary, according to the relative benefits such lands will receive from the activities of the district. In making such classifications the trustees shall consider the fertility of the soil, the proximity of the land to the watercourse (or, in the case of drainage benefits, its proximity to the ditch or a natural outlet), the location of the land relative to existing and proposed works of improvement of the district, its susceptibility to damage from floods or erosion, and other factors evidencing anticipated benefits or lack thereof to particular lands. The holdings of any one landowner need not necessarily be all in one class. The total number of acres owned by each landowner in each class and the number of acres benefited shall be determined. The total number of acres benefited in each class in the entire district shall be set forth in tabulated form. The scale of assessment upon the several classes of land shall be determined by the board of trustees.

(c) Following completion of such classification the trustees shall publish at least once a week for two successive weeks a notice of the time and place for a public hearing to hear the objections of all interested persons to the classification. The trustees shall also cause a copy of the notice to be mailed to each owner of classified lands. If any objection is made at the hearing and not sustained by the trustees their action thereupon shall be the final adjudication of the issues presented, subject to appeal to the courts.

§　10. Benefit Assessments: Estimates of Expenses; Levy and Collection of Assessment.

After the classification of lands has been completed, the trustees shall estimate as near as may be:

(i) The cost of the contemplated works of improvement and incidental expenses; and

(ii) The amount of all other expenses of the district (including expenses of maintaining the works of improvement, administrative expenses, and interest on borrowed funds):

(A) that have accrued or will accrue prior to the first fiscal year of the district during which assessments are turned over to the county authorities for collection, and

(B) that will accrue during such fiscal year and the two succeeding fiscal years. (The fiscal year of the district shall begin on July 1 and end on June 30.)

The trustees shall thereupon make an assessment of the amounts estimated pursuant to paragraphs (i) and (ii) above. For this purpose the trustees shall make out an assessment roll in which shall be entered the names of the landowners assessed so far as the same can be ascertained, and the amounts assessed against them, respectively, with a brief description of the parcels or tracts of land assessed. The said assessment roll shall also indicate the amount of the assessment installments to be paid during each of the first three fiscal years of the district by each landowner who elects to pay his assessment in installments.

§ 11. Benefit Assessments: Collection and Payment; Expenditure of Proceeds and of Other District Funds.

(a) The landowner against whom an initial assessment is made shall have the option of paying it in cash or, if he should so elect and give written notice of the fact to the secretary-treasurer of the district within 15 days after the confirmation of the assessment roll, in three equal annual installments.

(b) All watershed assessments shall be collected and enforced by the county tax collector in the same manner as county taxes. The tax collector shall be required on the first day of each month to make settlements with the secretary-treasurer of the district of all collections of watershed assessments for the preceding month, and to deposit all moneys so collected in an account maintained in the name of the district at an official depository designated by the district. Such account shall also be used for the deposit of all other funds of the district. Expenditures from such account may be made with the approval of the trustees of the district on requisition from the chairman and the secretary-treasurer of the district. For collecting the watershed assessments the tax collector shall be allowed a fee of ___ percent of the amount collected, except that, where the tax collector is on a salary basis, such fee shall be paid by the trustees into the general fund of the county.

§ 12. Authority to Borrow Money, Issue Bonds, and Accept Gifts.

The board of trustees shall have power to incur indebtedness and issue bonds to defray any part of the expenses of the district. If necessary to pay interest on and to amortize such indebtedness or bonds, the trustees shall levy an annual assessment on all lands within the district subject to assessment under sections 9-11 to pay such interest and to amortize such indebtedness or bonds. Such additional assessment shall be apportioned and collected in the same manner as the assessment provided for in section 11. The trustees on behalf of the district may accept, receive, and expend gifts, grants, or loans from whatever source received.

§ 13. Elections.

(a) All qualified voters residing within the watershed district shall be eligible to register for voting in referenda concerning creation of districts, elections of district officers, and all other district elections, and all qualified voters so registered shall be eligible to vote in such referenda and elections. For such elections and referenda the board of elections of each county wherein any part of the district lies, at county expense, shall provide polling places in said district and in their respective counties, and shall provide for a registrar or registrars and judges of election at each said polling place. In their discretion the board of elections may designate the general election polling places and election officials as polling places and election officials for such election (for registration as well as for elections). The said board shall provide for the printing and distribution of ballots in the same way they provide ballots for county and precinct offices.

(b) (i) For the election concerning creation of a district each board of elections shall provide for a new registration of all qualified voters residing in the district and in their respective counties.

(ii) For any district election to be held subsequent to the referendum concerning creation of a district the said board or boards of elections may order a new registration of voters to be conducted as provided in paragraph (i) of this subsection. If no new registration is ordered the registration books shall be open for registration of new voters in the district and registration of any legal residents of the district (who are or could legally be enfranchised as qualified voters for regular general elections), shall be carried out in accordance with the general election laws as provided for local elections.

(c) (i) For the referendum concerning creation of a district, the form of the question shall be substantially the words "For Creation of the (insert name of district) Watershed District" and "Against Creation of the (insert name of district) Watershed District," which alternates shall appear separated from each other on one ballot containing (opposite and to the left of each alternate), squares of appropriate size in one of which squares the voter may mark "X" to designate his choice.

(ii) For any district election to be held subsequent to the referendum concerning creation of a district, the ballots shall be printed separately, shall indicate the title and term of the office being voted for, and shall contain the names of all nominees certified to the board of elections and an instruction as to the number of candidates to be voted for. Write-in votes shall be treated as provided for write-in votes in the general election.

(iii) For the initial referendum, as well as subsequent elections and referenda, it shall be stated upon the ballots that if the voter tears or defaces or wrongly marks a ballot he may return it and get another.

§ 14. Supervision by State Board.

(a) Each watershed district (to the extent that moneys are made available therefor by the state or any of its agencies or political subdivisions, by any municipality, or otherwise) shall:

(i) By means of suitable measuring and recording devices and facilities and at intervals prescribed by the board, record the inflow of water into and release of water from such reservoirs of the district as may be designated by the board; and

(ii) Make periodic reports of such records as required by the board.

(b) The state board shall be the state agency to which watershed workplans developed under Public Law 566 (83rd Congress, as

amended) or otherwise for contemplated works of improvement shall
be submitted for review and approval or disapproval. The board shall
approve such workplans if, in its judgment, the workplans

    (i) Provide for proper and safe construction of proposed
works of improvement;

    (ii) Show that the construction and operation of the proposed
works of improvement (in conjunction with other such works and related structures of the district) will not appreciably diminish the flow
of useful water that would otherwise be available to existing downstream water users during critical periods; and

    (iii) Are otherwise in compliance with law.
No work of improvement may be constructed or established without the
approval of workplans by the board pursuant to this subsection. The
construction or establishment of any such work of improvement without
such approval, or without conforming to a workplan approved by the
board, may be enjoined. The board may institute an action for such injunctive relief in the _____ court of any county wherein such construction or establishment takes place, and the procedure in any such
action shall be as provided in _____.

    (c) In conjunction with any workplans submitted to the board under
subsection (b) of this section, a watershed district shall submit in such
form as the board may prescribe a plan of its proposed method of operations for works of improvement covered by the workplans and for
related structures. With the approval of the board, the district may
amend its initial plan of operations from time to time. Board approval
of the initial plan of operations shall not be required.

    (d) If the board has reason to believe that a watershed district is
not operating any work of improvement or related structure in accordance with its plan of operations as amended, the board on its own motion or upon complaint may order a hearing to be held thereon upon not
less than 30 days written notification to the district and complainant, if
any, by personal service or registered mail. Notice of such hearing
shall be published at least once a week for two successive weeks. In
connection with any such hearing the board shall be empowered to administer oaths; to take testimony; and, in the same manner as the
_____ Court, to order the taking of depositions; issue subpoenas;
and compel the attendance of witnesses and production of documents.
If the board determines from evidence of record that the district is not
operating any work of improvement or related structure in accordance
with its plan of operations, as amended, the board may issue an order
directing the district to comply therewith or to take other appropriate
corrective action. Upon failure by a district to comply with any such
order, the board may institute an action for injunctive relief in the
_____ Court of any county wherein such noncompliance occurs,
and the procedure in any such action shall be as provided in _____.

    (e) As used in this section the term 'critical periods' means
monthly periods, or other periods designated by the board when (in the
area affected) below-average streamflows coincide with above-average

utilization of water; *provided,* that where insufficient data are available
to permit reliable determinations concerning these matters, the board
may adopt as the 'critical period' for any particular area the period
June 15-September 15.

(f) The state board shall require as a condition of approving watershed workplans of a district under this section that, whenever the
district is directly benefited by the construction by another district of
a storage reservoir or other upstream improvement, the benefited dis-
strict shall reimburse the owner of the reservoir or improvement for
such part of the annual charges for interest, maintenance, and depreciation thereon as the board may deem equitable.

§ 15. Participation by Cities, Counties, Industries, and Others.

(a) Any industry, or private water user, the state of _____ ,
the United States or any of its agencies, any county, municipality, or
any other political subdivision may participate in watershed improvement district works or projects upon mutually agreeable terms relating to such matters as the construction, financing, maintenance, and
operation thereof.

(b) Any county or municipality may contribute funds toward the
construction, maintenance, and operation of watershed improvement
district works or projects, to the extent that such works or projects:

(i) Provide a source (respectively) of county or municipal
water supply; or protect an existing source of such supply or enhance
its quality or increase its dependable capacity or quantity; or

(ii) Protect against or alleviate the effects of floodwater or
sediment damages affecting, or provide drainage benefits for, (respectively) county or municipally owned property or the property (respectively) of county or municipal inhabitants located outside the boundaries
of such district but within the respective boundaries of such county or
municipality.

§ 16. Definitions.

Unless the context otherwise indicates, the following words, terms,
phrases, and references, as used in this act, have or include (as the
case may be) the following meanings:

(a) The word "acquire" means to acquire in any manner, whether
by condemnation, purchase, gift, devise, lease, lease-purchase arrangement, or otherwise.

(b) The term "board of trustees" or "trustees" means the board of
trustees of a watershed district.

(c) The phrase "dispose of" means to convey or dispose of in any
manner, whether by sale, lease, lease-purchase arrangement, or otherwise.

(d) The word "district" means a watershed district created under
this act.

(e) The "systems herein provided for" include drainage, flow regulation, water conservation, and flood prevention and control systems.

(f) The "projects herein provided for" include:

(i) Dams, reservoirs, weirs, channel improvements, levees,

and other like structures; parks; fishing, boating, swimming, picnicking, and other recreational facilities; wildlife or timber preserves; fish stocking projects; land treatment measures and practices; and dredging and related undertakings; all of which may be used (or useful or have present capacity for future use) in connection with low-flow regulation for dependable water supply; prevention and control of floods, erosion, and sedimentation; promotion of water recreation; or development and conservation of water resources and related land, forest, and wildlife resources;

(ii) Drains, ditches, canals, laterals, and other watercourses; undertakings to straighten, deepen, or widen the same; levees, embankments, tiles, tidal gates, and pumping plants; and other related works and undertakings; all of which may be used (or useful or have present capacity for future use) in connection with drainage improvement and reclamation of wet or overflowed land; and

(iii) All facilities incidental to or part of the aforenamed projects.

(g) The phrase "to publish notice" means to publish notice in at least one newspaper of general circulation published in each county wherein any part of the district lies, or if in any instance there is no such newspaper, then, in lieu thereof, in a newspaper of general circulation in the affected county.

(h) The terms "real property" and "personal property" include all manner of rights and interests therein.

(i) The term "state board" or "board" means the state water resources agency.

Article II, Watershed Membership Corporations

§ 17. Creation and Powers of Watershed Membership Corporations.

(a) Watershed membership corporations may be formed for any of the purposes for which a watershed district may be created, upon application filed with the state board by any number of persons (including corporations, and cities, counties, and other political subdivisions) not less than three. The application shall describe the territory within which the activities of the corporation would be conducted, and shall state the purposes for which the corporation is to be formed, the maximum number of directors to be selected (not less than three), the names and addresses of the original directors who are to manage the affairs of the corporation for the first year of its existence or until their successors are chosen, and the period, if any, limited for the duration of the corporation. The board shall approve all applications complying with the requirements of this subsection, and the corporate existence of a corporation shall commence as of the time of such approval.

(b) The corporation shall be governed by a board of trustees which, except in the case of the original trustees, shall be elected annually by the members. The provisions of subsection (a) of section 6 of this act shall apply to such board of trustees. All meetings of the trustees shall be open to the members of the corporation. The trustees shall direct the exercise of the functions of the corporation, except as otherwise stipulated by two-thirds vote of the members.

(c) The corporation may issue to its members certificates of membership, and each member shall be entitled to one vote at meetings of the corporation unless, by two-thirds vote of the members, additional voting power is granted to any member or class of members.

(d) The corporation shall have all of the powers of a watershed district under section 7 of this act [subject to the limitations set forth in subdivision (j) of such section], except that it shall not have the power of eminent domain nor the power to adopt rules or regulations under subsection (f) of such section affecting persons who are not members of the corporation. The corporation may accept, receive, and expend gifts, grants, or loans from whatever source received.

Article III, County Watershed Programs.

§ 18. <u>Alternative Method of Financing and Conducting Watershed Programs by County Government.</u>

(a) The board of county commissioners of any county is authorized to expend county funds, derived from tax or nontax sources, in the manner provided by this article for any of the purposes for which watershed districts may be formed under this act. Any board of county commissioners electing to proceed under this article shall have all of the powers of watershed districts under subsections (b) through (j) of section 7 of this act [subject to the limitations set forth in subdivision (j) of such section]. It is the intention of the legislature that such powers shall normally be exercised within all or part of a single watershed, or of two or more watersheds tributary to one of the major drainage basins of the state, but exceptions to this policy may be permitted in appropriate cases.

(b) The board of county commissioners may itself directly exercise such powers or, for that purpose, may create a watershed improvement commission to be composed of three members appointed by the board. The terms of office of the members of the commission shall be six years, with the exception of the first two years of existence of the commission, in which one member shall be appointed to serve for a period of two years, one for a period of four years, and one for a period of six years; thereafter all members shall be appointed for six years, and shall serve until their successors have been appointed and qualified. Vacancies in the membership of the commission occurring otherwise than by expiration of term shall be filled by appointment to the unexpired term by the board of county commissioners. The commission shall hold its first meeting within 30 days after its appointment as provided for in this act, and the beginning date of all terms of

office of commissioners shall be the date on which the commission
holds its first meeting. The provisions of section ___ concerning the
organization and compensation of the elected board of trustees of a watershed district shall apply to the commission. The commission shall
provide the board of county commissioners 30 days prior to July 1
a proposed budget for the fiscal year commencing on July 1 and shall
provide the board of county commissioners an audit by a certified public accountant within 60 days after the expiration of the fiscal year
ending on June 30.

(c) The board of county commissioners may create a single watershed improvement commission for the entire county or may create
separate commissions for individual projects or watersheds.

(d) Counties which carry out watershed programs under this article shall be subject to supervision by the state board pursuant to section 14 to the same extent as are watershed districts, and, for this
purpose, the words "districts" and "watershed districts," wherever
they occur in such section, shall be read as referring to counties.

(e) Any industry or private water user, the state of _____, the
United States or any of its agencies, any municipality, any other county,
or any other political subdivision may participate in county watershed
programs hereunder in the same manner and to the same extent as
provided by section 15 with respect to participation in watershed district programs. Two or more counties may jointly conduct a watershed program and expend county funds therefor and, in the discretion
of their respective boards of commissioners, may create a single watershed commission to carry out such program. The number of members of such commission, and their terms of office, shall be determined by the boards of county commissioners. Such commission shall
have the powers of a watershed commission created under subsection
(b) of this section and shall be subject to the provisions of such subsection concerning the initial meeting, organization, compensation,
budgets, and audits.

§ 19. Article Intended as Supplementary.

This article is intended to provide an alternative method of financing and operating watershed programs, supplementary to the method
set forth in Article I of this act.

§ 20. Transfer and Continuation of Programs. [1]

A watershed program initiated under this article may be discontinued as a county program and thereafter transferred to or renewed
as a watershed district or watershed membership corporation program
under Articles I and II, respectively, upon compliance with the provisions of said articles for initiating such programs. A watershed district program initiated under Article I may be discontinued as a district program and thereafter transferred to or renewed as a county or
watershed membership corporation program under this article and

---

[1] The second and third sentences of this section were added as a result of a suggestion
made by John C. O'Byrne.

Article II, respectively, upon compliance with the provisions of said articles for initiating such programs. A watershed membership corporation program initiated under Article II may be discontinued as a membership corporation program and thereafter transferred to or renewed as a district or county program under Article I and this article, respectively, in accordance with the provisions of said articles for initiating such programs.

ANNOTATION

There are certain omissions to be noted which should be remedied in actual watershed district enabling legislation. In order to conserve space, no effort has been made to deal with the question of how to count undivided interests in land for purposes of petitions to create districts under section 3 and nominating petitions under section 5(d).

The standards of administrative, engineering, and economic feasibility here employed in section 4(b)(3) are found in several state watershed district laws. In some circumstances and some jurisdictions such standards may be of questionable constitutionality.

The election procedures embodied in sections 4(c), 5(c), and 13 are derived from North Carolina laws concerning general elections, and the particular language used, in all probability, would be inappropriate in other jurisdictions. Some space-saving omissions have been made; for example, in the provisions of section 13 concerning the details of registration.

It may be necessary for constitutional reasons to insert standards to guide the state board in passing upon regulations filed with it under section 7(f).

Many necessary or desirable procedural provisions relating to benefit assessments have been left out of sections 9 through 11 because of space limitations. Sufficient material has been included only to make clear the general pattern of classification of land, and levy and collection of assessments. Among the omitted provisions are details concerning notice of classification; constitutionally prerequisite provisions concerning notices and hearings as to assessment rolls (these could be similar to those set forth in the act for land classifications); express authority for assessments subsequent to the initial assessment; and helpful details, such as forms illustrating interest computation for delinquent assessments and an assessment receipt book.

State constitutions may require bond referenda, not provided for in section 12, at least where the credit of a district is pledged.

The "state board of water resources," defined in section 16(i), is intended to refer to that board or commission (if any) in the particular state which has over-all responsibility for supervising state water activities. The act makes no effort to deal with the matters of dissolving or merging districts, changing district boundaries, and consolidating existing districts, all of which should be and ordinarily are covered in state watershed district laws.

JOHN R. GREENMAN

JOHN C. O'BYRNE

Comment

AN ADMIRABLE DRAFT of an "illustrative" law has been presented by Milton Heath. He would be the first to agree that a legislative draft is illustrative. There is no such thing as a model law. The complexities of the policy decisions that must be made in each state are exceeded only by the detail of adjustment of the resolutions of policy to local law, procedure, and existing political organization.

In our limited space and time we can only try to add to Heath's comments on the vital issues of policy upon which such a law is based. Otte, in the previous paper, suggested the first issue. Every state has many types of districts. Should new districts be created or should existing ones be improved? The rash of *ad hoc* legislation of the last few years illustrates either choice.

Heath made his decision in offering us a watershed district law which provides a legal basis for new multipurpose watershed districts. But acceptance of that alternative suggests the need for a method of replacing with desirable multipurpose districts the obsolete special districts that are now in existence. Procedures for terminating existing districts and coordinating the new district with existing laws must be developed. Heath's mention in his introduction of the "need for dovetailing" recognizes the extent of the problems inherent in a new layer of district organization.

Although Heath's watershed district law is drafted in broader context than Public Law 566, we are concerned primarily with districts that can serve as local organizations under that law. Only two real alternative forms of local organization exist. One is consensual or contractual — an arrangement whereby local people group themselves and bind themselves by agreement. A specific example of this is Heath's watershed membership corporation (sec. 17).[1] The other form involves some kind of governmental or quasi-governmental structure — a district. These lines are not sharp. It is possible for a contractual organization to have greater power and control over its members than a political subdivision. A major problem under Public Law 566 has been the absence of power in local governmental units. Otte points out that 33 states have districts that can be made to function under Public Law 566, but in ten of them it is necessary to use two or more units as co-sponsors.

---

[1] Section numbers refer to the Model Watershed District Law.

John R. Greenman is Professor of Agricultural Economics and Assistant Director, Science and Engineering Research Center Studies, University of Florida. He has served on the staff of the USDA, the Bureau of the Budget, and as Assistant Economic Commissioner with the ECA. John C. O'Byrne is Professor of Law and Director of the Agricultural Law Center, College of Law, State University of Iowa. He has been Visiting Professor of Law at the University of Texas and at Northwestern University Law School.

311

Only a governmental unit can exert the force of the state to bring a recalcitrant brother into line with the group. If the group is to be formed by other than unanimous action, if the recalcitrant brother's land is to be taken, if he is to be charged for his share of costs without his consent, if he is to be compelled to refrain from certain uses of his land, the power of the state must be exerted.

Herein lies the major policy hurdle. Heath's own legislature refused to grant such power to the district. Recent experience in the Florida legislature suggests that the broad powers embodied in Heath's draft may cause powerful interests in limited areas of a state to block its passage as a general law.

If the issue is resolved to force the recalcitrant brother to participate without his consent, the whole political and constitutional background of protection of the rights of the individual comes into play. This raises a plethora of local issues that can be decided only against the interplay of state institutions and the federal constitution. Notice how much of Heath's draft is necessarily concerned with problems of notice, hearing, and "due process" (secs. 3, 4, 9), and how often he warns of the need to adjust an illustrative clause to local law.

If it is agreed that the power of the state shall be exerted at all, the policy issue arises on how much power the district shall have. The usual corporate powers of a district raise few issues. These include powers to contract, to sue, to own property, to accept gifts and grants, to employ personnel, to establish operating rules, to cooperate with other units, to collect fees, and such businesslike powers. The need for powers to plan and survey, to construct and install improvements, to operate and maintain structures, will be conceded if the purpose of the district is settled.

The issues arise sharply on the power of eminent domain, power to levy general taxes, power to levy special assessments, power to borrow, and the power to enact and enforce land use regulations. The power of eminent domain and the power to levy special assessments for improvements seem to come easiest. A power to borrow is suspect, as is a power to levy limited general taxes. These powers are granted reluctantly. The power to enact and enforce land use regulations is still beyond legislative acceptance in most states.

From these broad problems stem the narrower ones, all to be determined within the context of state jurisdiction. Are the procedural guarantees to be provided at the formation of the district, or will they be reserved until the district begins to act? In Heath's draft the district organization and a detailed plan of operation are packaged together for approval by state board and referenda (secs. 3, 4). Would it be better to organize the district, either by election or administrative action, and thereafter bring up the detailed plans?

Closely related is the matter of how autonomous the local district should be in formation and operation. First, what is the relationship with the state level — the water agency, state board of health, the wildlife and recreation agencies, and so forth (secs. 14, 15). Second, what is the relationship to other local organizations — city, county, special purpose districts? (secs. 14, 15). Any district will face the normal problems of overlapping boundaries and related purposes, but in some states the general-purpose unit will provide services, e.g., tax assessment and collection by the county.

Such determinations are inseparable from the question of special or multipurpose districts. Purposes can range from narrow conceptions of flood control and conservation to the multiple purposes of Heath's districts involving water management and control, recreation, wildlife, water supply, power, and pollution control (secs. 2, 7, 8). As the purposes enlarge, the problems of coordination with state and local units intensify (secs. 14f, 15). The county or general-purpose unit should be able to accomplish some of its purposes through or in cooperation with the watershed district (sec. 18). Where the district may include parts of more than one county, the relationships proliferate (sec. 18).

Who will be the members or voters of a district? Heath discovered that under his local law he had to use "qualified voters" (sec. 14), but his petitions and nominations are made by landowners (secs. 3, 5). In other states, should the voters be all landowners, or only those landowners affected? Can voting power be related to the extent of landholdings? Do different classes of voters vote on different issues? Fundamental to all of these is the question of how much of the activities of the district must be based upon vote or referenda. As the purposes expand, the pattern of district activity touches more persons and comes closer in operation to a general-purpose unit.

Our further comments are more in the nature of suggestions to states considering such a law. Heath would agree that he, too, would consider all these and many more in planning a general multipurpose water district law for any state.

We have heard suggestions during these meetings that the purported analyses used to justify the establishment of watershed districts are, in some instances at least, not without serious bias in favor of the establishment of such districts. No doubt we can all agree that at an early stage in the consideration of a water district, unbiased information is needed concerning the advantages and disadvantages of the district. Perhaps unbiased information and analyses cannot be expected from "captive" economists and lawyers in action agencies that have a vested interest in the establishment of such districts. While we are not unaware of the difficulties involved, we believe that a general multipurpose district law such as Heath has proposed might well include provision for an independent agency to develop unbiased information and analyses for use in establishing and operating watershed districts.

Any watershed district law must contain specific provisions relating it to the organic water law of the state and to any state water or resources control unit. Heath's act requires state board approval of the district and its plans (secs. 3, 7f). But is this enough to coordinate the district's activities? The model water use act requires advance approval by the state agency of any district rule or regulation and of the exercise of eminent domain.[2]

There is no express provision in the model act for the capture and use of surplus waters. Nor is there an express provision for the use of such water on nonriparian land. In fact, the draft act negates any change in basic water law (sec. 7). Inclusion of these provisions should facilitate more efficient and more complete use of available water. More efficient use of available water would also be facilitated by the inclusion of a provision authorizing the board of trustees of a district to regulate wasteful, non-beneficial use of water.

Heath's introductory remarks suggest that provision should be made for periodic re-evaluation of benefits and assessments, for dissolving or merging districts, and for changing district boundaries, but the draft does not deal with these items. Over time, original determinations of benefits and assessments may prove to be inadequate and inequitable. Likewise, it may become desirable to enlarge or combine districts.

CONCLUSION

The model act is a complex document not readily subject to discussion in limited space and time. The detail of specific provisions, local mechanics, and state procedure must be analyzed in the light of the legal and political patterns of each state. The policy decisions will be made again in every state in which such a law is contemplated.

Heath has done an excellent job in providing us with an example from which to work. He has given us some insight into the complexity of the undertaking. In our discussion we have sought to expand upon points that struck us as important. To conclude in another way, Heath's model is very attractive, but a little more clothing here and there might make her even more attractive to the public of some states.

---

[2] Section 205, Model Water Use Act, National Conference of Commissioners on Uniform State Laws, in "Water Resources and the Law," University of Michigan Law School, Ann Arbor, 1958.

Harry A. Steele is Chief, Land and Water Research Branch, Farm Economics Research Division, USDA. In 1933-34 he worked on land conservation for the National Resources Planning Board in Brookings, South Dakota, and from 1935-54 was an agricultural economist with the Bureau of Agricultural Economics in Lincoln, Nebraska.

Chapter 20

HARRY A. STEELE

Suggestions for Fostering Optimum Watershed Development

AT THE REQUEST of the committee planning this volume, I have asked several people, "What are your suggestions for fostering optimum watershed development?" I have received nine replies covering a wide variety of subjects and suggestions. The time and effort these people put into their replies are greatly appreciated. I have attempted to summarize their suggestions under seven major headings. So far as possible, I have tried to present the ideas of the various respondents without interjecting comments of my own. I have tried to maintain their concepts, but I may have changed meanings inadvertently in some instances. In case of doubt, the reader is referred to the responses reproduced at the end of this résumé. In trying to keep the summary short, I did not include all the comments made by the various respondents. In most instances, I was able to use the specific suggestions, but eliminated some of the more general observations. Again, I refer you to the individual statements for this material.

RESEARCH AND BASIC DATA

Several respondents mentioned the need for more research and basic data, or assumed that this need would be met and confined their

315

suggestions to other things. Four, however, made specific recommendations.

Gladwin E. Young indicated that there are major opportunities to improve the basic data on which present calculations are made in engineering, water and land interrelationships, and economic phases of project development. Although research in many of these categories is difficult and costly, more real progress is being achieved now than at any time in the past, and this is being done with widespread support from local watershed interests. Gilbert F. White raised the question of the need for sounder methods of estimating flood damages and of computing possible benefits from flood reduction. He indicated that it is not enough to define general methods. Fieldworkers need, for example, to have relatively precise stage-damage curves for various seasons, crops, and structures which will enable them to check quickly the guesses made by farmers and local observers. White also suggested the need for observation of changes in the use of flood plains which result from the planning and construction of watershed programs. Too often, the estimates of probable benefits are not checked by observation of what in fact occurs in flood-hazard areas.

Fred A. Clarenbach stated that more adequate provision should be made for collection and interpretation of basic data concerning the effects of land treatment and structural measures under a variety of conditions in natural watersheds. He felt that this need had been recognized by many competent and disinterested engineers and economists but that the proponents of watershed programs had not given it sufficient support.

John B. Bennett said that under present procedures for formulating watershed programs, perhaps the most obvious improvement in specific projects would result from improved basic data — both physical and economic. Although it will seldom be possible to have all the data desired before proposing a project, any improvements along this line would constitute a valuable contribution to the long-range improvement of watershed development. According to Bennett, another important contribution to the improvement of watershed development would be achieved through conducting postconstruction evaluations of selected watershed projects. An objective comparison over a reasonable period of years of actual results with the results that had been assumed in the project justification would add valuable information that could be used to perfect the planning process. It would serve also to clarify the goals that can be attained through watershed programs. Such a postconstruction evaluation should cover both the physical and economic aspects of the project.

PLANNING

There are many suggestions regarding planning. Young pointed out that while additional research information would undoubtedly help improve the optimum development, we are sure also that improvements can and will be made in project planning only as experience is gained through actual construction and operation of projects.

A. C. Spencer was concerned with the effect that limiting flood storage to 5,000 acre feet has on the design of projects and the formulation of watershed plans. He felt that the 250,000-acre limitation on size of the watershed is sufficient to prevent conflict between the watershed program and the large flood control reservoirs, and that the removal of the 5,000-acre foot limitation would be helpful. He indicated that the administrative procedures for allocating planning assistance to various states and watersheds did not always reflect the greatest amount of interest and need for flood control work. He felt that the practice of allocating state contributions to planning on the basis of the willingness and ability of local people to contribute might lead to the wrong priorities in watershed development. He felt that state funds should be from state appropriations and allocated on the same basis as priorities for federally financed planning parties.

Norman E. Landgren was also concerned with the problem of allocating watershed funds between different watersheds. He felt that optimum watershed development would not be reached if funds were allocated entirely on the basis of the willingness of local people to sponsor projects. The requirement of a high degree of local interest in watershed development is a necessary condition before the federal government can participate actively in project formulation and implementation. Undoubtedly, however, this policy has tended to divert public expenditures for watershed development to some watersheds that may rank comparatively low in terms of net benefits achieved from the limited funds available. Landgren suggested an inventory of all potential watersheds to provide rough estimates of the cost of several levels of project intensity within each watershed and rough estimates of the benefits associated with each level, and the approximate division of cost between local participants and the federal government. Development of such an inventory would provide a guide as to which watersheds would produce the greatest net benefits from limited watershed expenditures. An educational program to inform local people within potentially high net benefit watersheds about the economic advantages of and possibilities for watershed development would be needed to implement the inventory program.

The need for speeding up planning, designing, and preparing specifications was stressed by Othie R. McMurry. He pointed out the lag between applications filed, plans completed, and actual construction. He recognized that time is necessary for review and compliance with various state and federal laws, but felt that both federal and state efforts could be speeded up. He suggested that the states might contribute more to the planning parties and also streamline their own procedures to provide more speedy review.

Clarenbach felt that the gross shortcomings and distortions in the economic analysis of watershed projects should be eliminated. If the federal government is to pay the lion's share of the cost, then benefits and costs should be considered from a national viewpoint. He thought that small projects should be evaluated not only in the light of conditions and prospective development in larger basins, but also in the light of national needs and relevant broad national policy considerations.

The problem of prime importance is bringing a watershed program into harmony with comprehensive basin plans, according to Howard L. Cook. He felt that this subject was of vital importance to all who have striven to bring about acceptance of the idea that the United States should have comprehensive and unified plans for the development, conservation, and utilization of the resources of its major river basins. Cook suggested specifically that techniques must be developed to insure that all reservoirs constructed in a river basin constitute elements of a basin-wide reservoir system to best meet all of the needs that can be satisfied by development of that basin's resources. This means an effort should be made to find the best combination of small, large, and intermediate-sized reservoirs for each major basin. It also means federal assistance, whether under Public Law 566 or other legislation, should not be made available for the construction of any reservoir until it has been determined that the reservoir would fit into and constitute an integral part of a good basin-wide reservoir system.

Bennett stated that a factor to consider is the relation between plans for development of a watershed and plans for development of the larger area of which the watershed is a part. Since the sponsors of watershed programs are frequently soil conservation districts or other local groups concerned with limited areas, and since considerable emphasis is placed on local initiative in planning the watershed program, he felt that insufficient attention is given to effective, coordinated water-conservation and water-use planning for larger areas. Neither is there at present, he pointed out, any really effective mechanism at the regional or national levels to encourage breadth of view in considering the interrelations between the watershed programs and other programs that may affect or be affected by them.

White suggested that the present administrative organization appears to draw up workplans without a clear link to integraged river basin plans on the one hand or to integrated farm plans on the other. For example, he stated that there does not appear to be a mechanism for assuring that the sum of the watershed projects for a basin is reconciled with larger scale plans for water use in the major stream channels of the basin. Likewise, the projects concentrate on certain cropping and engineering improvements without considering economic or social measures that might affect farm income and stability.

COST-SHARING

The separable cost-remaining benefit method of allocating costs hinders the participation of small towns and agricultural interests in the addition of conservation storage to floodwater-retarding structures, according to Spencer. He pointed out that the potential need for conservation storage should be met at the time of construction, and that the policy should be set so as to encourage local participation in and financing of such storage. He felt that local interests should pay the full additional cost of adding conservation storage (separable costs), but should not pay a part of the joint cost of the project, as they would under the separable cost-remaining benefit method of calculation. Assuming that a reservoir was justified as a flood control structure, Spencer suggested that local people be given the option of adding conservation storage by paying the added or separable cost.

Clarenbach was of the opinion that a key to responsible development of watersheds is in the cost-sharing arrangements. He recalled that the watershed protection and flood prevention program was launched with emphasis on the idea that each project is a local undertaking with federal help, not a federal project with local help. He felt that the program had drifted away from this concept. He suggested that federal subsidies for flood control, irrigation, and drainage be greatly reduced or eliminated, particularly at a time when the Department of Agriculture is struggling with mounting crop surpluses. He felt a cost-sharing formula that would limit the federal share to a fixed percentage, say 25 percent, of construction cost would be desirable.

White asked whether repayment policies do not favor certain forms of watershed treatment. He asked whether repayment policies might not encourage local groups to seek watershed work in preference to Corps of Engineers projects, and whether in the watershed program reservoirs might not be preferred to land treatment because they require less local contribution.

The need for better state enabling legislation and local organization to meet their responsibilities was stressed by several respondents. Young indicated that one of the major contributions to optimum watershed development lies in the field of improved state enabling legislation and improved administration of state and local responsibilities. This is a field for rewarding effort for someone in almost every state who could work with soil conservation districts and other watershed groups or agencies as may be provided under state law.

Landgren and McMurry both stressed the need for local organizations with power to acquire reservoir sites and rights-of-way by condemnation, and with the power of taxation to finance a share of construction costs and operation and maintenance costs. It was pointed out that the lack of these powers is certain to affect the selection and design of projects. This lack will become more serious as the program develops.

It was Clarenbach's belief that local sponsors should be truly responsible units of local government (or a state government) that possess all requisite legal and fiscal powers and the resources for adequate administration. Spencer pointed out that there is a need for cosponsorship of watershed programs by soil conservation districts and another subdivision of the state government having powers of eminent domain and taxing authority.

AUTHORIZATION

Interagency review was mentioned by Cook and Clarenbach. Cook felt that watershed projects should be reviewed in relation to comprehensive basin-wide plans, and that if the watershed program is to reinforce, rather than to subvert, the nation's efforts to unify and make more effective its resource development programs, means must be found to insure that watershed projects shall be planned and carried out as integral parts of comprehensive river basin programs. Clarenbach indicated that provision should be made for more effective review of watershed project plans by other federal agencies. He felt that the present limitation on time allowed for review usually does not permit adequate interagency consultation and consideration in the review process. In contrast, McMurry and Spencer both felt that too much time elapses between the preliminary planning and the final construction. Spencer was concerned also about the limitation on new starts as set by the United States Bureau of the Budget. He felt that setting the limitation in terms of numbers of watersheds was not desirable, and that if it were necessary to set a limitation, it should be set from a monetary standpoint, with discretion as to the size and number of watersheds selected for construction.

MAINTENANCE AND OPERATIONS

Spencer pointed out that as responsibilities for maintenance and operation require definite organization and specific arrangements, local people must have the answers to several questions. The first is: What is maintenance? He defined it as consisting of two parts: first, the management and land treatment of the watershed to slow down runoff and reduce sediment to the absolute minimum. This would increase the life of all the structures. The second part of maintenance included taking all the necessary steps to insure that nothing impeded the water control structures from functioning as designed. Prompt performance of needed maintenance jobs such as restoration of depleted vegetation and repair of cracks, separated joints, and eroded spillways would be a necessity.

A second question is: What will maintenance cost? Spencer indicated that not enough experience had been gained to permit accurate estimates, so Texas has developed a program of estimating costs in accordance with the size of watershed projects. This procedure provides for building up a reserve that will be available to meet emergency costs and place less financial burden on local people at any given time.

A third question is: What kind of organization can and should

assume maintenance responsibilities? Spencer suggested cosponsorship by a soil conservation district, which would arrange for desirable
land treatment measures and would undertake the responsibility of operation, inspection, and supervision of maintenance work; and cosponsorship by another subdivision of state government with legal and financial powers to levy taxes in order to raise revenue for construction,
maintenance, and operation costs, and with the power of eminent domain to secure easements on rights-of-way necessary for projects.

LAND USE REGULATIONS

Not many suggestions were made regarding land use regulations
and alternative ways of achieving program benefits. White raised the
question as to whether watershed projects might not stimulate intensity
in the use of flood plains so that net annual flood losses might be increased rather than decreased.

Clarenbach suggested that far more serious attention should be
given to various alternatives to headwater reservoirs and other upstream engineering measures for flood prevention. He stated that in
some watersheds, if all appropriate and recommended land treatment
and land management measures were carried out, few or none of the
costly engineering measures would be economically justified. Stricter
requirements regarding land treatment and management should be instituted, and proper local and state land use regulations for uplands and
lowlands should in some instances be prerequisite to federal funds for
a project. Clarenbach indicated that flood-plain zoning is an important
tool that has been almost completely neglected in the watershed program, and that undoubtedly the restriction of flood-plain use by law
would frequently be the most economical means for minimizing flood
damage. He suggested that sometimes even outright public purchase
of flood-plain lands might be better than more costly attempts to protect them.

RELATED PROGRAMS

McMurry stressed the need for adequate educational activities regarding the watershed program. He indicated that many farm owners
and operators in local communities and the public in general are not
sufficiently acquainted with the provisions, operations, objectives, and
results of the watershed program. He suggested additional extension
activity in this area. If the inventory of potential watershed development suggested by Landgren were carried out, an educational program
would be needed to point out the areas that would benefit most from
watershed development. Landgren suggested that such a program be
used to bring about interest in local sponsorship of watershed programs in these areas.

The relation of the watershed program to forest lands was pointed out by Warren T. Murphy. Forest lands constitute a very important segment of the rural watersheds of this country. They amount to as much as 54 percent of the land area, exclusive of cities, highways, and so forth, in the 34 most industrialized states. With increasing emphasis on conservation and utilization of water resources, the condition of the forest watershed lands is assuming greater importance.

Except for the 27 percent of our forests in public ownership, the forest lands in watersheds are under the control of about 4-1/2 million individual owners. Most of these ownerships are small. The improvement of forest watersheds depends largely upon the desires and abilities of these landowners to operate their forest holdings under good principles of forest management. An important aspect of this is their ability to operate their forest properties as financially profitable undertakings. The situation regarding land ownership imposes conditions and limitations upon any program of forest land improvement. This is a major factor and immediately places programs for watershed improvement in a setting that differs from that of construction of a reservoir or an aqueduct where land is acquired by the constructing agency and the structure built as one operation in a short period of time.

By contrast, the treatment of land for watershed improvement purposes has largely defied the familiar project approach to structural phases of water resource development. Much needs to be done to remove obstacles to the practice of good forestry. Murphy felt that, for the most part, the broad national and state forestry programs offer the best immediate hope for improving forest watershed conditions by making the practice of forestry feasible and economically possible.

The principal project-type program now in operation that affects forest watershed lands is the watershed protection and flood prevention program. Murphy indicated that this program has limited possibilities for application on a broad scale in watersheds that are composed largely of forest lands. This is because of the requirement that flood prevention benefits, to be realized downstream, must be sufficient to support the structural measures of the program. To a considerable extent, forest watersheds are located in regions where downstream values within the area limitation of a watershed project are relatively low.

Looking ahead, Murphy suggested that the future presents a challenge for new ideas and a strengthening of some of the old approaches. For example, he thought that when the private owners of forest land have little incentive to maintain satisfactory watershed conditions, it is conceivable that downstream beneficiaries of good watershed management might enter into contracts with forest landowners and pay an annual fee to these landowners for maintaining the watersheds in good condition.

Multiple-purpose approaches that involve a combination of fish, wildlife, and recreational use of lands and streams with watershed objectives may offer promise under some situations. This might include acquisition by public agencies of forest lands that are marginal for good management under private ownership. Such lands could be utilized as public forests and hunting and recreation areas, while serving the watershed objectives.

In closing, I should like again to express my appreciation to the nine people who responded to my inquiry. I believe they have made several suggestions worthy of serious consideration.

THE RESPONDENTS' STATEMENTS

A. C. SPENCER, *Executive Director,*

Texas State Soil Conservation Board

With one exception, Public Law 566 provides an excellent medium for cooperation between local people, local subdivisions of the state government, and the federal government in carrying out, on a small watershed basis, complete soil, water, and plant conservation programs.

The 5,000 acre-foot limit on flood storage for any single structure is a hindrance in some cases. The wide expanse of hill country range land in some parts of Texas frequently provides sites for larger structures. If a greater number of smaller sites is required, additional easement problems are encountered. Added expense of smaller sites in some instances may render a potential project not economically feasible. We think the 250,000-acre limitation on size of watersheds is sufficient limitation to keep one agency from treading on another's toes.

Some administrative procedures or stipulations cause more problems than do deficiencies in the law. The allocation of planning assistance on a state basis ignores the principle of carrying on flood control work where there is the greatest amount of interest and need, and where the land and people are the most ready. It is our understanding that each state that has a sufficient number of applications under Public Law 566 to occupy a planning party is assigned one. The state of Texas has received 148 watershed applications (86 have been approved) and has one party financed with Public Law 566 funds, while states with as few as 20 applications also have one planning party. Texas also has one planning party operating on trust funds furnished by local watershed groups.

While it may be healthy for local people, where financially able, to pay the cost of developing the plan, this procedure allows inferior projects — in terms of need, number of people benefited, and conservation treatment applied — to be authorized and developed ahead of more worthy projects. Financial ability to pay for the development of a plan should not be a major consideration in determining priority of planning. State participation in the cost of planning should be financed by appropriated funds and the same criteria used for determining planning priorities as under Public Law 566.

The present separable cost-remaining-benefits policy hinders the participation of small towns as well as agricultural interest in the addition of conservation storage to floodwater-retarding structures. We believe that if a potential need for storage for beneficial use is present, this need should be met at the time of construction. Any policy that discourages the meeting of future water needs is not in the best interest of the general welfare. We think that local interests should pay the full *additional* cost attributable to conservation storage but should not share joint costs with other project purposes.

The Bureau of the Budget has restricted the Public Law 566 program to only 100 *new starts* for the two fiscal years 1959 and 1960. The tendency, both with the U. S. Department of Agriculture and the states, will be to authorize the larger projects for operations. The effect of this administrative procedure is to defeat the Public Law 566 purpose of being a small watershed act.

A more logical approach, if limits must be imposed, would be for the Department of Agriculture to be permitted to obligate a certain sum of money each year for Public Law 566 projects. A state could then use its allotted funds on fewer large projects or more smaller projects.

Since maintenance and operations responsibilities of local organizations require definite organization and specific arrangements, local people must have the answers to such questions as:

1. What is maintenance? The first and primary essential to proper maintenance is the slowing down of runoff and reduction of the sedimentation rate to the absolute minimum. Slowed down runoff reduces the amount of water that will flow around the emergency spillway, and reduced sedimentation rate increases the length of life of the sediment pool. Second, proper maintenance includes taking all necessary steps to insure that nothing impedes the structure's functioning as designed. The prompt performance of needed maintenance jobs such as restoration of depleted vegetation and repair of cracks, separated joints, and eroded spillways is a necessity.

2. What will maintenance cost? Conclusive evidence of dollars and cents costs of maintenance are not available. However, a rule-of-thumb maintenance plan has been developed and is being used in Texas. This plan provides that the local sponsoring organizations will create for each watershed project a maintenance reserve fund by depositing $200 per year for each structure in the watershed and $200 per year for each mile of channel improvement work in the watershed until an amount equal to the following has accumulated.

Structures

$1,000 for each of the first 10 structures

750 for each of the second 10 structures

500 for each of the third 10 structures

250 for each of the fourth 10 structures

Channel Improvement

$1,000 for each of the first 10 miles

750 for each of the second 10 miles

500 for each of the third 10 miles

250 for each of the fourth 10 miles

By these criteria a small project that has 3 structures and 2 miles of channel improvement would accumulate $5,000 in a maintenance fund. On the other hand, for a large project containing 40 structures and 20 miles of channel improvement, the formula would require the accumulation of $42,500 in a maintenance reserve fund.

However, experience seems to indicate that the formula should be used for the larger projects only until $25,000 to $30,000 is accumulated, and this balance maintained thereafter. The accumulation of a maintenance fund of from $5,000 to $30,000 may seem large. However, we must consider the fact that a large amount of capital may have been invested in each project. It is the responsibility of the local people to see that this investment returns the maximum possible benefits over the longest period of time. Percentage-wise, maintenance cost is very small in proportion to the total investment.

3. What kind of organization can and should assume maintenance responsibilities? Public Law 566 requires that a subdivision or combination of subdivisions of state government sponsor the projects. A soil conservation district is usually at least a cosponsor of an upstream flood prevention project because of its responsibility for the application and maintenance of land treatment measures. In most states, however, soil conservation districts cannot levy taxes and have no assured source of income; consequently, in most instances it is desirable for some other subdivision of state government to be a cosponsor with the soil conservation district. There are a variety of these districts such as soil conservation subdistricts, conservancy districts, water control and improvement districts, counties, cities, and drainage districts.

The cosponsoring subdivisions of state government should have (1) taxing authority or an assured source of income to meet maintenance, operations, and other costs; and (2) power of eminent domain to secure the necessary property or easements.

GLADWIN E. YOUNG, *Deputy Administrator,*

Soil Conservation Service

It seems more realistic and profitable at the moment to consider this question in the legislative setting in which the watershed program now operates than to try to speculate on how it might operate under some different authorization.

Public Law 566 was a logical next step that was almost certain to be taken, sooner or later in some form, as a consequence of two major programs authorized by Congress two decades ago. I have reference to the legislation setting forth the policies and the program for nation-wide flood control and the legislation establishing a nation-wide soil conservation program.

It was inevitable, as experience was gained in the operations of these two major programs, that the interrelationships between watershed lands and water resources would become a vital consideration for both programs. As a matter of fact, the original legislation for both programs specifically recognized this interrelationship.

In the actual operation of the two programs a very large gap remained between them. On the one hand, the flood control program for the major rivers was beamed largely at benefits to major urban centers and major river bottom lands. On the other hand, the soil conservation program was directed mostly toward assisting individual farmers to plan and apply conservation management to their land and to the surface water with which they had to deal.

Congressman Clifford Hope, a major sponsor of the Watershed Protection and Flood Prevention Act, has said that this act was intended to close the gap between the flood control program of the Corps of Engineers and the farm conservation program of the Soil Conservation Service.

The concept back of the watershed program is that it use the principles of both the flood control program and the soil conservation program and adapt them to the minor tributaries. It is intended that it shall not only reduce or prevent flood damage and reduce land deterioration, but shall also contribute to development and efficient use of all land and water resources.

This approach makes sense, and for that reason it has been given widespread support. Although the program is still in early stages, some watershed projects have now been completed and are ready for observation and measurement of projected benefits.

How well the 171 projects authorized for operations by June 1, 1959, actually turn out will depend on the accuracy and soundness of a whole series of estimates and judgments that have gone into planning and executing the projects.

Watershed projects developed under this program are partially paid for by local watershed communities and are to be entirely operated and maintained by them. This in itself dictates that the projects shall be fully acceptable to the local sponsors, shall be designed within their financial and legal limits, and shall meet the objectives which they seek.

One of the major contributions to optimum watershed development lies in the field of improved state enabling legislation and improved administration of local and state responsibilities. This is a field of rewarding effort for someone in almost every state who could work with soil conservation districts and other watershed groups or agencies as may be provided under state law.

There are also major opportunities to improve the basic data on which present calculations are made in engineering, water, and land interrelationships, and in the economic phases of project development. These research needs are recognized and generally outlined by federal agencies. Actual research in many categories is very difficult and costly. Nevertheless, more real progress is under way now than at any time in the past, and with widespread support from local watershed interests.

While additional research information would undoubtedly help achieve optimum development, we are sure also that improvements can and will be made in project planning only as experience is gained through actual construction and operation of projects.

In summary, it is my conviction that the watershed program is soundly conceived, that it is now a definite and continuing part of the nation's land and water policy, and that improvements will continue to come from efforts to improve local participation, as well as in policies and procedures under existing legislation or any modifications of it.

OTHIE R. McMURRY, *Director,*

Iowa Natural Resources Council

We find many farm owners and operators, local communities, and the public in general not sufficiently acquainted with the provisions, operations, objectives, and results of a watershed program. It appears that expanded educational effort is needed to better acquaint the farmers and local communities with the watershed programs. I believe that additional money should be provided to the Federal Extension Service and earmarked for watershed specialists. This is over and above the educational efforts of the Soil Conservation Service personnel in their work with the individual farmers in planning and applying the soil conservation plans.

I believe that many people in Iowa are anxious to see the watershed program under Public Law 566 move ahead at a much faster pace. It requires time, in any new program, to work out policies, procedures, and administrative details for actual operation. There may be some short cuts or streamlining that could be adopted in the planning procedures, or additional personnel could be secured to take care of planning needs. I believe that the federal government should provide for the professional and technical personnel for this activity, with the state and local communities providing the additional subprofessional help needed.

There appears to be considerable lapse of time between the preliminary workplans and the detailed plans and specifications for the individual structural measures needed in any given watershed. Every effort should be made to reduce the time involved between the preliminary plans and the final plans for construction.

The state of Iowa recently enacted a water rights law which requires permits for the impoundment of surface water. The plans and specifications for individual structures need to be submitted at the earliest opportunity to reduce the time lag in processing and issuance of permits and thus facilitate construction.

The 57th General Assembly of Iowa enacted legislation in 1959 granting the power of eminent domain to soil conservation districts on a watershed or subdistrict basis. To date, all land easements and rights-of-way for watershed projects have been provided free of charge by the farmers involved. As work progresses in larger watershed areas, however, farmers may not be willing to provide right-of-ways for the larger structures voluntarily. Funds for the purchase of right-of-ways and the financing of operation and maintenance costs are provided by a uniform tax on all the agricultural land within the watershed. I believe that there is still a need for a system whereby costs are assessed on a benefit basis if we are to secure the ultimate potential provided in Public Law 566.

WARREN T. MURPHY, *Director*

Division of Flood Prevention and River Basin Programs,

U. S. Forest Service

Forest lands occupy a large proportion of rural areas and exert a material influence upon soil stabilization and streamflow characteristics of watersheds. In the continental United States, about 34 percent of the total land area is classed as forest land, including all commercial and noncommercial types of forest areas. In the 34 states (the 31 most eastern and the three Pacific Coast states) in which 87 percent of our people reside and in which the bulk of the nation's manufacturing activities is located, 54 percent of the total land surface is forest land, exclusive of land in cities, industrial sites, highways, and similar uses. In the Southeast the proportion of total area classed as forest land is even greater. Of additional significance is the fact that watersheds located in the highest precipitation zones are watersheds with a very high proportion of land area classed as forest lands. Therefore, the condition, management, and improvement of the forest lands is a matter of real concern to planners and operators of water control, utilization, and conservation projects.

Most of the problems associated with watershed cover improvement are common to cultivated and pasture lands, as well as to forest lands. However, the remarks made here are concerned primarily with forest lands. In the first place, the large number of small land-ownership tracts imposes special conditions and limitations upon any program of forest land improvement. This places programs for watershed cover improvement in a different setting from the construction of a reservoir or an aqueduct, where land is acquired by the constructing agency and the structure is built as one operation in a short period of time. By contrast, the treatment of land for watershed improvement purposes has largely defied the project approach so familiar with structural phases of water resources development.

Of the 489 million acres of timberlands in the United States classed as commercially productive, 73 percent are privately owned and 27 percent are in various forms of public ownership. The forest lands in private ownership are held in about 4-1/2 million individual ownerships.

Thus, a very important aspect of watershed planning should be the formulation of effective programs to induce the many owners of small tracts of woodland to put them into good hydrologic condition and keep them that way. Since the improvement of hydrologic condition and the stabilization of forest soil does not necessarily result in a marketable product from which the landowner can receive a cash income, the development of a program for watershed cover improvement must usually be tied in with activities which will enhance the production of marketable products. However, such motivations as civic pride, interest in fish and game, and a pure interest in improvement of water resources may also play a part in obtaining landowner cooperation.

There are a number of means of fostering optimum watershed development as this relates to forest lands. Considering the widespread need for improving forest watersheds, general programs having national and state-wide application offer the best promise. These include:

1. Programs for the protection of forest lands and trees.

    a. Organized fire prevention and control. Broadly speaking, an adequate program of organized fire prevention and control is the basic program required for the improvement of watershed conditions in forested watersheds. Not only does it result in the improvement of the hydrologic condition of the forest floor, but it also minimizes one of the most serious hazards to the practice of sustained-yield forestry by landowners.

    b. Forest pest control. The control of tree-destroying insects and diseases is another prerequisite in the long-time practice of forestry. Where a pest problem exists control programs should be placed in operation.

2. Programs of assistance to landowners.

    a. Forest management assistance. Technical forestry assistance is available through most state foresters and should be provided to advise the landowner on timber harvesting methods that will minimize soil disturbance and help maintain good watershed conditions, as well as do a better job of forestry on the ground.

    b. Agricultural conservation program. Financial assistance to farmers in carrying out conservation practices on forest lands is of material help in getting better forestry accomplished on the ground.

    c. Tree planting assistance. Reforestation of many watershed areas is urgently needed. Landowners in many states are provided trees at minimum cost for reforestation purposes.

    d. Technical assistance in farm planning. Farmers need assistance in the proper planning of their farms for conservation of soil and water, maintenance or placing of land in forests, and protecting woodlands from fire and grazing.

    e. Special tax provisions for forest lands. Some states have special tax legislation to encourage the practice of forestry. Public values inherent in good management of forest lands from a watershed standpoint may be preserved by these tax provisions.

f. Forest credit. Often credit is needed by forest landowners in order to assist them in placing their property under good forest management.

3. Education in forest land management can help provide improved watershed
cover conditions.

4. Research on all aspects of forestry activities, from the economics of forestry
through protection, forest influences on watersheds, establishment, management, harvesting, and forest inventories, to better utilization of the forest
product, offers many opportunities for improving forest watersheds, or may
lead to better forestry incentives.

The principal project-type program now in operation affecting forest watershed lands is the watershed protection and flood prevention program. This program has limited possibilities for application on a broad scale in watersheds that
are largely composed of forest lands, due to the requirement that flood prevention
benefits, to be realized downstream, must be sufficient to support the structural
measures of the program. To a considerable extent forest watersheds are located
in regions where downstream values within the area limitation of a Public Law
566 project are relatively low.

Holding of land in public ownership or public acquisition of land, in whole or in
part, for watershed protection purposes is another approach to watershed cover
improvement. During a fifty-year period ending about 1940 this approach was
widely applied. Lands in public ownership, such as national and state forests or
municipal watersheds, are being managed with a primary concern for watershed
values.

There are perhaps other approaches to watershed cover improvement that
may warrant study. For example, where upland landowners have little incentive
to maintain satisfactory watershed conditions, it is conceivable that downstream
landowners might enter into contracts with the upstream landowners and pay an
annual fee for maintaining the watersheds in good condition.

Multiple-purpose approaches involving the combination of fish, wildlife, and
recreational use of lands and streams with watershed objectives may offer promise under some situations. This might include public hunting and park areas on
marginal-type lands.

Safeguarding increasingly important water facilities becomes a challenge for
new ideas and a strengthening of some of the old approaches in watershed protection and improvement.

GILBERT F. WHITE, *Professor*,

Department of Geography,

University of Chicago

In addition to the endemic problem of determining the hydrologic effect of
watershed projects, there are at least four questions which seem persistently to
arise:

1. What are sound methods of estimating flood damages and of computing
possible benefits from flood reduction?

Benefits from predicted prevention of flood losses and from intensification of land
use in flood plains apparently form the major share of benefits other than on-site

benefits. Because long and systematic records of losses ordinarily are not available and because survey parties cannot be expected to make detailed investigations of the economic impact of flooding, the estimates are subject to a wide margin of error and interpretation. It is not enough to define general methods. The field workers need, for example, to have relatively precise stage-damage curves for various seasons, crops, and structures which will enable them to check quickly the common guesses made by farmers and local observers. In these and other ways the unfortunate range of loss estimate can be reduced, and the validity of the benefit computations improved.

2. What changes in flood-plain use are resulting from the planning and construction of watershed programs?

All too often the estimates of probable benefits are not checked by observation of what in fact occurs in flood hazard areas. There is little evidence as to the degree of intensification that follows improvements upstream. This may be more or less than commonly assumed. Moreover, it is possible that to the extent that use changes in areas of relatively high-frequency flooding, the net annual flood losses may increase rather than decrease as a result of the watershed programs. There is some evidence that greater public discussion of a possible watershed project in certain areas encourages more encroachment than can be offset by flow reduction.

3. Do the repayment policies favor certain forms of treatment work?

The present policies for setting the amount of project costs which will be repaid by project beneficiaries appear to bias the acceptable design of watershed treatment works in two directions. There are indications that local groups are encouraged to seek Public Law 566 help in preference to Corps of Engineers projects because of the more liberal financing arrangements and to favor flood control over works for other purposes.

There also are suggestions that works such as reservoirs are preferred to land improvement measures because they require less local contribution and that, because of legal restrictions on size, several costly small reservoirs are preferred to one cheap reservoir. In both directions the policies might be considered to favor work which has lower economic returns but higher federal participation, and to foster irresponsible local action. It would be important to learn whether, in practice, either bias results.

4. Does the current organization favor integrated planning on either a drainage area basis or a farm basis?

The present administrative organization appears to draft workplans without a clear link to integrated river basin plans on the one hand or to integrated farm plans. For example, there does not appear to be a mechanism for assuring that the sum of watershed projects for a basin is reconciled with larger scale plans for water use in the major stream channels of the basin. Likewise, the projects concentrate on certain cropping and engineering improvement without considering economic or social measures which might affect farm income and stability. The aim seems to be to prepare a single plan without canvassing alternative ways of achieving the same aims. Thus, engineering and land treatment methods of reducing flood losses are considered to the exclusion of other structural and land use means of reducing flood losses. Wildlife restoration through water storage is not compared with land acquisition, game management, and other alternative approaches. Cropping practices are not compared with marketing arrangements as means of improving farm income. It would be desirable to know how far the present planning is, in practice, able to go in taking account of these other social instruments.

NORMAN E. LANDGREN, *Graduate Assistant,*

Department of Economics and Sociology,

Iowa State University

Benefits of water control measures transcend farm boundaries and may be dissociated from the costs of application. Such dissociation inhibits individual firms from making water control investments which promise net benefits to the watershed group but which would be uneconomic to the individual firms. Through watershed organization it is possible to distribute development costs among watershed participants so that group benefits are maximized without reducing the welfare of any individual participant.

Optimum watershed development would require the meeting of certain economic criteria at three levels of decision-making. These levels are (1) appropriations for watershed development in competition with other governmental activities, (2) allocations of limited funds *among* competing watersheds, and (3) allocations of limited funds among competing uses *within* watersheds. To the extent that economic criteria are violated at any of these levels of decision-making, watershed development will be suboptimum in a purely economic sense.

Many of the problems in watershed planning are associated with inadequacies of physical and economic data, methodological procedures, and analytical techniques for evaluating alternative development plans. Even though advancements in these areas have been encouraging, much research remains to be done. The orientation of current research is such, however, that investigations into allocation problems within watersheds will continue.

The appropriation of public funds among the many alternative investment possibilities is determined through the political process. Appropriation decisions made through the political process presumably reflect the desires of society and, thus, must be accepted as representing substantially the "correct" distribution of public funds among the many competing expenditure possibilities.

Once an appropriation has been made, however, its allocation among competing demands within an activity becomes susceptible to economic analysis. The appropriated funds should be allocated in such a manner that benefits are maximized to the extent that knowledge, time, and statutory restrictions permit.

Thus, improvement in watershed development will come mainly from improving procedures for allocation of funds among watersheds, since initial appropriations for watershed development are politically and socially determined and current research is so oriented that rapid progress is being made on problems of the optimum allocation of funds among measures within watersheds.[1]

The Public Law 566 program does not enable the optimum allocation of expenditures among watersheds. The expenditure of funds in watersheds which yield net benefits less than could be attained by the same expenditure in other watersheds results in suboptimum allocation of funds among watersheds. If funds for watershed development were unlimited, this sort of suboptimum allocation would not represent a significant problem. But funds for watershed development are not unlimited; thus, the loss to society from suboptimum allocation of funds among watersheds could be substantial — the loss of benefits foregone from potential higher net-benefit watersheds never developed.

---

[1] Expenditure decisions among watersheds are not independent of expenditure decisions within watersheds. To maximize program benefits, the scale of a project within any individual watershed is limited by benefits achievable from the same incremental expenditure in another watershed. The distinction is made only to simplify the presentation.

Public Law 566 requires a high degree of local interest. This requirement has undoubtedly tended to divert public expenditures for watershed development into watersheds with intensive local interest even though such watersheds may rank comparatively low in net benefits. The degree of suboptimum allocation of funds is unknown, since not all watersheds have been planned. At least part of the solution to the problem of suboptimum allocation of funds among watersheds lies in ascertaining which watersheds promise the greatest net benefits. This suggests the need for an inventory of all potential Public Law 566 watersheds irrespective of the degree of local interest within the watersheds.

Such an inventory should be designed to provide rough estimates of the costs of several levels of project intensity within each watershed, rough estimates of the benefits associated with each level, and the approximate division of the costs between local participants and the federal government as specified by Public Law 566. Estimates would by necessity have to be approximate to complete such an inventory program within a reasonable period of time. Crude methods of predicting damages and their reduction through alteration of watershed variables would be applicable. Accuracy would have to be sacrificed to expedite the inventory.

Such an inventory would indicate those watersheds with the greatest net benefit potential. In many watersheds there would be an absence of local interest in watershed development. Inasmuch as a high degree of local interest is necessary for Public Law 566 projects, an educational problem exists in those watersheds which critically need development but within which local interest is absent.

A watershed inventory program alone probably would not be sufficient to bring about substantially better allocation of funds among watersheds. A positive educational program directed towards informing local people within potentially high net-benefit watersheds about watershed development must supplement the inventory program. Once local interest in these watersheds has been stimulated, the necessary local initiative probably would be forthcoming to qualify for assistance in watershed planning and development within the existing framework of Public Law 566.

A basic weakness in many states which impedes local-state-federal collaboration in watershed development is inadequate authorized powers of local districts. Particularly evident is the lack of authority to acquire land under eminent domain and to raise revenue through taxes. Inability to acquire structural sites through condemnation, if necessary, may result in a structural plan for a watershed which promises substantially lower net benefits than would be the case if the best sites could be acquired. This may be particularly true if there is interdependency between structures on these sites and other structures. Denial of the taxing power to local districts restricts them to projects which require only a small local financial contribution. The absence of either or both of these powers in local districts can result in the adoption of watershed plans which are suboptimum.

Incomplete information from which decisions regarding the allocation of limited watershed development funds among competing watersheds are made and inadequate acquisition and tax powers of local sponsoring districts represent two major obstacles to optimum watershed development. Inefficient use of public funds will continue until these obstacles are overcome.

FRED A. CLARENBACH, *Professor*,

Department of Political Science,

University of Wisconsin

A main key to responsible development of watersheds is in the cost-sharing arrangements. The watershed protection and flood prevention program was launched with great emphasis on the idea that "each project is a local undertaking with federal help, not a federal project with local help." The workplan, more-over, "must be the plan of the local organization for solving its watershed prob-lems." Experience over several years, however, has revealed anew the incon-gruity of having Uncle Sam pay all but a small fraction of the cost of a "local undertaking" for land improvement. Beneficiaries on the local scene, including owners of urban and rural lands whose properties may be much enhanced in value, have insufficient incentive to careful economic planning. When benefits to real estate and other interests are heavily local and "somebody else" pays the big end of the cost, a program tends to fall within the political economy of the pork barrel.

The roots of this condition are deep in the complex of the country's pluralistic pressure politics, in our sprawling and ill-coordinated governmental arrange-ments, and in a widespread popular and official susceptibility to whatever may be flying the shining banners of "Soil Conservation" and "Flood Prevention." No doctor of political economy can suggest an effective combination of remedies that the collective patient would now be willing to take. Probably the condition will become much worse, in terms of amounts of wasteful outlays, before it can get better. A rapid multiplication and intensification of water problems in many lo-calities could conceivably force a reluctant Congress not only to restrain pork barreling proclivities among its own members, but also to make sensible provi-sion of executive machinery for adequately comprehensive and coordinated plan-ning and installation of water control projects. If or when that day arrives, a set of reorganized and decently cooperative national agencies might properly provide the prime responsible leadership in broad and well-conceived water programs in which current types of "watershed" projects and activities would be more appro-priately related to other major features of basin development. In such a regime, the national government should not merely invite, but should firmly require, as a condition of federal aid, appropriate participation by responsible state and local governments in planning, construction, operation, maintenance, and *paying for* the works of improvement.

Meanwhile, in the absence of miraculous reorganization and broad upgrading of the actual rules of the game, continuous discussion and repeated proposal of various limited steps should be encouraged. Among the suggestions that warrant consideration are these:

1. Greatly reduce or entirely eliminate the heavy federal subsidies for flood control, irrigation, and drainage in the watershed program. When some agencies of the Department of Agriculture struggle with mounting crop surpluses and pay farmers handsomely to withdraw land from crop use, there can be little justifica-tion for large subsidies for uneconomic protection and reclamation of other lands. An easily applicable rule for cost-sharing — with the incidental advantage of elim-inating some current types of bargaining — would set the federal share at a fixed percentage, say 25 percent, of construction costs.

2. Insist that projects can be sponsored only by truly responsible units of local government (or a state government) that possess all requisite legal and fis-cal powers and the resources for adequate administration. A jerry-gathered paper confederation of local agencies, interested mainly in getting as much as Uncle Sam will pay for, is not an appropriate local sponsor.

3. Provide for more effective review of watershed project plans by other federal agencies. The present limitations on time allowed for review usually do not permit adequate interagency consultation and consideration in the review process.

4. Provide far more adequately for collection and interpretation of basic data concerning the effects of land treatment and structural measures under a variety of conditions in natural watersheds. This absolutely fundamental requirement for sensible planning in a large program has been heavily stressed and often repeated by many competent and disinterested engineers and economists. Yet, many federal bureaucrats and their congressional and pressure group allies continue to indicate by their behavior that they are by no means keen to know or to have others make full and proper inquiry into the real effects of their multiplying projects. These interests seem to feel safer moving ahead as fast as possible and largely in the dark, apparently fearing that more light might discredit much of the program.

5. Eliminate gross shortcomings and distortions in the economic analysis of watershed projects. If Uncle Sam is to pay the lion's share of the cost, then both benefits and costs should be considered from a *national* viewpoint. Effects of small projects should be evaluated not only in the light of conditions and prospective developments in larger basins, but also in the light of national needs and relevant broad national policy considerations.

6. Give far more serious attention to various alternatives to headwater reservoirs and other upstream engineering measures for "flood prevention." In *some* watersheds, if all appropriate and recommended land treatment and land management measures were carried out, few or none of the costly engineering measures would be economically justified. Stricter requirements regarding land treatment and management should be instituted, in practice as well as on paper; and proper local and state land use regulations (for uplands and lowlands) should in some cases be prerequisite to federal funds for a project. Clearly, flood-plain zoning is an important tool that has been almost completely neglected in the watershed program; and undoubtedly the restriction of flood-plain use by law would frequently be the most economical means for minimizing flood damage. Sometimes even outright public purchase of flood-plain lands might be better than more costly attempts to protect them.

HOWARD L. COOK, *Chief,* [2]

Special Projects Branch, Planning Division, Civil Works

Corps of Engineers

Meshing watershed development with river basin development is a subject of vital interest to all who have striven to bring about acceptance of the idea that the United States should have comprehensive and unified plans for the development, conservation, and utilization of the resources of its major river basins, or other regions. For unless the "watershed" program is used to implement such comprehensive regional plans, it is inevitable that it will be used to undermine them.

The basic concept of the comprehensive river basin plan had its beginnings in the "First Conservation Crusade" early in the present century. It has taken a half century for the nation to reach the point at which it can be said that the implementation of this concept has become a national goal. Evidence of this is the

---

[2] The opinions are those of the author and do not necessarily represent official views.

acceptance of the basic idea by groups as diverse as the President's Water Resources Policy Commission established by President Truman, the "Hoover" Commission established by the Congress, and the Presidential Advisory Committee on Water Resources Policy established by President Eisenhower. Additional evidence is the recent establishment by the Congress of the United States Study Commissions for the Southeast and Texas. During the 1950's there was but one important effort to reverse the trend and return to the piecemeal approach of the past. This was the introduction of the legislation which later became Public Law 566. Of this legislation the Task Force on Water Resources and Power of the Hoover Commission observed: "The [Act] provides for a piecemeal approach that runs counter to the trend of the last half century toward comprehensive and coordinated river development [and]...encourages the subdivision of major river basins into a myriad of small watersheds, each of which may be independently planned and developed."

Subsequent events have demonstrated that the fears of the Task Force were not unfounded, and that if the watershed program is to reinforce, rather than to subvert, the nation's efforts to unify and make more effective its resource development programs, means must be found to insure that watershed projects shall be planned and carried out as integral parts of comprehensive river basin programs.

More specifically, techniques must be developed which will insure that all reservoirs constructed in a river basin constitute elements of a basinwide reservoir system which best meets all of the needs that can be satisfied by development of that basin's resources. This means that an effort should be made to find the best combination of small, large, and intermediate-sized reservoirs for each major basin. It also means that federal assistance, whether under Public Law 566 or other legislation, should not be made available for the construction of any reservoir until it has been determined that it would fit into, and constitute an integral part of, a good basinwide reservoir system. In the same way there should be for each basin an over-all plan for the best use of the water available for irrigation before it is committed to either small irrigation projects in headwater watersheds or major irrigation projects. These, of course, are merely illustrative examples of the need for the meshing of watershed plans with basin plans.

A number of other watershed problems are also of very great importance. However, at this stage of development of the Public Law 566 program the problem of bringing it into harmony with comprehensive basin plans must be given precedence.

JOHN B. BENNETT, *Assistant Director,*

Technical Review Staff, Office of the Secretary,

Department of the Interior

If we assume continuation of present procedures for formulating watershed programs, perhaps the most obvious improvement in specific projects would result from improved basic data — both physical and economic. Although it will seldom be possible to have all the data desired before proposing a project, any improvements along this line would constitute a valuable contribution to the long-range improvement of watershed development.

A second factor to consider is the relation between plans for development of a watershed and the plans for development of the larger area of which it is a part.

Since the sponsors of watershed programs are frequently soil conservation districts or other local groups concerned with limited areas, and since considerable emphasis is placed on local initiative in planning the watershed program, insufficient attention is given to effective coordinated water conservation and use planning for larger areas. Neither is there at present any really effective mechanism at the regional or national levels to encourage breadth of view in considering the interrelations between the watershed programs and other programs which may affect or be affected by them. The extent to which such coordinated planning is significant depends, in part, on the goals which are controlling.

Another important contribution to the improvement of watershed development would be achieved through conduct of postconstruction evaluations of selected watershed projects. Since we know that present procedures are not infallible, it is axiomatic that improvement can be made in the formulation of watershed protection projects. An objective comparison over a reasonable period of years of actual results with the results which had been predicted in the project justification would add valuable information which could be used to perfect the planning process. It would also serve to clarify the goals which can be attained through watershed programs. Such a postconstruction evaluation should cover both the physical and economic aspects of the project.

Index

337